OXFORD
G N V Q
CORE SKILLS

PLEASE NOTE
There is a newer edition of this book in stock

Application of
NUMBER

BRIAN GAULTER & LESLYE BUCHANAN

COLLEGE OF TECHNOLOGY

D0300934

Oxford University Press

Oxford University Press, Walton Street, Oxford OX2 6DP

Oxford New York
Athens Auckland Bangkok Bombay
Calcutta Cape Town Dar es Salaam Delhi
Florence Hong Kong Istanbul Karachi
Kuala Lumpar Madras Madrid Melbourne
Mexico City Nairobi Paris Singapore
Taipei Tokyo Toronto

and associated companies in
Berlin Ibadan

Oxford is a trademark of the Oxford University Press

© B. Gaulter and L. Buchanan 1994

First published 1994

A CIP catalogue record for this book is available from the British
Library.

All rights reserved. No part of this publication may be reproduced,
stored in a retrieval system, or transmitted, in any form or by any
means, without the prior permission in writing of Oxford
University Press. Within the UK, exceptions are allowed in respect
of any fair dealing of the purpose of research or private study, or
criticism or review, as permitted under the Copyright, Designs and
Patents Act, 1988, or in the case of reprographic reproduction in
accordance with the terms of licences issued by the Copyright
Licensing Agency. Enquiries concerning reproduction outside
those terms and in other countries should be sent to the Rights
Department, Oxford University Press, at the address above.

ISBN 0 19 914581 4

Typeset and designed by Gecko Limited, Bicester, Oxon

Printed and bound in Great Britain by
Butler & Tanner Ltd, Frome and London

Contents

GNVQ LEVELS MATRIX

Book section	GNVQ Level 1	2	3	4
1.1	✓			
1.2	✓			
1.3			✓	
1.4			✓	
2.1	✓			
2.2	✓			
2.3	✓			
2.4	✓			
2.5				✓
3.1	✓			
3.2	✓			
3.3	✓			
3.4	✓			
4.1		✓		
4.2		✓		
4.3		✓		
4.4	✓			
5.1	✓			
5.2	✓			
6.1	✓			
6.2		✓		
6.3		✓		
6.4		✓		
6.5		✓		
7.1	✓			
7.2		✓		
7.3		✓		
7.4		✓		
7.5		✓		
8.1	✓			
8.2	✓			
8.3		✓		

Book section	GNVQ Level 1	2	3	4
9	✓			
10.1	✓			
10.2		✓		
10.3		✓		
10.4			✓	
10.5		✓		
10.6		✓		
10.7		✓		
10.8				✓
11.1		✓		
11.2			✓	
11.3	✓			
11.4	✓			
12.1	✓			
12.2	✓			
12.3	✓			
12.4	✓			
12.5	✓			
12.6	✓			
12.7	✓			
13.1	✓			
13.2	✓			
13.3	✓			
13.4	✓			
13.5				✓
13.6	✓			
14				✓
15.1		✓		
15.2		✓		
15.3		✓		
15.4			✓	
15.5		✓		

Book section	GNVQ Level 1	2	3	4
16.1		✓		
16.2		✓		
17.1	✓			
17.2			✓	✓
17.3			✓	✓
17.4				✓
17.5		✓		
17.6			✓	✓
17.7			✓	
17.8			✓	
17.9		✓		
17.10	✓		✓	
18.1				✓
18.2			✓	
18.3	✓			
18.4	✓			
18.5			✓	
18.6			✓	
18.7				✓
19.1	✓			
19.2	✓			
19.3	✓			
19.4	✓			
19.5		✓		
20.1	✓			
20.2		✓		
20.3		✓		
20.4		✓		
21.1				✓
21.2				✓
21.3				✓
21.4				✓
22.1				✓
22.2				✓
22.3			✓	

There is a separate Matrix for each vocational area in the Assignments section (see pp.275, 288, 298, 307, 320).

Introduction

The book is written for students following a GNVQ course. All such courses list core skills that have been designed from the common skills used by BTEC, the profiling schemes used by RSA, and the general profiles used by City and Guilds. It is necessary for a student to show competence in *every* one of these skills.

One of the core skill units is *Application of Number*, which is concerned with using Mathematics in the context of a particular vocational area.

There are different levels of GNVQ, each of which is broadly equivalent to a specific level of academic achievement:

- GNVQ Foundation (Level 1) is comparable with 4 GCSE grade Es.
- GNVQ Intermediate (Level 2) is comparable with 4 GCSE grade Cs.
- GNVQ Advanced (Level 3) is comparable with 2 A-level grade Es.
- GNVQ Level 4 is comparable with a first degree.
- GNVQ Level 5 is comparable with a higher degree.

A complete list of the Elements and Ranges Techniques for each of the Levels is given on *pp vii–viii.*

This book is designed principally for students working at Intermediate and Advanced Levels. Students who are competent in the core skills at their level are encouraged to extend their skills by working towards the next level. We have therefore included all the skills needed for Application of Number for GNVQ Level 4, and where Level 4 competences are included, these are shown in the text with an asterisk. Students working at Application of Number Level 2 (or Level 1) should use the grid opposite, which gives the GNVQ level reflected in each topic.

There will be many circumstances where colleges feel that it is desirable for a student to have periods of teaching or workshop help, specifically to use learning material devoted to the core skills in Application of Number.

This book will be particularly useful as a resource for that purpose. A student should be able to identify weaknesses in a particular competence and then study that section in this book, either in a formal classroom situation or as part of a self-supported study programme.

The Application of Number competences need to be shown in a student's portfolio. These competences are usually shown by means of assignments which students do as part of their vocational units. It is important that the assignments are designed so that students can show all the competences required at their GNVQ level. All students need to realise that they must produce, in their assignments, work which clearly demonstrate their core skill competences.

At the end of this book is a section of assignments designed specifically to enable a student to demonstrate his or her core competences. This section is based on each of the 1993–94 GNVQ vocational areas. However, it is intended primarily to be used as a guide. Each assignment should be regarded as the starting point in the student's vocational area and developed into a more open-ended task. It is also essential that any assignment should relate closely to the topics which the student has followed in his or her vocational studies.

Students using textbooks sometimes worry if the solution at the end of the book differs slightly from their own answer. Very often this is caused by a misunderstanding about accuracy. In this book answers involving money should be given to the nearest penny and exact answers should always be given where possible. Where appropriate, other levels of accuracy can be required, and in Probability, fractional answers can be expected. As a guide, students should use at least four figures in their working and give answers to three significant figures. The answer must be rounded to the third figure.

Finally, we would like to thank all those who have helped with the preparation of this book, especially Malcolm Bennett for his valuable contribution in preparing the assignments, and the publisher's reader, who checked all the mathematics at manuscript stage. Those who gave permission for us to reproduce previously published material are listed in the Acknowledgements on p. 342.

We hope that this book will be of great benefit to lecturers and students alike. If you have any suggestions for enhancing its usefulness in future editions, please contact us via the Oxford office of OUP.

Brian Gaulter and Leslye Buchanan
Hampshire, 1994

GNVQ Techniques

The techniques required for each of the GNVQ levels are listed with bullet points below. A student needs to show competence in every skill listed at the appropriate level.

Application of Number Level 1

ELEMENT 1.1:

Gather and process data at Core Skill Level 1.

- Make estimates based on familiar units of measurement, checking results.
- Conduct a survey on an issue of the individual's choice.
- Convert between different units of measurement using tables, graphs and scales.

ELEMENT 1.2:

Represent and tackle problems at Core Skill Level 1.

- Solve whole-number problems involving addition and subtraction.
- Solve problems involving multiplication and division.
- Use fractions, decimals and percentages to describe situations.
- Use simple formulae expressed in words.
- Find perimeters, areas and volumes.

ELEMENT 1.3:

Interpret and present mathematical data at Core Skill Level 1.

- Use mathematical terms to describe common 2D shapes and 3D objects.
- Construct and interpret statistical diagrams.
- Use the mean and range of a set of data.
- Use symbols and diagrams.

Application of Number Level 2

ELEMENT 2.1:

Gather and process data at Core Skill Level 2.

- Make estimates based on familiar units of measurement, checking results.
- Conduct a survey on an issue of the individual's choice.
- Convert between different units of measurement using tables, graphs and scales.
- Design and use an observation sheet to collect data.
- Design and use a questionnaire to survey opinion.

ELEMENT 2.2:

Represent and tackle problems at Core Skill Level 2.

- Solve whole-number problems involving addition and subtraction.
- Solve problems involving multiplication and division.
- Use fractions, decimals and percentages to describe situations.
- Use simple formulae expressed in words.
- Find perimeters, areas and volumes.
- Use networks to solve problems.
- Find areas of plane shapes and volumes of simple solids.
- Calculate with fractions, decimals, percentages and ratios.
- Solve simple equations.
- Know and use the formulae for finding the area and circumference of circles.

ELEMENT 2.3:

Interpret and present mathematical data at Core Skill Level 2.

- Use mathematical terms to describe common 2D shapes and 3D objects.
- Construct and interpret statistical diagrams.
- Use the mean and range of a set of data.
- Use symbols and diagrams.
- Use 2D representation of 3D objects.
- Identify all the outcomes of combining two independent events.

Application of Number Level 3

ELEMENT 3.1:

Gather and process data at Core Skill Level 3.

- Make estimates based on familiar units of measurement, checking results.
- Conduct a survey on an issue of the individual's choice.
- Convert between different units of measurement using tables, graphs and scales.
- Design and use an observation sheet to collect data.
- Design and use a questionnaire to survey opinion.
- Organise data into groups and classifications.

ELEMENT 3.2:

Represent and tackle problems at Core Skill Level 3.

- Solve whole-number problems involving addition and subtraction.
- Solve problems involving multiplication and division.
- Use fractions, decimals and percentages to describe situations.
- Use simple formulae expressed in words.
- Find perimeters, areas and volumes.
- Use networks to solve problems.
- Find areas of plane shapes and volumes of simple solids.
- Calculate with fractions, decimals, percentages and ratios.
- Solve simple equations.
- Know and use the formulae for finding the area and circumference of circles.
- Use symbolic notation to express the rules of sequences.
- Solve equation or simple inequalities.
- Carry out calculations in plane and solid shapes.

ELEMENT 3.3:

Interpret and present mathematical data at Core Skill Level 3.

- Use mathematical terms to describe common 2D shapes and 3D objects.
- Construct and interpret statistical diagrams.
- Use the mean and range of a set of data.
- Use symbols and diagrams.
- Use 2D representation of 3D objects.
- Identify all the outcomes of combining two independent events.
- Given the probability of exclusive events calculate the probability of a combined event.

Application of Number Level 4

ELEMENT 4.1:

Element 4.1: Gather and process data at Core Skill Level 4.

- Make estimates based on familiar units of measurement, checking results.
- Conduct a survey on an issue of the individual's choice.
- Convert between different units of measurement using tables, graphs and scales.
- Design and use an observation sheet to collect data.
- Design and use a questionnaire to survey opinion.
- Organise data into groups and classifications.
- Design a questionnaire/experiment to test a hypothesis.
- Use sampling to investigate a 'population'.

ELEMENT 4.2:

Represent and tackle problems at Core Skill Level 4.

- Solve whole-number problems involving addition and subtraction.
- Solve problems involving multiplication and division.
- Use fractions, decimals and percentages to describe situations.
- Use simple formulae expressed in words.
- Find perimeters, areas and volumes.
- Use networks to solve problems.
- Find areas of plane shapes and volumes of simple solids.
- Calculate with fractions, decimals, percentages and ratios.
- Solve simple equations.

- Know and use the formulae for finding the area and circumference of circles.
- Use symbolic notation to express the rules of sequences.
- Solve equations or simple inequalities.
- Carry out calculations in plane and solid shapes.
- Calculate with numbers expressed in standard form.
- Manipulate algebraic formulae, equations or expressions.
- Co-ordinate a number of features or variables in solving problems.
- Express general laws in symbolic form.
- Use the gradients of graphs found by constructing tangents.

ELEMENT 4.3:

Interpret and present mathematical data at Core Skill Level 4.

- Use mathematical terms to describe common 2D shapes and 3D objects.
- Construct and interpret statistical diagrams.
- Use the mean and range of a set of data.
- Use symbols and diagrams.
- Use 2D representation of 3D objects.
- Identify all the outcomes of combining two independent events.
- Given the probability of exclusive events calculate the probability of a combined event.
- Construct and interpret a cumulative frequency curve.
- Interpret graphs which represent particular relationships.

1 *Basic Numeracy*

Even in prehistoric times the basis of arithmetic was being developed. The earliest number system was one, two, many. When races began to settle and become farmers, craftsmen and traders, there was a need for more sophisticated number systems for counting, recording and calculation. As different civilisations evolved, they developed different number systems. Our system is based on the number 10. Other civilisations used different systems based on the number 60 (Babylonian), 20 (Mayan) or 5. The Romans used letters to represent numbers (e.g. I, V, X, C for 1, 5, 10, 100).

When trade and communication spread beyond the local area to the rest of the country and abroad, it became essential to have a common system of numbers which was efficient.

The **decimal** system, based on the number 10, was eventually accepted as the most convenient. Its advantages are that any number can be written using only ten symbols, 0, 1, 2, 3, 4, 5, 6, 7, 8, 9 (called **digits**) and **place value**.

1.1 *Integers and decimal fractions*

Place value

An abacus is a frame with beads sliding on wires, which was used as a counting aid before the adoption of the ten digits. It is still used for this purpose in parts of Asia.

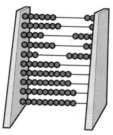

Beads on the first wire have the same value of 1 unit, but a bead on the second wire has a value which is the total of the beads on the first wire, i.e. 10. Each bead on the third wire then has the value $10 \times 10 = 100$, and so on.

The **decimal system** works in the same way, but with digits written in columns instead of beads on wires. Working from right to left, each column is worth 10 times the previous column:

$$15 = 5 \times 1 + 1 \times 10 = \text{fifteen}$$
$$352 = 2 \times 1 + 5 \times 10 + 3 \times 100 = \text{three hundred and fifty two}$$
$$1234 = 4 \times 1 + 3 \times 10 + 2 \times 100 + 1 \times 1000$$
$$= \text{one thousand, two hundred and thirty four}$$

If there is no digit in a particular column, the place is filled by 0, which is called a **place-holder**.

$$105 = 5 \times 1 + 1 \times 100 = \text{one hundred and five}$$
$$150 = 5 \times 10 + 1 \times 100 = \text{one hundred and fifty}$$

Note. Whole numbers are also called **integers**.

Similarly, working from left to right, each column is worth one tenth of the previous column.

Each number in the column to the right of the units column is worth $1 \div 10$, i.e. one tenth, which is a **decimal fraction**.

To separate whole numbers from decimal fractions a **decimal point** is used:

$0.1 \quad = \frac{1}{10} \quad =$ one tenth
$0.01 \quad = \frac{1}{100} \quad =$ one hundredth
$0.001 = \frac{1}{1000} =$ one thousandth

Multiplication and division by 10, 100, 1000, etc., is very easy in the decimal system.

EXAMPLE 1

Multiply 34 by: **a** 10 **b** 1000

a When a number is multiplied by 10, each digit becomes worth 10 times more, i.e. moves **1 column** to the **left**.
The empty space in the units column is filled by a zero:
$34 \times 10 = 340$

b When a number is multiplied by 1000, each digit becomes worth $10 \times 10 \times 10$ more, i.e. moves **3 columns** to the **left**.
The three empty spaces in the units, tens and hundreds columns are filled by zeros:
$34 \times 1000 = 34000$

With numbers of more than four digits, it is usual to leave a small gap after each group of three digits, e.g. 34 000.

EXAMPLE 2

Divide 2030 by: **a** 10 **b** 100

a When a number is divided by 10, each digit becomes worth 10 times less, i.e. moves **1 column** to the **right**.
The zero in the units column is no longer needed:
$2030 \div 10 = 203$

b When a number is divided by 100, each digit is worth 10×10 times less, i.e. moves **2 columns** to the **right**.
The 3 in the tens column will move into the **tenths column**:
$2030 \div 100 = 20.30$ or 20.3

EXERCISE 1.1

1 What value do the following digits have in the given number?

   a 5 in 250   **d** 4 in 624

   b 7 in 1725   **e** 6 in 12.6

   c 3 in 3012   **f** 2 in 34.529

2 Write the following numbers in order of size, smallest first:

   a 54   17   45   10   21   86

   b 104   23   14   230   32   203

   c 60   6   600   61   610   601

   d 99   101   11   110   1001   999

   e 399   400   300   297   420

3 What is the largest number which can be made from the digits 1, 7, 5 and 0?

4 What is the smallest number which can be made from the digits 3, 9, 6 and 2?

5 Find the answers to the following multiplications:

a 43×10 **d** 13.2×10 **g** 5.16×100

b 167×100 **e** 5.9×100 **h** 7.03×1000

c 20×1000 **f** 93.58×10 **i** 0.13×1000

6 Find the answers to the following divisions:

a $320 \div 10$ **d** $4030 \div 100$ **g** $2.7 \div 1000$

b $300 \div 100$ **e** $65 \div 100$ **h** $0.51 \div 10$

c $4000 \div 100$ **f** $65 \div 1000$ **i** $0.02 \div 100$

7 What number is formed when:

a 1 is added to 99   **c** 1 is added to 4099

b 2 is added to 398   **d** 2 is added to 6198?

Decimals and the four rules

The four rules of arithmetic are **addition, subtraction, multiplication** and **division**. It is generally easiest to perform calculations involving decimals on a calculator (see Unit 2). However, in simple cases, you should also be able to find an answer without the aid of a calculator.

EXAMPLE 1

a Add 34.5, 9.7 and 56.12.

b Subtract 91.72 from 164.6.

First, write the numbers in a column so that the decimal points are in line, then each digit is in its correct place.

a
```
    34.5
     9.7
   56.12
  100.32
```

b
```
  164.60
   91.72
   72.88
```

EXAMPLE 2

a Multiply 271.3 by 9

b Divide 384.8 by 7

a
```
   271.3
       9
  2441.7
```

b
```
     54.9
  7)384.3
```

EXERCISE 1.2

Calculate, without the aid of a calculator:

1	$36.2 + 5.7$	7	24.2×7
2	$104.9 + 75.4$	8	78.04×9
3	$6.7 + 51.09 + 76.18$	9	147.5×12
4	$72.9 - 56.2$	10	$54.6 \div 7$
5	$89.13 - 72.42$	11	$650.79 \div 9$
6	$121.6 - 69.85$	12	$526.46 \div 11$

Combining the four operations

Does $3 + 4 \times 2 = 7 \times 2 = 14$
or
does $3 + 4 \times 2 = 3 + 8 = 11$?

When more than one **operation** is used in a calculation there has to be an agreed order for combining the numbers.

The order used in the calculation is:

 (i) brackets
 (ii) multiplications and divisions
 (iii) additions and subtractions.

$\therefore 3 + 4 \times 2 = 3 + 8 = 11$

EXAMPLE

Find: **a** $7 + 3 \times 6 - 1$ **b** $(7 + 3) \times 6 - 1$ **c** $7 + 3 \times (6 - 1)$

a $7 + 3 \times 6 - 1 = 7 + 18 - 1 = 24$

b $(7 + 3) \times 6 - 1 = 10 \times 6 - 1 = 60 - 1 = 59$

c $7 + 3 \times (6 - 1) = 7 + 3 \times 5 = 7 + 15 = 22$

EXERCISE 1.3

The answers to questions 1–10 should be found without the aid of a calculator. (You may use a calculator to check your answers.)

1	$5 + 7 \times 3$	6	$(21 + 17 - 10) \div 4$
2	$(5 + 7) \times 3$	7	$16 \div 4 - 20 \div 5$
3	$10 \div (5 - 3)$	8	$528 \div (150 - 142)$
4	$10 \div 5 - 1$	9	$150 - 90 \div 45 - 15$
5	$11 - 15 \div 3 \times 2$	10	$(150 - 90) \div (45 - 15)$

11　An artist buys 9 paint brushes costing 56p each.
　　How much change will be received from a £10 note?

12 Canvas costs £3.50 per square metre.
How many square metres can be bought for £14?

13 An office buys two computers for £889.08 each (including VAT) and a
laser printer costing £1643.83. The budget for this expenditure is £3500.
How much money remains after the purchases?

14 A theatre can seat 564 people in the stalls, 228 in the circle, and 196 in the
balcony.

   a How many people can the theatre seat in total?

Seats in the stalls cost £4.50, circle seats cost £6.50, and balcony seats
cost £3.75.

   b How much will the theatre take in ticket sales if it has a full house?

15 A freelance typist works at 60 wpm. She charges 0.25p per word.

   a How long will she take to type a document which is 7620 words long?

   b How much will she receive for this document?

16 Packs of 40 nappies cost £6.95.
How many packs can be bought for £50?
How much change will be received?

17 Mrs Halliday uses her own estate car when she delivers meals on wheels
and keeps a record of her mileage.

Week of 20/1/94	Mon	Wed	Fri	Sun
Mileage	12.3	11.5	13.9	9.8

For the week shown above:

   a what was her total mileage for the week?

   b how much does she claim for the week if she claims 27.2p per mile?

18 The diagram shows an extract from a holiday brochure:

Hotel	Golden Sands		Park Royal		Ocean Lodge	
Dates	14 days	21 days	14 days	21 days	14 days	21 days
Mar 2 – Mar 29	323	368	337	382	284	321
Mar 30 – Apr 26	373	425	387	439	334	377
Apr 27 – May 24	338	385	352	400	299	339
May 25 – Jun 21	367	418	382	434	329	372
Jun 22 – Jul 19	399	455	414	470	361	408
Single room supp.	£2.30 per day		£2.70 per day		£2.90 per day	

Find the cost of a holiday for three adults staying at the Park Royal for 14
days from May 25. The third adult will require a single room.

19 It costs £44.50 per day to hire a car plus £0.06 per mile travelled.
How much does it cost to hire a car for 3 days to travel 450 miles?

20 A foundry makes accessories for fireplaces. A pair of brass fire dogs weighs 1.7 kg, a set of fire irons weighs 2.04 kg, and a fire screen weighs 3.65 kg.

   a What is the total weight of the accessories for one fireplace?

   A van can carry a load of up to 1000 kg.

   b How many sets of the above accessories can the van carry?

21 A machine cuts lengths of hollow metal rod for lamps. Each section is 20.6 cm long.

   a How many sections can be cut from a 200 cm length of rod?

   b What length of rod will be wasted?

1.2 *Directed numbers*

The negative sign has two distinct uses in mathematics:

(i) as a **subtraction** operation, e.g. $6 - 4 = 2$,
(ii) as a **direction** symbol, e.g. $-7°C$.

If we wish to show a temperature which is 7°C *below* zero, we can write $^{-}7°C$ or $-7°C$.

If a car travels 20 miles in one direction and then 15 miles in the reverse direction, we can write the distances travelled as $^{+}$**20 miles** and $^{-}$**15 miles**.

The numbers $^{-}7$, $^{+}20$ and $^{-}15$ are called **directed numbers**.

On your calculator you will see that there are two keys with negative symbols:

$\boxed{-}$ for subtraction

$\boxed{+/-}$ for direction.

Directed numbers can be represented on a horizontal or a vertical number line.

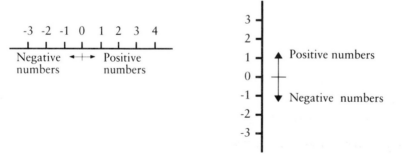

Addition and subtraction

Think of additions and subtractions of numbers as movements *up* and *down* the vertical number line.

Start at zero, move up 7 and then down 3.
Your position is now 4 *above* zero.

$$\text{i.e. } 7 + (-3) = +4$$

Subtracting two numbers is the same as finding the difference between them:

$$5 - (-3)$$

is the difference between being 3 *below* zero and being 5 *above* zero on the number line.

From 3 below to 5 above you must move up 8. Therefore

$$5 - (-3) = +8 \text{ } or \text{ } 5 - (-3) = 5 + 3 = 8$$

(Note that $-(-3) = +3$.)

$$-4 - (-2)$$

is the difference between being 2 below zero and being 4 below zero.

From 2 *below* to 4 *below* you must move DOWN 2, i.e.

$$-4 - (-2) = -2$$

or use the rule $- \times - = +$ to give

$$-4 - (-2) = -4 + 2 = -2$$

```
 7 ─
 6 ─
 5 ─
 4 ─
 3 ─
 2 ─
 1 ─
 0 ─
-1 ─
-2 ─
-3 ─
-4 ─
-5 ─
-6 ─
-7 ─
```

EXERCISE 1.4

Find the answers to the following, without the aid of a calculator:

1 **a** $-5 + 7$ **c** $-2 + -8$ **e** $-21 + 27$ **g** $-19 + 19$

   b $3 + (-7)$ **d** $16 + (-12)$ **f** $35 + 5$ **h** $-35 + (-14)$

2 **a** $7 - 8$ **c** $-9 - 4$ **e** $-10 - (-7)$ **g** $25 - (-25)$

   b $12 - (-5)$ **d** $11 - (-9)$ **f** $-15 - (-15)$ **h** $100 - 64.$

Multiplication and division

Going *up* 2 three times would mean you were now 6 *above* zero. So

$$(+2) \times 3 = +6$$
$$\text{or} \quad 2 \times 3 = 6 \qquad \text{also } 3 \times 2 = 6$$

Going *down* 2 three times would mean you were now 6 *below* zero. So

$$(-2) \times 3 = -6$$
$$\text{or} \quad -2 \times 3 = -6 \qquad \text{also } 3 \times -2 = -6$$

But what is $(-2) \times (-3)$?

Remember that $-(-6) = +6$

and $\qquad (-2) \times 3 = -6 = -(2 \times 3)$

$\therefore \qquad (-2) \times (-3) = -(2 \times -3) = -(-6) = +6$

i.e. the reverse of moving 6 *down* is moving 6 *up*.

The rules for multiplication and division are similar:

Two numbers with like signs give a positive answer.
Two numbers with unlike signs give a negative answer.

EXAMPLE 1

Find the product of $-4 \times -7 \times -3$

$$(-4 \times -7) \times -3 = +28 \times -3$$
$$= -84$$

EXAMPLE 2

Evaluate $(-12 \div 4) \times -6$

$$(-12 \div 4) \times -6 = -3 \times -6$$
$$= +18$$

EXERCISE 1.5

Do *not* use a calculator in the following questions:

1   **a** -3×6 **d** $-7 \div -4$ **g** $8 \div -\frac{1}{2} \div -2$ **j** $\dfrac{20 \times -6}{-4 \times -3}$

    b $15 \div -5$ **e** $10 \times -3 \div 2$ **h** $(-3 + -6) \times -4$

    c -7×-4 **f** $-3 \times -3 \times -3$ **i** $-7 \div (3 - (-4))$

1.3 *Powers and roots*

Powers

Patterns of dots like this

| 1 | 4 | 9 | 16 |

form squares, and the numbers 1, 4, 9, 16, . . . are called the **square numbers**.

The square numbers are also formed by finding the product of an integer with itself:

$$1 \times 1 = 1$$
$$2 \times 2 = 4$$
$$3 \times 3 = 9$$
$$4 \times 4 = 16, \text{etc.}$$

The sums of odd numbers also produce the square numbers:

$$
\begin{aligned}
1 &= 1 \\
1 + 3 &= 4 \\
1 + 3 + 5 &= 9 \\
1 + 3 + 5 + 7 &= 16 \\
1 + 3 + 5 + 7 + 9 &= 25, \text{ etc.}
\end{aligned}
$$

If any number is multiplied by itself, the product is called the square of the number. For example:

the square of 1.2 is 1.44
the square of $\sqrt{2}$ is 2.

The square of 3 or 3 squared $= 3 \times 3 = 3^2$, and the 2 is called the **index**.

Similarly:

the cube of 4 = 4 cubed $= 4 \times 4 \times 4 = 4^3$

and

the fourth power of 2 $= 2 \times 2 \times 2 \times 2 = 2^4$

Roots

The square of 4 $= 4 \times 4 = 16$.
The number 4, in this example, is called the **square root** of 16, i.e. the number which when squared will give 16.

16 has another square root because $-4 \times -4 = 16$.

Hence the square roots of 16 are $+4$ and -4.

The symbol $\sqrt{}$ indicates the positive square root and hence $\sqrt{16} = +4$.

Similarly, the cube root of a number is the number which when multiplied by itself three times equals the given number. For example:

the cube root of 64 or $\sqrt[3]{64} = 4$
(since $4^3 = 4 \times 4 \times 4 = 64$)

EXERCISE 1.6

1 Write down the first 10 square numbers.

2 Write down the first 6 cube numbers.

3 Find the positive square roots of the following numbers:

   a 25 b 121 c 625 d 225 e 196

4 a Find the cube root of (i) 27 (ii) ⁻64
(iii) 729

   b Find the fifth root of 32.

   c Find the fourth root of (i) 81 (ii) 625

5 Write 25 as the sum of a sequence of odd numbers.

6 What is the third power of 2?

7 What is 3 cubed?

8 Write down the cube root of:

   a 8 b 27 c 216 d $\frac{1}{8}$ e ⁻64

9 What is the fourth root of 81?

10 Evaluate $5^2 \times \sqrt{16}$.

1.4 *Factors and multiples*

A **factor** is an integer which divides into a given number exactly, i.e. there is no remainder.

For example: 3 and 4 are factors of 12.

A **multiple** of a number is the number multiplied by any integer.

For example, multiples of 6 are 12, 18, 24, and so on.

12 is a multiple of 3 and of 4, since 3 and 4 are factors of 12.

EXAMPLE 1

Find all the factors of 42 and list them in pairs, the product of which is 42.

The factors of 42 are 1, 2, 3, 6, 7, 14, 21, 42.

Listed in pairs they are $1 \times 42, 2 \times 21, 3 \times 14, 6 \times 7$.

EXAMPLE 2

Which of the following numbers are multiples of 9?

a 63   b 732   c 1944

a $63 \div 9 = 7$ means that 63 is a multiple of 9.
b $732 \div 9 = 81.3$ means that 732 is not a multiple of 9.
c $1944 \div 9 = 216$ means that 1944 is a multiple of 9.

EXERCISE 1.7

1   Find all the factors of each of the following and list the factors in pairs, the product of which is the number itself:

a 15   b 27   c 36   d 64   e 100

2   a Write down the factors of (i) 48 (ii) 72.

b List the factors which are common to 48 and 72.

3   Of which of the following numbers is 4 a factor?
34   64   144   642   116   2620

4   State which of 5, 10, 20, 25 are factors of the following:

a 300   b 1050   c 470   d 875   e 2360

5   Which of the following numbers are divisible by   a 3,   b 6,   c 15?

125   240   87   96   146   255   1073

2 *Using a Calculator*

2.1 *Approximations*

Most calculators display answers of up to 10 digits.

In most cases, this is too many digits. Therefore, when using a calculator, it is necessary to give an *approximate* answer which contains fewer digits (but which has a sensible degree of accuracy).

There are two methods in common usage:
rounding to a number of **decimal places** (e.g. 2 decimal places or 2 d.p.) and rounding to a number of **significant figures** (e.g. 3 significant figures or 3 s.f.).

The rule for rounding to, for example, 2 decimal places is:

If the digit in the third decimal place is **5 or more, round up**, i.e. increase the digit in the second decimal place by 1.
If the digit in the third decimal place is **less than 5, round down**, i.e. the digit in the second place remains the same.

EXAMPLE 1

Give the following numbers, from a calculator display, to 2 d.p.
7.92341,   25.675231,   0.06666. .,   0.9999999. .

Calculator display	Degree of accuracy required (2 d.p.)	Answer correct to 2 d.p.
7.92341	7.92|341	7.92
25.675231	25.67|5231	25.68
0.066666 .	0.06|6666 .	0.07
0.9999999 . .	0.99|99999 . .	1.00

The rules for significant figures are similar, but you need to take care with zeros.

Zeros at the beginning of a decimal number or at the end of an integer are not counted as significant figures, but must be included in the final result. All other zeros are significant.

For example, 70 631.9 given correct to 3 significant figures is 70 600.

The three significant figures are 7, 0 and 6. The last two zeros are not significant (i.e. do not count as fourth and fifth figures), but are essential so that 7 retains its value of 70 thousand and 6 its value of 6 hundred.

EXAMPLE 2

Give the following numbers, from a calculator display to 3 s.f.
7.92341, 25.675231, 0.066666. .,24380., 0.999999. .

Calculator display	Degree of accuracy required (3 s.f.)	Answer correct to 3 s.f.
7.92341	7.92|341	7.92
25.675231	25.6|75231	25.7
0.066666..	0.0666|66..	0.0667
24380.	243|80.	24400
0.999999..	0.999|999..	1.00

In the last example, the digit 1 becomes the first significant figure, and the two zeros are the second and third figures.

EXERCISE 2.1

Give each of the following numbers to the accuracy requested in brackets:

1	9.736	(3 s.f.)	6	4.1983	(2 d.p.)
2	0.36218	(2 d.p.)	7	1245.4	(3 s.f.)
3	147.49	(1 d.p.)	8	0.00425	(3 d.p.)
4	28.613	(2 s.f.)	9	273.6	(2 s.f.)
5	0.5252	(2 s.f.)	10	459.97314	(1 d.p.).

2.2 *Estimation*

The answer displayed on a calculator will be correct for the values you have entered, but a calculator cannot tell you if you have pressed the wrong key or entered your numbers in the wrong order.

Each number you enter into the calculator should be checked for accuracy and the final answer should be checked by comparing it with an *estimated* answer.

EXAMPLE

Estimate the value of 31.41×79.6.

31.41 is approximately 30
79.6 is approximately 80

An estimated value is therefore $30 \times 80 = 2400$.

If the calculator displays, for example, 25002.36, a mistake has been made with the decimal point, and the answer should read 2500.236

EXERCISE 2.2

1 By rounding all numbers to 1 significant figure, find an estimated value of each calculation:

a 52.2×67.4

b 6143×0.0381

c 607×1.86

d $607 \div 1.86$

e $48.2 \div 0.203$

f $3784 \div 412$

g $\dfrac{520.4 \times 8.065}{99.53}$

h $\dfrac{807}{391.2 \times 0.38}$

2 Find an estimate for each of the following calculations, by choosing an appropriate approximation for each number:

a $82.3 \div 9.1$

b $0.364 \div 6.29$

c $\dfrac{31.73 \times 6.282}{7.918}$

3 By finding an estimate of the answer, state which of the following calculations are obviously incorrect. (Do not use a calculator.)

a $8.14 \times 49.6 = 403.74$

b $23.79 \div 5.57 = 4.27$

c $324 \div 196 \times 0.5 = 226$

d $3.14 \times 9.46^2 = 882.35$

e $23.79 \div 0.213 = 11.169$

f $\dfrac{42.3 \times 3.97}{1635} = 10.27$

g $\sqrt{1640} = 40.5$

h $\sqrt{650} = 80.6$

i $(0.038)^2 = 0.00144$

j $(0.205)^3 = 0.0862$

2.3 *Degrees of accuracy*

Whenever you solve a numerical problem, you must consider the accuracy required in your answer, especially if you cannot obtain an exact answer. In Section 2.1, you saw how to correct an answer to a number of significant figures or decimal places. Section 2.3 shows you how to select an appropriate degree of accuracy.

Sometimes the answer to a numerical problem is an integer, and this gives you an exact answer. Fractions are also exact, but their decimal equivalents are often inexact. For example, suppose you were able to buy sixteen pencils for £3 but wanted to buy only one. Each pencil would cost $£\frac{3}{16}$.

As a decimal this would be 18.75 pence, but obviously you cannot pay 18.75 pence for an individual pencil. The shopkeeper would work in the smallest unit of currency, which is one penny. To make sure that she did not lose money she would round up the price to 19p.

┌─ **EXAMPLE 1** ─────────────────────────────────

Sara makes a 12-minute local phone call, at a rate of $4\frac{1}{2}$ minutes per unit of charge. British Telecom always rounds up the number of units.

How many units will Sara be charged for?
No. of units charged for is 12/4.5 = 2.6666.
The 2.6666 is rounded up to the next integer.
∴ Sara is charged for 3 units.

└──

Sometimes you will need to **round down** a mathematical answer as the following example shows.

┌─ **EXAMPLE** ──────────────────────────────────

Pam changes 7254 French francs into pounds at the rate of 8.4 francs to £1. The bank, not wishing to be generous, decides to round down to the nearest penny the money it will give Pam.

How much does Pam receive?

7254 French francs = £7254/8.4 = £863.57143

∴ Pam receives £863.57

└──

EXERCISE 2.3

1 Twelve pens cost £6.20. What would be charged for one pen?

2 A tin of paint covers $12\,\text{m}^2$.
How many tins are required to cover an area of $32\,\text{m}^2$ with two coats of paint?

3 A local phone call takes 20 minutes. At $4\frac{1}{2}$ minutes per unit, how many units are charged for?

4 An office orders plastic sleeves which cost £2.67 for a box of 100.
How much should be charged:
a for ten   b for one?

5 A TV room $5.6\,\text{m}^2$ is to be carpeted. The carpet chosen is 3 m wide and is sold in metre lengths. How many metres should be bought?

6 Visitors to a day centre pay £1.70 per week of five days towards the cost of tea and biscuits. How much should someone visiting for one day be charged, if the centre is not to make a loss?

7 Eleven students receive a bill for £120 after an evening out.
How much should each pay?

8 A booking agency normally sells a block of four tickets for £15.43. It agrees to sell them individually.
How much should it charge for one ticket if it does not wish to lose money through individual sales?

9 A factory used 26 818 units of electricity at 5.44p per unit.
What is the cost of the electricity used?

10 In a car factory, pieces of glass fibre 0.9 m are cut from a roll which is 24 m long.
How many pieces can be cut from one roll?

2.4 *The keys of a calculator*

To use your calculator most effectively, you must become familiar with the keys and their functions.

The booklet that accompanies your calculator will tell you the order in which the keys are used for calculations.

For example, to find $\sqrt[4]{5}$ the keys required on most calculators are

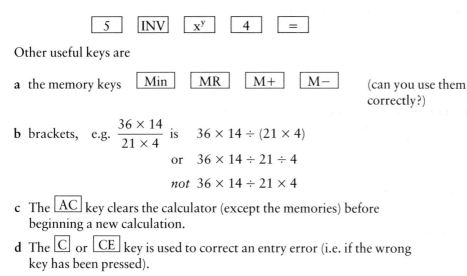

$$\boxed{5} \quad \boxed{\text{INV}} \quad \boxed{x^y} \quad \boxed{4} \quad \boxed{=}$$

Other useful keys are

a the memory keys $\boxed{\text{Min}} \quad \boxed{\text{MR}} \quad \boxed{\text{M+}} \quad \boxed{\text{M}-}$ (can you use them correctly?)

b brackets, e.g. $\dfrac{36 \times 14}{21 \times 4}$ is $\quad 36 \times 14 \div (21 \times 4)$

$\qquad\qquad\qquad$ or $\quad 36 \times 14 \div 21 \div 4$

$\qquad\qquad\qquad$ *not* $36 \times 14 \div 21 \times 4$

c The $\boxed{\text{AC}}$ key clears the calculator (except the memories) before beginning a new calculation.

d The $\boxed{\text{C}}$ or $\boxed{\text{CE}}$ key is used to correct an entry error (i.e. if the wrong key has been pressed).

The key clears the last entry made (either a figure or an operation), provided it is pressed immediately after the error has been made.

The correct entry can then be made and the sequence continued.

For example, $6 + 3 \boxed{\text{C}} 2 =$ will produce the answer to $6 + 2$.

EXERCISE 2.4

1 $386.9 \div 32.87$ (to 1 d.p.)

2 $2756 \div 0.03741$ (to 3 s.f.)

3 $\sqrt{\dfrac{79.5}{10.9}}$ (to 3 s.f.)

4 0.000356×385.7 (to 3 d.p.)

5 $(7.1 + 4.01) \times 8$ (to 3 s.f.)

6 $\dfrac{1}{0.0345}$ (to 3 s.f.)

7 $(4.63)^2$ (to 3 s.f.)

8 $2.1 + 3.41 \times 7.01$ (to 3 s.f.)

9 $\dfrac{3.8 \times 2.9}{17.1 \times 0.82}$ (to 3 d.p.)

10 $\frac{1}{2}(246.3 + 1092.8 + 376.4 + 49.8)$

11 $\dfrac{3.1 \times 15.2}{7.01 \times 8.11}$ (to 3 d.p.)

12 $\sqrt{\pi \times 38.4}$ (to 2 s.f.)

13 $\sqrt[3]{4 + 3.7 + 28.1}$ (to 1 d.p.)

*2.5 Standard form

Standard form is used when dealing with very large or very small numbers.

In standard form the number is always written as a number between 1 and 10 multiplied by a power of 10, i.e. as

$$A \times 10^n \text{ where } 1 \leq A < 10 \text{ and } n \text{ is an integer.}$$

This form is also known as **scientific notation**.

EXAMPLE 1

The velocity of light is 300 000 000 metres per second.

Write this number in standard form.

(i)   Write down A, the number between 1 and 10: 3.0

(ii) Count the number of places to the *right* which the decimal point must be moved to give the velocity of light: 8 places.

(iii) Write the number in standard form: 3.0×10^8

or $$300 000 000 = 3.0 \times 100 000 000$$
$$= 3.0 \times 10^8$$

EXAMPLE 2

0.000 000 000 000 000 000 000 000 001 67 kg is the mass of a hydrogen atom.

Write this number in standard form.

(i) $A = 1.67$

(ii) In this case the decimal point must be moved 27 places to the *left*, $n = -27$

(iii) In standard form, the mass $= 1.67 \times 10^{-27}$ kg.

EXAMPLE 3

Convert 3.15×10^4 to a 'normal' number.

$n = 4$ so the decimal point must be moved 4 places to the right:

$$3.15 \times 10^4 = 31 500$$

or $$3.15 \times 10^4 = 3.15 \times 10 000$$
$$= 31 500$$

EXAMPLE 4

Multiply (2.7×10^4) by (5×10^{-2})

$$\begin{aligned}(2.7 \times 10^4) \times (5 \times 10^{-2}) &= (2.7 \times 10\,000) \times (5 \div 100) \\ &= 13.5 \times 100 \\ &= 1.35 \times 1000 \\ &= 1.35 \times 10^3\end{aligned}$$

Using a calculator:
$$(2.7 \times 10^4) \times (5 \times 10^{-2}) = 2.7 \boxed{\text{EXP}} \, 4 \, \boxed{\text{X}} \, 5 \, \boxed{\text{EXP}} \, 2 \, \boxed{+/-}$$

(On some calculators the exponential button is $\boxed{\text{EE}}$.)

Calculator display is $\qquad\qquad$ 1350

$$= 1.35 \times 10^3 \text{ (in standard form)}$$

If it is possible to use your calculator in scientific mode, the same sequence of operations will produce the answer in standard form displaying

1.35 $\qquad$ 03 $\qquad$ or possibly 1.35^{03}

which is then written as 1.35×10^3.

(Some calculators round calculations to 2 s.f. displaying the answer as 1.4^{03}, which is then written as 1.4×10^3.)

EXAMPLE 5

Divide (2.7×10^4) by (5×10^{-2}).

$$\begin{aligned}(2.7 \times 10^4) \div (5 \times 10^{-2}) &= 27\,000 \div 0.05 \\ &= 540\,000 \\ &= 5.4 \times 10^5 \text{ (in standard form)}\end{aligned}$$

Using your calculator gives

$$\begin{aligned}(2.7 \times 10^4) \div (5 \times 10^{-2}) &= 2.7 \ \boxed{\text{EXP}} \, 4 \div 5 \, \boxed{\text{EXP}} \, 2 \, \boxed{+/-} \\ &= 540\,000 \\ &= 5.4 \times 10^5 \text{ (in standard form)}\end{aligned}$$

Working in the scientific mode will give the correct answer 5.4^{05}

which is conventionally written as 5.4×10^5.

Numbers in standard form can be added and subtracted, provided the power of 10 is the same in each number.

If the powers of 10 are *not* the same, convert each number to a normal number before adding or subtracting or convert to a common power of 10.

EXAMPLE 6

Evaluate $(4.3 \times 10^4) - (8.7 \times 10^3)$

$$(4.3 \times 10^4) - (8.7 \times 10^3) = 43\,000 - 8700$$
$$= 34\,300$$
$$= 3.43 \times 10^4$$

EXERCISE 2.5

1   Write the following numbers in standard form:

   a 790 000

   b 0.004 6

   c 31 300

   d 0.000 094 1

   e 100 000

   f 0.000 282

   g 15.7×1000

   h $4700 \times 10\,000$

   i 0.00034×100

   j $0.0027 \div 1000$

   k $5000 \div 10\,000$

   l $0.000028 \div 200$

2   Write the following numbers in normal form:

   a 7.53×10^3

   b 2.4×10^2

   c 1.9×10^{-3}

   d 8.37×10^{-1}

   e 4.51×10^{-2}

   f 4.042×10^4

   g 3.192×10^6

   h 9.74×10^{-4}

   i 6.8×10^{-6}

3   Evaluate the following, giving your answers in standard form:

   a $(3 \times 10^2) \times (2 \times 10^2)$

   b $(1.4 \times 10^{-3}) \times (3.7 \times 10^3)$

   c $(8 \times 10^3) \div (2 \times 10^2)$

   d $(5.3 \times 10^3) + (8.2 \times 10^3)$

   e $(4.6 \times 10^3) \times (5.9 \times 10^{-1})$

   f $(3.6 \times 10^4) \div (9.0 \times 10^5)$

   g $(2.7 \times 10^{-2}) \times (1.6 \times 10^{-3})$

   h $(3.3 \times 10^4) - (4.6 \times 10^3)$

   i $(4.5 \times 10^{-3}) - (5.0 \times 10^{-3})$

   j $(1.32 \times 10^{-1}) \div (2.2 \times 10^{-3})$

4   The distance from the Earth to the Sun is about 9.29×10^7 miles and from the Earth to the Moon is about 2.38×10^5 miles.
   How many times greater is the distance to the Sun than the distance to the Moon?

5   Light travels at a speed of 3.0×10^8 metres per second.

   If the distance from the Earth to the Sun is approximately 1.5×10^8 km, how long does it take the Sun's light to reach the Earth?

EXERCISE 2.6

1   The weight of 100 m of fine thread is 2.3 g.

   a Find the weight of 1 m and state this weight in kg in standard form.

   b Find the length of thread which has weight 2×10^{-4} kg.

2   A mill produces 350 m of a particular material.
   State this length (in cm) in standard form.

   One designer buys 8.34×10^3 cm
   How many metres of the material does the mill have left?

3   The revenue of the budget in West Samoa in 1990 was W\$ 1.21×10^8.
   The population was 1.6×10^5.
   What was the revenue raised per person?

4   The capacity of a computer is 40 megabytes where 1 megabyte is 10^3
   kilobytes. 1 kilobyte is 1.024×10^3 bytes.
   Express the capacity of the computer in bytes in standard form.

5   In Peter's blood there are 4.7×10^{12} blood cells per litre. Peter's body
   contains 4.9 litres of blood.
   How many red blood cells are there in Peter's body?

6   The population of the USA in 1992 was 2.55×10^8, of whom $\frac{1}{19}$
   were over 75 years old.
   How many were over 75?

7   The number of people attending a sports centre is 132 000 during a year:

   a Give this number in standard form.

   b Find the average number of people attending on each day.

8   The length of a round-the-world yacht race is 3.3×10^4 miles. A boat
   averages 311 miles per day.
   How many days does the yacht take to complete the race?

9   In 1992, Martinique imported goods worth $\$1.7 \times 10^9$. The population
   of the island was 3.7×10^5.
   What was the value of the goods imported per person (to the nearest
   dollar)?

10 In 1991 the coal reserves in the USA were estimated to be 2.15×10^{11}
   tons. The production was 9.44×10^8 tons.
   At this rate of production, how many years would the reserves last?

3 *Fractions*

3.1 *Types of fraction*

A fraction is a number which can be written as a ratio, with an integer divided by an integer, e.g. $\dfrac{7}{9}$ or $-\dfrac{2}{3}$.

If a shape is divided into a number of equal parts and some of those parts are then shaded, the shaded area can be written as a fraction of the whole.

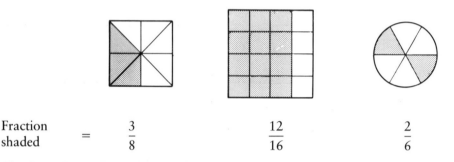

| Fraction shaded | = | $\dfrac{3}{8}$ | $\dfrac{12}{16}$ | $\dfrac{2}{6}$ |

The **denominator** (lower integer) denotes the number of parts into which the shape was divided.

The **numerator** (upper integer) denotes the number of parts which have been shaded.

Fractions which have a smaller numerator than denominator are called **proper** fractions, e.g. $\dfrac{1}{2}$, $\dfrac{5}{12}$, $-\dfrac{28}{60}$

If the numerator is larger than the denominator, the fraction is an **improper** fraction, e.g. $\dfrac{12}{5}$, $-\dfrac{7}{2}$, $\dfrac{72}{18}$

A **mixed number** is a number composed of an integer and a proper fraction, e.g. $3\dfrac{1}{2}$, $-24\dfrac{3}{4}$, $4\dfrac{5}{6}$

3.2 *Equivalent fractions*

We could consider the larger square above to be divided into four columns instead of sixteen squares.

The shaded area is then $\dfrac{3}{4}$ of the whole. This means that $\dfrac{12}{16} = \dfrac{3}{4}$

$\dfrac{12}{16}$ and $\dfrac{3}{4}$ are called **equivalent fractions** because they have the same value.

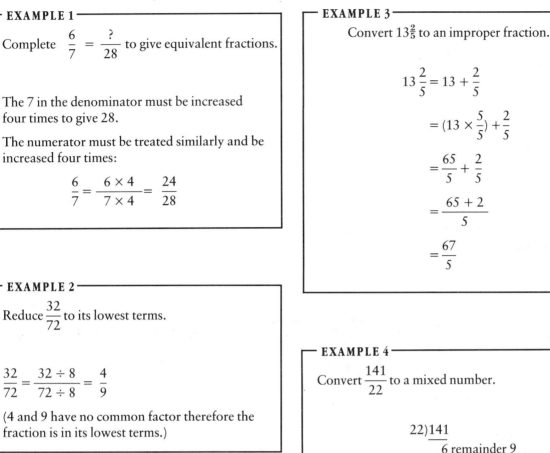

EXAMPLE 1

Complete $\dfrac{6}{7} = \dfrac{?}{28}$ to give equivalent fractions.

The 7 in the denominator must be increased four times to give 28.

The numerator must be treated similarly and be increased four times:

$$\frac{6}{7} = \frac{6 \times 4}{7 \times 4} = \frac{24}{28}$$

EXAMPLE 2

Reduce $\dfrac{32}{72}$ to its lowest terms.

$$\frac{32}{72} = \frac{32 \div 8}{72 \div 8} = \frac{4}{9}$$

(4 and 9 have no common factor therefore the fraction is in its lowest terms.)

EXAMPLE 3

Convert $13\frac{2}{5}$ to an improper fraction.

$$13\frac{2}{5} = 13 + \frac{2}{5}$$

$$= \left(13 \times \frac{5}{5}\right) + \frac{2}{5}$$

$$= \frac{65}{5} + \frac{2}{5}$$

$$= \frac{65 + 2}{5}$$

$$= \frac{67}{5}$$

EXAMPLE 4

Convert $\dfrac{141}{22}$ to a mixed number.

$$22)\overline{141}$$
$$ 6 \text{ remainder } 9$$

$$\frac{141}{22} = 6\frac{9}{22}$$

EXERCISE 3.1

1 Complete each of the following to give equivalent fractions:

   a $\dfrac{4}{5} = \dfrac{?}{10}$

   b $\dfrac{2}{3} = \dfrac{?}{12}$

   c $\dfrac{3}{4} = \dfrac{?}{24}$

   d $\dfrac{1}{4} = \dfrac{?}{36}$

   e $\dfrac{21}{30} = \dfrac{?}{10}$

   f $\dfrac{16}{18} = \dfrac{8}{?}$

2 Reduce the following fractions to their lowest terms:

   a $\dfrac{10}{15}$ b $\dfrac{18}{24}$ c $\dfrac{22}{99}$ d $\dfrac{21}{63}$

   e $\dfrac{75}{100}$ f $\dfrac{40}{60}$ g $\dfrac{30}{65}$ h $\dfrac{64}{96}$

3 A particular shade of green paint is made by mixing 60 g of blue powder paint with 30 g of yellow powder paint.
   What fraction of the mixture is blue paint?

4 A secretary's working day is 8 hours long. On one particular day, $4\frac{1}{2}$ hours were spent typing and $1\frac{1}{2}$ hours on the telephone.
What fraction of the working day was spent:
a typing   b telephoning?

5 A dental chart shows that a patient with a full set of 32 teeth has 6 fillings.
What fraction of the teeth are filled?

6 In a group of 240 tourists travelling on a charter flight, 180 requested seats in the non-smoking section.
What fraction of the passengers were in the smoking section?

7 A printing firm produces 350 books in a day. 200 of these are to be exported.
What fraction of the day's production is exported?

8 Convert the following mixed numbers to improper fractions:

a $2\frac{2}{9}$ b $5\frac{1}{6}$ c $4\frac{11}{12}$ d $11\frac{1}{10}$

e $8\frac{3}{4}$ f $12\frac{2}{3}$ g $7\frac{3}{20}$ h $20\frac{3}{7}$

9 Convert the following improper fractions to mixed numbers, in their lowest terms:

a $\frac{9}{7}$ b $\frac{36}{5}$ c $\frac{30}{9}$ d $\frac{61}{8}$

e $\frac{153}{11}$ f $\frac{127}{12}$ g $\frac{132}{15}$ h $\frac{94}{4}$

3.3 *Operations involving fractions*

Addition and subtraction

Only fractions *of the same type* can be added or subtracted, i.e. they must have the same denominator.

The method for addition or subtraction is:

(i) Find the smallest number which is a multiple of all the denominators.

(ii) Change each fraction to an equivalent fraction with the new denominator.

(iii) Add and/or subtract the fractions.

(iv) If the answer is an improper fraction, convert to a mixed number.

(v) Give the answer in its lowest terms.

EXAMPLE 1

Evaluate $\dfrac{5}{8} - \dfrac{3}{4} + \dfrac{1}{5}$

40 is the smallest number that is a multiple of all the denominators.

The sum in equivalent fractions is $\dfrac{5 \times 5}{8 \times 5} - \dfrac{3 \times 10}{4 \times 10} + \dfrac{1 \times 8}{5 \times 8} = \dfrac{25}{40} - \dfrac{30}{40} + \dfrac{8}{40}$

$= \dfrac{3}{40}$ which is a fraction in its lowest terms.

EXAMPLE 2

Evaluate $1\frac{2}{3} + \frac{3}{4} - 2\frac{1}{12}$

$$1\frac{2}{3} + \frac{3}{4} - 2\frac{1}{12} = 1 + \frac{2}{3} + \frac{3}{4} - \left(2 + \frac{1}{12}\right)$$

$$= 1 + \frac{2}{3} + \frac{3}{4} - 2 - \frac{1}{12}$$

The smallest multiple of all the denominators is 12.

The sum in equivalent fractions is $\dfrac{12}{12} + \dfrac{8}{12} + \dfrac{9}{12} - \dfrac{24}{12} - \dfrac{1}{12}$

$$= \frac{12 + 8 + 9 - 24 - 1}{12}$$

$$= \frac{4}{12} = \frac{1}{3} \text{ in its lowest terms}$$

EXERCISE 3.2

Evaluate the following:

1 $\dfrac{2}{5} + \dfrac{3}{4}$

2 $\dfrac{7}{8} - \dfrac{5}{6}$

3 $\dfrac{5}{12} + \dfrac{1}{4}$

4 $1\dfrac{1}{2} - \dfrac{3}{4}$

5 $4\dfrac{1}{6} - 3\dfrac{2}{3}$

6 $3\dfrac{4}{5} + 1\dfrac{1}{4}$

7 $3\dfrac{1}{2} - 4\dfrac{1}{4} + 2\dfrac{3}{4}$

8 $3\dfrac{5}{8} - 1\dfrac{1}{4} - 1\dfrac{1}{2}$

9 A clear glaze for pottery is made by mixing feldspar, flint, whiting and china clay.
One half of the mix is feldspar and one fifth is china clay. Flint and whiting are mixed in equal amounts.

What fraction of the mix is flint?

10 a Photographic prints $4\frac{1}{2}$ in wide by $3\frac{1}{2}$ in are to be mounted in an album which has pages $9\frac{3}{4}$ in wide by $13\frac{1}{4}$ in.

How many prints can be mounted on one page?

b The photographs are to be equally spaced on the page. What width are the margins:
a across the page   **b** down the page?

11 Three quarters of an office's stationery budget is spent on paper, one sixth on envelopes, and the remainder on miscellaneous items.
What fraction is spent on miscellaneous items?

12 To encourage customers to pay their bills, a firm gives a discount of $\frac{1}{20}$ of the bill if it is paid on time and a further discount of $\frac{1}{12}$ of the bill for early payment.

What fraction of the bill is deducted for early payment?

13 A dietician, advising clients on suitable diets, found that $\frac{3}{4}$ of her clients were overweight, $\frac{1}{6}$ suffered from arthritis and the remainder from coeliac disease.

a What fraction were coeliac sufferers?

b If her clients numbered 36 at the time, how many needed a gluten-free diet?

14 A cold remedy is sold as a powder in sachets. $\frac{4}{5}$ of each powder is aspirin and $\frac{2}{25}$ is ascorbic acid. The remainder is caffeine.

a What fraction is caffeine?

b How much of each ingredient does 500 mg of powder contain?

15 The proprietor of a B & B establishment mixes his own breakfast cereal. This consists of $2\frac{1}{2}$ cups of oats, $\frac{1}{4}$ of a cup of wheat germ, and $\frac{2}{3}$ of a cup of raisins and nuts.

What is the total number of cups in this mixture?

16 During a three-day holiday break, $1\frac{1}{2}$ in of rain fell on the first day, $1\frac{3}{4}$ in on the second day and $3\frac{3}{4}$ in on the third day.

How much rain fell altogether?

17 An axle of diameter $2\frac{3}{4}$ inches is fitted into the centre of the hub of a wheel which has a diameter of $3\frac{1}{8}$ inches.

How much clearance is there between the axle and the inside of the hub on each side?

18 In a self-assembly unit, a wood top, $\frac{5}{8}$ in thick, is screwed to a metal frame $1\frac{1}{4}$ in thick.

What is the maximum length of screw that can be used?

Multiplication and division

The rules for multiplication and division of fractions are very different from those for addition and subtraction.

The fractions do not have to have the same denominator, but they must not be mixed numbers.

Answers should be given in their lowest terms and as mixed numbers, if necessary.

To divide by a fraction, invert it and then multiply by the inverted fraction.

EXAMPLE 1

Multiply $\dfrac{18}{25}$ by $\dfrac{5}{6}$

$$\frac{18}{25} \times \frac{5}{6} = \frac{18 \times 5}{25 \times 6} = \frac{90}{150} = \frac{3}{5} \qquad or \qquad \frac{18}{25} \times \frac{5}{6} = \frac{\overset{3}{\cancel{18}} \times \overset{1}{\cancel{5}}}{\underset{5}{\cancel{25}} \times \underset{1}{\cancel{6}}} = \frac{3 \times 1}{5 \times 1} = \frac{3}{5}$$

EXAMPLE 2

Evaluate $1\dfrac{3}{4} \times 2\dfrac{2}{7}$

The mixed numbers are converted to improper fractions:

$$\frac{7}{4} \times \frac{16}{7} = \frac{7 \times 16}{4 \times 7} = \frac{112}{28} = 4 \qquad or \qquad \frac{7}{4} \times \frac{16}{7} = \frac{\overset{1}{\cancel{7}} \times \overset{4}{\cancel{16}}}{\underset{1}{\cancel{4}} \times \underset{1}{\cancel{7}}} = \frac{1 \times 4}{1 \times 1} = 4$$

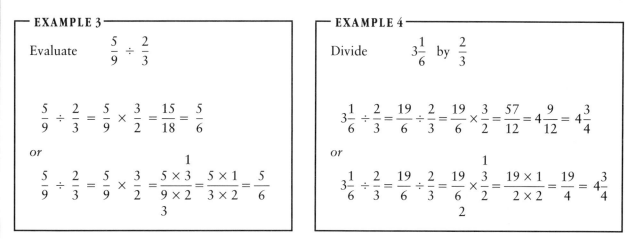

┌─ **EXAMPLE 3** ─────────────────────

Evaluate $\dfrac{5}{9} \div \dfrac{2}{3}$

$$\frac{5}{9} \div \frac{2}{3} = \frac{5}{9} \times \frac{3}{2} = \frac{15}{18} = \frac{5}{6}$$

or

$$\frac{5}{9} \div \frac{2}{3} = \frac{5}{9} \times \overset{1}{\frac{3}{2}} = \frac{5 \times 3}{9 \times 2} = \frac{5 \times 1}{3 \times 2} = \frac{5}{6}$$
$$\underset{3}{}$$

┌─ **EXAMPLE 4** ─────────────────────

Divide $3\dfrac{1}{6}$ by $\dfrac{2}{3}$

$$3\frac{1}{6} \div \frac{2}{3} = \frac{19}{6} \div \frac{2}{3} = \frac{19}{6} \times \frac{3}{2} = \frac{57}{12} = 4\frac{9}{12} = 4\frac{3}{4}$$

or

$$3\frac{1}{6} \div \frac{2}{3} = \frac{19}{6} \div \frac{2}{3} = \frac{19}{6} \times \overset{1}{\frac{3}{2}} = \frac{19 \times 1}{2 \times 2} = \frac{19}{4} = 4\frac{3}{4}$$
$$\underset{2}{}$$

EXERCISE 3.3

Evaluate the following:

1 $\dfrac{7}{8} \times \dfrac{4}{5}$ **2** $1\dfrac{2}{3} \times \dfrac{4}{5}$ **3** $6 \div \dfrac{1}{2}$ **4** $\dfrac{5}{6} \div \dfrac{3}{4}$ **5** $2\dfrac{1}{5} \times 3\dfrac{1}{4}$ **6** $5\dfrac{1}{7} \div 3$

7 The length of the head of an adult is about $\frac{1}{8}$ of the adult's height.
For a baby, the head is about $\frac{1}{3}$ of the total height.

  a An artist draws the figure of a lady which is $4\frac{4}{5}$ inches in length.
  What, approximately, should be the length of the head?

  b In the same picture, a baby is drawn with a head length of $\frac{1}{2}$ inch.
  What, approximately, should be the length of the baby from neck to foot?

8 A silversmith designs a kilt pin which is a sword $6\frac{1}{4}$ cm long. The hilt is $\frac{1}{5}$ of the total length and the cross-piece is $\frac{3}{5}$ of the blade.
What is the length of:

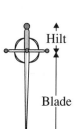

  a the hilt

  b the cross-piece?

9 In a small business, overtime is paid at one and a third (see Section 7.2). The basic hourly rate is £5.70 per hour.

  What is the overtime rate of pay per hour?

10 A5 paper is half the size of A4, which is half the size of A3.

  a What fraction of A3 size paper is A5?

  b How many sheets of A3 should be cut to make two dozen sheets of A5?

11 In a healthy person approximately $\frac{1}{15}$ of their weight is body fat.
How much body fat should a healthy person of $11\frac{1}{4}$ stones have?

12 Approximately $\frac{1}{7}$ of virgin oil consists of saturates.
Approximately, how many grams of saturates are contained in:

  a a 91 g bottle of oil

  b a $5\frac{1}{4}$ g helping of oil?

13 A large bowl contains three times the B&B proprietor's cereal mixture (see question 15, Exercise 3.2). Each guest receives $\frac{3}{4}$ of a cup of cereal for breakfast.
How many guests can be served with the contents of the bowl?

14 A travel company charges children $\frac{2}{3}$ of the cost of an adult's holiday price.

    a How much is charged for a child if the adult price is £432?

    b How many children are the equivalent, in cost, of ten adults?

15 A $1\frac{7}{8}$ in long screw has a thread which is $\frac{3}{5}$ of the length of the screw.

    How long is the thread?

16 A toy manufacturer makes sets of boxes which nest inside one another. One set is rectangular in shape and the length of each box is $1\frac{2}{3}$ times the width.

    a If the width of the largest box in the set is $4\frac{1}{2}$ inches, what is the length?

    b If the length of the smallest box is $4\frac{1}{6}$ inches, what is the width?

3.4 *The conversion between fractions and decimal fractions*

The fraction $\frac{7}{8}$ may be stated as $7 \div 8$.

Using a calculator, $7 \div 8 = 0.875$, and this is the **decimal fraction** which is equivalent to $\frac{7}{8}$.

EXAMPLE 1

Convert $3\frac{5}{6}$ to a decimal.

The integer part of the mixed number remains the same. Only the fractional part needs to be converted.

On the calculator $5 \div 6 = 0.8333333$ which is a recurring decimal.

$$3\frac{5}{6} = 3.8\dot{3} \text{ or } 3.83 \text{ (to 3 s.f.)}$$

All fractions convert to either a terminating or a recurring decimal. The dot above the 3 indicates that the 3 is a recurring decimal.

EXAMPLE 2

Convert 0.35 to a fraction in its lowest terms.

$$0.35 = \frac{35}{100} = \frac{7}{20} \text{ (dividing numerator and denominator by 5)}$$

EXERCISE 3.4

1 Write down the shaded area as (i) a fraction, (ii) a decimal fraction of the whole area.

a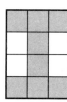

b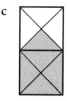

c

2 Convert the following fractions to decimals:

a $\dfrac{1}{10}$ **b** $\dfrac{1}{2}$ **c** $\dfrac{3}{4}$ **d** $1\dfrac{9}{20}$

e $4\dfrac{21}{25}$ **f** $2\dfrac{5}{6}$ **g** $7\dfrac{4}{9}$ **h** $3\dfrac{1}{7}$

3 Convert the following decimals to fractions:

a 0.5   **f** 2.8

b 0.25   **g** 3.6

c $0.\dot{6}$ **h** 2.15

d $1.\dot{3}$ **i** 0.125

e 1.3   **j** 0.375

4 Investigate the relationships between the fractional and decimal forms of:

a halves, quarters and eighths

b thirds, sixths and ninths.

5 Describe a quick method of converting to decimals:

a tenths   **b** fifths   **c** hundredths

d twentieths   **e** twenty-fifths.

In questions 6–11, where appropriate, write the answer:

(i) as a mixed number in its lowest terms

(ii) as a decimal correct to 2 d.p.

6 A designer draws a sketch for a new design of car. The length of the car on the sketch is $4\frac{1}{2}$ inches. The actual length of the car is 153 inches.

How many times larger is the actual car than the sketch?

7 a A chemist sells toothpaste in two sizes: 75 g and 125 g.

How many times larger is the 125 g tube than the 75 g tube of toothpaste?

b If the cost of the 75 g tube of paste is 48p what should the equivalent price of the 125 g tube be?

8 Traditionally, 1 quire of paper = 24 sheets
               1 ream of paper = 20 quires
Nowadays, however, a ream is generally 500 sheets.

a How many extra sheets are there in a ream?

b How many quires are there in a ream?

9 On a hospital ward, 40 minutes is spent every day checking patients' temperatures and blood pressures.

How many hours are spent on this activity in a 7-day week?

10 A tour bus driver has to travel 112 miles on the first leg of the journey. The driver expects to travel at an average speed of 35 mph.

What is his estimate of the time for this part of the journey?

11 A piece of machinery has two interlocking cogs.

Cog A has 35 teeth.
Cog B has 20 teeth.

How many turns does Cog B make for each turn of Cog A?

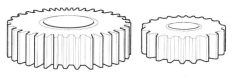

         Cog A   Cog B

4 *Ratio and Proportion*

4.1 *Ratio*

Carmen's parents give her a weekly allowance of £3.60.
Her younger brother, Leroy, is given an allowance of £1.20. Carmen receives three times as much allowance as Leroy. Here is another way of saying the same thing:

The ratio of Carmen's allowance to Leroy's allowance is **3 : 1**

Ratios can be written with a colon between the amounts, like this:

First quantity : Second quantity

or as a fraction, like this: $\dfrac{\text{First quantity}}{\text{Second quantity}}$

EXAMPLE 1

When Leroy is older, his parents decide that the ratio between his allowance and his sister's should now be 2 : 3.
If Carmen receives £3.90 per week, how much should they give Leroy?

$$\text{Leroy's allowance : Carmen's allowance} = 2 : 3 = \frac{2}{3}$$

$$\text{Leroy should receive } \frac{2}{3} \text{ of Carmen's allowance}$$

$$\text{Leroy's allowance} = \frac{2}{3} \times £3.90 = £2.60$$

EXAMPLE 2

A large jar of coffee costs £2.38 and a small jar costs 84p.
Express these prices as a ratio in its lowest terms.

Converting both prices to pence gives the ratio

Large jar : small jar = 238 : 84

The ratio can be reduced if 238 and 84 can both be divided by the same number (called a common factor).

The largest factor which is common to 238 and 84 may not be immediately obvious, in which case the reduction to lowest terms can be carried out in stages.

2 is a common factor of 238 and 84. Dividing by 2 reduces the ratio to
119 : 42

Possible factors of 42 are 2, 3, 6 and 7.
Only 7 is also a factor of 119.

Dividing by 7 gives the ratio in its lowest terms

$$= 17 : 6$$

EXERCISE 4.1

In questions 1–3, write all ratios in their lowest terms.

1 Two brothers have £20 and £24 in their respective savings accounts.
Express these amounts as a ratio.

2 Miss Morgan has £320 in her current account, £400 in her deposit account, and £800 in her savings account.
Express these amounts as a ratio.

3 A pound of grapes costs £1.60 and a pound of pears 72p. Write these prices as a ratio.

4 Write each pair of quantities as a ratio in its lowest terms:

a 60 m, 40 m   f 15 cm, 10 cm

b £2, 20p   g 750 g, 2 kg

c 0.6 cm, 0.05 cm   h 39 litres, 26 litres

d 0.4 m, 1.6 m   i 32 mph, 48 mph

e 1 ft, 9 in

5 Complete the following ratios:

a 3 : 4 = 6 : ?   d 240 : 400 = ? : 1

b 18 : 9 = ? : 1   e 20 : 1 = 64 : ?

c ? : 1 = 12 : 10   f 1 : ? = 5 : 13

6 Spring bulbs are planted in a border in the ratio of 3 yellow tulips to 2 pink tulips to 5 grape hyacinths.
If 615 yellow tulip bulbs are planted, how many pink tulip bulbs and how many grape hyacinth bulbs are planted?

7 Two terracotta pots have volumes in the ratio of 2 : 9. The smaller can hold 3 kg of peat.
What weight of peat can the larger pot hold?

8 The width of a marigold flowerhead in a photograph is 9 mm. In an enlargement the width is 6 cm.
Write these widths as a ratio.

9 Carl, Stephanie and Joanne deal with 425 clients in a year. The number of clients are in the ratio of 2 : 5 : 10.

a How many clients has Stephanie?

b How many more clients has Joanne than Carl?

10 The cost of a drug to a hospital is 75p and a rest home pays £4 for the same drug.
Write these prices as a ratio.

11 The daily feeds of two new born babies are in the ratio of 3 : 4. The smaller baby needs 21 fl oz per day.
How much milk does the larger baby need?

12 In a leisure centre, the width and height of a locker are 9 inches and 6 feet.
Write these measurements as a ratio.

13 Sara, Richard and Francesca hire cars on their holidays. The number of miles travelled by them are in the ratio 4 : 3 : 6. The total mileage travelled is 3120 miles.

a How many miles does Richard travel?

b How many more miles does Francesca travel than Sara?

14 The length of a hacksaw blade is 32 cm and its width is 8 mm. Write these measurements as a ratio.

15 A garage dealing in Ford cars sells Fiestas, Escorts and Mondeos in the ratio of 4 : 5 : 2. In one month 363 of these cars are sold.
How many were Mondeos?

4.2 *Division in a given ratio*

FAIR SHARES FOR ALL!!

This does not necessarily mean equal shares for all.

For example, if three partners invest different amounts of money in a business, they might expect the profits to be shared in proportion to their investment.

EXAMPLE 1

Divide £672 between Emily, Faye and Geoff in the ratio 7 : 5 : 9 respectively. How much does each person receive?

Method
 (i) Find the total number of shares.
 (ii) Find the amount of one share.
(iii) Find the amount each receives.

Calculation
 (i)   Total number of shares = $7 + 5 + 9$ $= 21$

 (ii)   Amount of one share = $\dfrac{£672}{21}$ $= £32$

(iii)   Emily receives $£32 \times 7$ $= £224$
                            Faye receives $£32 \times 5$ $= £160$
                            Geoff receives $£32 \times 9$ $= £288$

(*Check.* $224 + 160 + 288 = 672$.)

EXAMPLE 2

Three partners, A, B and C, invest money in a small business. The amounts they invest are £10 000, £12 000 and £6000, respectively.

At the end of the first year of trading the profits from the business are £14 350.

They each receive profits in proportion to their investment.
How much does each partner receive?

The investments are in the ratio 10 000 : 12 000 : 6000
                                       $= 5 :   6   :   3$
The total number of shares $= 5 + 6 + 3$ $= 14$
One share of the profits $= £14 350 \div 14$ $= £1025$
A receives 5 shares $= £1025 \times 5$ $= £5125$
B receives 6 shares $= £1025 \times 6$ $= £6150$
C receives 3 shares $= £1025 \times 3$ $= £3075$

(*Check.* $5125 + 6150 + 3075 = 14 350$.)

EXERCISE 4.2

1 Divide £650 in the ratio 2 : 3.

2 Divide £12 000 in the ratio 1 : 3 : 4.

3 Divide £104 in the ratio 6 : 4 : 3.

4 Mrs Chandra shared £4000 among her three children in the ratio 7 : 5 : 4.
How much did each receive?

5 The Shang Dynasty in China was making bronze artifacts more than three thousand years ago.

The bronze they used was an alloy of copper and zinc in the ratio (by weight) of 17 : 3.
What weights of copper and zinc were used to make a bronze bowl weighing 1.6 kilograms?

6 The number of necklaces, bracelets and earrings made by a jeweller are in the ratio of 4 : 5 : 8. In one week, she made 68 pieces of jewellery.
How many of the pieces made were bracelets?

7 X and Y invested money in a home computing business. X put in £6000, but Y could only afford £4000. The profits were divided in the same ratio as their investment.

a At the end of the first year the profits were £10 530.
How much did each receive?

b At the end of the second year X's share of the profits was £9456.
How much was the total profit?

c After two years Y increased his investment to £5000. At the end of the year his share of the profits was £8270.
How much did X receive?

8 Four office workers run a pools syndicate and each week pay £4.95, £6.60, £3.30 and £4.95 respectively for their entry. When they win £104 616 they divide the winnings in the ratio of their weekly contribution.
How much does each receive?

9 A drug company representative gives 72 trial samples of a drug to two doctors in the ratio of 3 : 5.
How many samples does each doctor receive?

10 On one day, a hospital casualty department saw 140 accident victims. The ratio of casualties caused by motor accidents, accidents in the home, sporting accidents and others was 4 : 5 : 3 : 2.
How many casualties were the result of motor accidents?

11 a Every summer, Grandma gives her grandchildren money to spend on holiday in the ratio of their ages. When David is 10 years old, Emily is 6 years old.

(i) What is the ratio of their ages, in its simplest form?

(ii) If Grandma gives the children £12 to share, how much does each child receive?

b Next year the children again share £12 between them in the ratio of their ages.
How much (to the nearest 1p) does each receive?

12 The cost of hiring a coach from Bournemouth to London for a day trip was £78. The breakdown of the cost into labour, fuel, overheads and profit was in the ratio of 4:4:3:2.
How much of the cost was for the driver?

13 On one day, a toy manufacturer makes 2072 fashion dolls dressed either in disco wear or in riding gear. The ratio of dolls in disco wear to riding gear is 7:1.
How many dolls are wearing disco wear?

14 A company makes 1056 television sets. The number of portable, small screen and large screen models is in the ratio of 4:15:3.

a How many portable television sets are made?

b How many of the televisions are small screen models?

4.3 *Direct proportion*

If two quantities increase, or decrease, at the same rate, they are said to be in
direct proportion.

For example, if you double your speed of walking you will travel twice as far in
the same period of time.

EXAMPLE

Mrs Wall usually buys 12 pints of milk each week and pays the milkman
£3.72. In a week when she has visitors, she buys 3 extra pints. How much
is her milk bill for that week?

$$12 \text{ pints of milk cost £3.72}$$

$$1 \text{ pint of milk costs } \frac{£3.72}{12} \ (=31\text{p})$$

$$(12 + 3) \text{ pints of milk cost } \frac{£3.72}{12} \times 15$$

$$= £4.65$$

EXERCISE 4.3

1   Find the cost of 6 lb of apples if 4 lb cost £2.12.

2   The baker's shop sells cheese biscuits for £1.52
    per quarter pound.
    How much would 7 oz cost? ($\frac{1}{4}$ lb = 4 oz).

3   Pic'n'Mix sweets cost 56p per quarter pound.
    How much would you be charged for 9 oz?

4   A printer charges £1.15 for 25 posters.
    How much should be charged for 40 posters?

5   A designer sells coasters in packs of 18 for
    £19.80. In order to increase sales, the designer
    decides to offer them also in packs of 4.
    How much should he charge for a pack of 4
    coasters?

6   A tax adviser charges clients per letter sent. John
    pays £352 when 16 letters are sent. How much
    should Camilla pay if her tax affairs require 11
    letters?

7   An accountant charges £369 for 12 hours of her
    professional services.
    How much should she charge for 14 hours?

8   A rest-home needs 24 care assistants when there
    are 6 residents.
    How many assistants does it need when there
    are 11 residents?

9   Amy burns up 75 calories when she swims for
    15 minutes.
    How many calories does she use up when she
    swims for 40 minutes?

10 On an organised hike, it is estimated that hikers
    take $3\frac{1}{2}$ hours to walk $10\frac{1}{2}$ miles.
    How long will it take them to walk 12 miles at
    the same speed?

11 A timeshare agent is paid for each person he
    persuades to look at a new development.
    Alastair sends 32 people and is paid £1312.
    How much does Jason receive when he sends 45
    people?

12 A carpenter uses 48 screws to fit 4 doors.
    How many screws does he need to fit 7 doors?

13 Two spanners are in the ratio of 4 : 11. The
    smaller is $\frac{1}{4}''$.
    What size is the larger spanner?

4.4 *Scale diagrams and models*

Scale Diagrams

Scale diagrams are two-dimensional representations of three-dimensional shapes. If the scale diagram is to be a faithful representation of the original, all the corresponding measurements of the original and the scale diagram must be in the same proportion.

The **scale** is the proportion by which each measurement has been reduced.

In order to fit a diagram onto paper, the measurements have to be 'scaled down'.
Once this has been done, you have a 'scale diagram'.

A scale is expressed either as a comparison between 2 lengths:

e.g. 1 cm : 2 m

or as a ratio:

e.g. 1 : 200.

For example, a scale of 2 centimetres to 1 metre means that every length of 1 metre on the original is represented by a length of 2 centimetres on the scale diagram, i.e. the measurements are all in the ratio of 1 : 50 and all the measurements of the scale diagram are $\frac{1}{50}$ of those of the original.

EXAMPLE 1

The scale of a diagram is 1 : 5. AB in the scaled diagram is 4 cm.
Find the original length AB.

$$\text{Original length} = 5 \times 4\,\text{cm}$$
$$= 20\,\text{cm}$$

EXAMPLE 2

A scale diagram of a playing field is drawn on a scale of 1 : 500.

a What distance on the ground is represented by 6.3 cm on the scale diagram?

b What distance on the scale diagram represents 82 m on the ground?

a 1 cm represents 500 cm

$$6.3\,\text{cm represents } 500 \times 6.3\,\text{cm} = 3150\,\text{cm} = \frac{3150}{100}\,\text{m}$$

$$= 31.5\,\text{m}$$

Actual distance = Scale × Length on scale diagram

b $500 \, \text{cm} = \dfrac{500}{100} \, \text{m} = 5 \, \text{m}$

5 m is represented by 1 cm
1 m is represented by 0.2 cm
82 m is represented by $82 \times 0.2 \, \text{cm} = 16.4 \, \text{cm}$

or $\text{Length on diagram} = \dfrac{\textbf{Actual length}}{\textbf{Scale of diagram}}$

$= \dfrac{82 \times 100}{500} \, \text{cm}$

$= 16.4 \, \text{cm}$

EXAMPLE 3

The length of a kitchen is 4.8 m. The length on a scale diagram is 6 cm.
Find the scale used.

$$\text{Scale} = \frac{\textbf{Original length}}{\textbf{Scaled length}}$$

Converting all units to centimetres gives

$$\text{Scale} = \frac{4.8 \times 100}{6}$$

$$= 80$$

The scale of the diagram is 1 : 80.

EXERCISE 4.4

1 Convert the following actual lengths to
scale diagram lengths using the scales given:

Actual length	Scale
a 5 metres	1 : 500
b 120 metres	1 : 2500
c 11 metres	1 : 10
d 14.4 centimetres	1 : 5

2 Convert the following diagram lengths to the
original lengths using the scales given:

Diagram length	Scale
a 2 centimetres	1 : 10
b 3.1 centimetres	1 : 40
c 2.8 centimetres	1 : 60
d 3 inches	1 : 300
e 4.5 inches	1 : 20

3 The end of a roll of dress material is shown
below on a scale of 1 : 40.

Find: **a** the width of the material

b the length of one pattern of the
material (before it repeats).

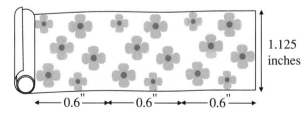

1.125 inches

← 0.6″ → ← 0.6″ → ← 0.6″ →

4   A designer sketches a dress
    The height of the model on whom the dress will
    be shown is 5′ 9″. Find:

    a the scale used in drawing the sketch

    b the length of the dress.

5   The plan of an office is shown on a scale of
    1 : 50.

    a What are the dimensions of a desk in metres?

    b What is the minimum distance between the
        two desks?

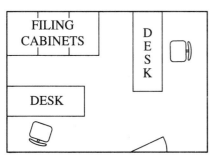

6   A company is hoping to build a 'green field site
    factory'. On an Ordnance Survey map scale
    1 : 2500, the rectangular plot of land is 4 cm by
    18 cm.
    What are the actual dimensions of the field?

7   The plan of a room in a rest-home is shown
    below on a scale of 1 : 80.
    Find the area of the room in m².

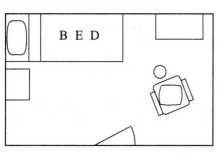

8   The plan of a ward in a cottage hospital is
    shown below.
    The beds are 3′ by 6′. Find:

    a the scale of the plan

    b the size of the ward.

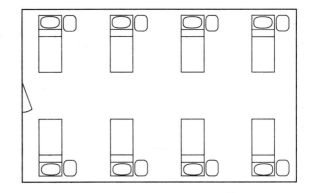

9   The diagram shows the accurate drawing of a
    car to a scale of 1 : 50. Find the length and
    height of the car in metres.

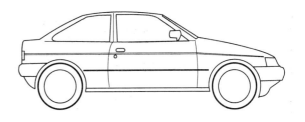

10 The plan shows the machine-tool section of a
    manufacturing company. Each work station is
    at least 2.4 m from the next work-station.
    Find:

    a the scale of the plan

    b the area of a work-station.

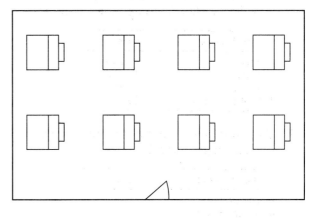

Models

A model is a replica, usually much smaller in size, of an original object. As with scale diagrams, if the model is to be a faithful representation of the original, all the corresponding measurements of the original and the model must be in the same proportion.

EXAMPLE 1

A model of an aircraft is made to a scale of 1 cm : 1.8 m.

a The length of the aircraft is 43 m. What is the length of the model?

b The width of the cargo hold on the model is 4.2 cm.
What is the width of the cargo hold on the aircraft?

a 1.8 m is represented by 1 cm

  1 m is represented by $\dfrac{1}{1.8}$ cm

  43 m is represented by $\dfrac{1}{1.8} \times 43$ cm

  $= 23.9$ cm

b 1 cm represents 1.8 m
  4.2 cm represents 1.8×4.2 m
  $= 7.56$ m

EXAMPLE 2

The wing-span of a Boeing 747 is 59.6 metres. A model of the aircraft has a wing-span of 29.8 centimetres.
To what scale was the model made?

  29.8 cm represent 59.6 m

  1 cm represents $\dfrac{59.6}{29.8}$ m $= 2$ m $= 200$ cm

The scale is '1 cm represents 200 cm' or 1 : 200

Provided both lengths have the same units,

$$\text{Scale} = \frac{\text{Original length}}{\text{Scaled length}}$$

EXERCISE 4.5

1 A doll's house is made to a scale of 1 centimetre representing 30 centimetres.

   a What are the measurements, in the doll's house, of the following:

     (i) a 2.1 m high door

     (ii) a carpet measuring 4.2 m × 3.6 m

     (iii) a plate of diameter 24 cm?

   b What would be the full-scale sizes of the following doll's house furnishings:

     (i) a chair of height 3.1 cm

     (ii) a candlestick 4.5 mm high

     (iii) a picture 23 mm × 20 mm?

2 **a** When Alice ate a cake marked 'Eat me' she found herself enlarged on a scale of 1 to 1.9. If she was previously 4 ft 10 in tall, how tall was she after eating the cake?

   b When Alice drank the contents of the bottle labelled 'Drink me', she shrank to a height of 10 inches.
If the miniature Alice had feet which were 3.6 cm long, how long were the feet on the enlarged Alice?

3 An 'N' gauge model railway is made to a scale of $\frac{1}{150}$. The roof of a model station is 136 mm long.

   a How long would the actual station roof be?

   b Taking 30 cm = 1 foot, calculate the actual length of the roof in feet.

4 A model of a stage set is made to a scale of 1 : 20.

   a A table is 1.2 m by 0.6 m.
What are its dimensions on the model?

   b A bed is the model is 6.2 cm wide.
What is its actual width?

5 An architect produces a model of a housing development to a scale of 1 : 125.

   a A house will be 11 m wide.
What is its width on the model?

   b A road on the model is 4 cm wide.
What will be its actual width?

6 In a children's home, the children produce a model of an outside play area using Lego bricks. A roundabout in the model is 6 cm wide and represents an actual roundabout 9 m wide.

   a What is the scale of the model?

   b A slide is 4 m long.
What should be its length in the model?

7 A travel agent made a window display of the Pyramids to promote a special offer. The height of the tallest display pyramid is 3 feet. The actual pyramid is 90 m high.

   a What is the scale of the display?

   b Each side of the pyramid's base is 188 m.
What should be the base length of the pyramid in the window?

8 A model replica of a plane is shown below. The length of the plane is 47 m.

   a What is the scale of the model?

   b What is the width of the model?

   c What is the width of the plane?

5 *Measurement*

5.1 *Metric and imperial units*

In 1971 the British monetary system was decimalised. We stopped using pounds, shillings and pence (£ s d) and started using pounds and 'new' pence (£ p). Since then, many more units have changed from imperial to metric units:

We now buy petrol in litres, not gallons.
We buy material in metres instead of yards.
The standard length of a ruler is 30 centimetres, not 12 inches.
The weather forecast gives temperatures in degrees Celsius rather than in degrees Fahrenheit.

We do, however, still use some imperial measures:

Distances are given in miles and speed restrictions in miles per hour.
Although most grocery items are labelled with weights in both grams and ounces, fruit, vegetables and sweets are bought in pounds and ounces.
Milk and beer are still sold in pints.
Carpets are often sold in feet and yards.

The advantage of the metric system over the imperial is the ease with which one unit can be converted to another.

Metric units

The metric system is a decimal system and units are converted by multiplying or dividing by powers of 10 (i.e. 10, 100, 1000).

Each prefix to a standard measure (e.g. metre, gram, litre) indicates the relative size:

$$\begin{array}{ll}
\text{kilo (k)} \quad \text{means } 1000 \times & \text{deci (d)} \quad \text{means } \dfrac{1}{10} \times \\[2mm]
\text{hecto (H) means } 100 \times & \\[2mm]
\text{deka (D)} \quad \text{means } 10 \times & \text{centi (c)} \quad \text{means } \dfrac{1}{100} \times \\[4mm]
& \text{milli (m)} \quad \text{means } \dfrac{1}{1000} \times
\end{array}$$

The most common metric units in everyday use are:

Length Metre (m)	Weight Gram (g)	Capacity Litre (l)
1 kilometre = 1000 metres	1 kg = 1000 g	1 litre = 100 cl
1 centimetre = 10 millimetres	1 g = 1000 mg	1 litre = 1000 ml
1 metre = 100 centimetres	1 tonne = 1000 kg	1 cl = 10 ml
1 metre = 1000 millimetres		

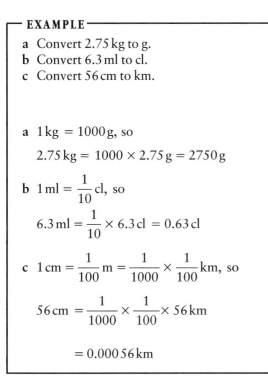

┌─ **EXAMPLE** ─────────────────────────

a Convert 2.75 kg to g.
b Convert 6.3 ml to cl.
c Convert 56 cm to km.

a 1 kg = 1000 g, so

2.75 kg = 1000×2.75 g = 2750 g

b 1 ml = $\dfrac{1}{10}$ cl, so

6.3 ml = $\dfrac{1}{10} \times 6.3$ cl = 0.63 cl

c 1 cm = $\dfrac{1}{100}$ m = $\dfrac{1}{1000} \times \dfrac{1}{100}$ km, so

56 cm = $\dfrac{1}{1000} \times \dfrac{1}{100} \times 56$ km

= 0.000 56 km

Estimation of measurements

You should be able to estimate many familiar measurements – for example, the length of a room. You may then use an accurate measurement to check your estimation.

┌─ **EXAMPLE** ─────────────────────────

Estimate the height of a room.

Most houses have a ceiling height of between 2.3 m and 2.4 m. Suitable estimates would be:
2 m, using one significant figure:
2.3 m or 2.4 m, using two significant figures
or $2\frac{1}{2}$ m.

An estimate of 3 m would be too large, and 2.34 m would be too great a degree of accuracy.

EXERCISE 5.1

1 Estimate, in turn, each of the following (or substitute your own choice):

a the height of a friend

b the length of the classroom

c the length of a sheet of A4 paper.

d the width of a sheet of A5 paper

e the length of your stride

f your handspan

g the circumference of your wrist

h the dimensions of the college car park.

When you have estimated the lengths, measure them, to an appropriate degree of accuracy and record the results on a table:

Object	Estimated length	Actual length	Measuring device
a Height of student			
b Length of room			
etc.			

2 Choose the most appropriate metric unit to measure:

a the height of a building

b the capacity of a bottle of ink

c the weight of a baby

d the length of a journey

e the thickness of a brass screw.

3 Place the following lengths in order, beginning with the smallest:
750 m, $\frac{1}{2}$ km, 5000 mm, 4860 cm.

4 Which is larger: $\frac{3}{8}$ kg or 370 g?

5 Change:

a 1232 m to km   e 1.62 cl to ml

b 0.032 m to mm   f 12.7 km to m

c 626 g to kg   g 59.1 ml to litres

d 0.731 litres to cl   h 3.4 tonnes to kg

6 The weight of sliced meat is marked on the packet as 0.23 kg.
What is the weight in grams?

7 A hotel restaurant uses 100 kg of potatoes per day.
A load of 2 tonnes is delivered.
How many days supply is this?

8 A silver ingot weighs 1550 g.
How many kg is this?

9 A length of cable has a diameter of 26.5 mm.
What is its diameter in cm?

10 A bottle of disinfectant holds 739 ml.
To make up a solution for cleaning the floors, 5 ml of disinfectant are added to 4.5 litres of water.
How many litres of solution can be made from the bottle?

Imperial units

The most common imperial units in everyday use are:

Length	Weight	Capacity

1 mile = 1760 yards
1 yard = 3 feet (ft or ')
1 foot = 12 inches (in or ")
	1 ton = 20 hundredweight
	         (cwt)
	1 cwt = 112 pounds (lb)
	1 lb = 16 ounces (oz)
	1 stone = 14 pounds
		1 gallon = 8 pints
		1 pint = 20 fluid
		         ounces (fl oz)

┌─ **EXAMPLE** ───┐

a Convert 76″ to feet and inches.

b Convert 6 lb 5 oz to ounces.

c Convert 18 pints to gallons.

a 12 in = 1 ft,   so $76'' = \dfrac{76}{12}$ ft $= 6\dfrac{4}{12}$ ft $= 6'\ 4''$

b 1 lb = 16 oz,   so   6 lb 5 oz = $(6 \times 16) + 5$ oz = 101 oz

c 8 pt = 1 gal,   so   18 pt = $\dfrac{18}{8}$ gal = 2.25 gal

└──┘

EXERCISE 5.2

1 Repeat question 1 of Exercise 5.1 using imperial units for the measurements.

2 Change:

   a 39 in to feet   **e** 3 lb 7 oz to oz

   b 40 oz to lb and oz   **f** 20 pints to gallons

   c $16\frac{1}{2}$ ft to yards   **g** $3\frac{1}{2}$ gallons to pints

   d 2 ft 3 in to inches   **h** 0.7 pint to fluid ounces

3 A recipe requires 15 fluid ounces of water, but the measuring jug is calibrated in pints.
How many pints of water should be measured?

4 The dimensions of a room are 12′ 9″ by 10′ 6″.
What is the perimeter of the room in:

   a feet   **b** yards?

5 A grocery store divides a block of cheese weighing 4 lb $9\frac{1}{2}$ oz into twelve equal portions.
How much does each portion weigh?

6 A 'flat' for a stage set is 15 ft high by $7\frac{1}{2}$ ft wide.
What are its dimensions in yards?

7 Churns of milk in a dairy hold 5 gallons.
How many one pint bottles can be filled from each churn?

8 A baby's bottle holds 8 fluid ounces of milk.
How many bottles can be filled from 2 pints of milk?

9 A cricket pitch has a length of 1 chain = 22 yd.
Ian knows that his stride is about 1 yard in length, so he paces out the distance between the wickets by taking 22 strides.
In fact, his stride is 34 inches in length.
What is the actual length of his pitch in yards, feet and inches?

10 An 18″ TV has a screen which is 18 inches wide and 14 inches high.
What are the dimensions of the screen in feet?
Give your answer correct to 2 d.p.

5.2 *Conversion between metric and imperial units*

It is often necessary, for comparison, to convert from imperial to metric units or vice versa.

If a rough comparison is all that is required, an approximate conversion factor can be used. For large quantities, or where a correct comparison is required, a conversion factor of the appropriate degree of accuracy should be used.

Approximate conversion		More accurate conversion	
5 miles	≈ 8 km	1 mile	$= 1.609$ km
1 yard	≈ 1 m	1 yard	$= 0.914$ m
1 foot	≈ 30 cm	1 foot	$= 30.48$ cm
1 inch	$\approx 2\frac{1}{2}$ cm	1 inch	$= 2.54$ cm
1 kg	≈ 2 lb or 2.2 lb	1 kg	$= 2.205$ lb
1 litre	$\approx 1\frac{3}{4}$ pints	1 litre	$= 1.76$ pt
		1 gallon	$= 4.55$ litres

EXAMPLE 1

The contents of a packet of sugar weigh 250 g.
What weight, in ounces, should be printed on the packet?

Merchandise must carry an accurate description, and therefore the weight given must be correct to a reasonable degree of accuracy.
The weight stated on a packet, tin, etc., is usually the minimum weight of the contents.

$$\text{The conversion used is } 1\,\text{kg} = 2.205\,\text{lb}$$
$$\therefore\ 1000\,\text{g} = 2.205 \times 16\,\text{oz} = 35.28\,\text{oz}$$
$$1\,\text{g} = 0.035\,28\,\text{oz}$$
$$250\,\text{g} = 0.035\,28 \times 250\,\text{oz}$$
$$= 8.82\,\text{oz}$$

The minimum weight of the sugar is 8.8 oz.

EXAMPLE 2

A family, on a self-catering holiday in Europe, wish to buy the equivalent in weight of 3 lb of potatoes and $\frac{1}{2}$ lb of butter.
How much of each item should they buy?

Exact weights are not required.

$$\text{The conversion used is } 2\,\text{lb} \approx 1\,\text{kg}$$
$$\text{or } 1\,\text{lb} \approx 0.5\,\text{kg}$$
$$\text{so } 3\,\text{lb} \approx 1.5\,\text{kg}$$
$$\text{and } \tfrac{1}{2}\,\text{lb} \approx 0.25\,\text{kg} = 250\,\text{g}$$

They should buy $1\frac{1}{2}$ kg of potatoes and 250 g of butter.

EXERCISE 5.3

1   Which is greater: 5 miles of 9 kilometres?

2   Vegetables are sold in tins of various sizes.
    What weight, in ounces to the nearest 0.1 oz,
    should be printed on a tin if the contents weigh:

    a 425g   **b** 440g   **c** 415g?

3   A shop prepacks its groceries and labels the
    packets with both metric and imperial weights.
    For each of the following items, calculate the
    missing weight:

    a 1 lb of mince

    b 150g of cooked ham

    c 5 lb of potatoes

    d 0.74 lb of cheese

    e 14.2g of dried herbs.

4   **a** What is the equivalent of 1 litre of petrol in
    gallons?

    b A driver buys 20 litres of petrol.
    Approximately how many gallons of petrol
    does he buy (correct to 1 d.p.)?

5   The specifications for a particular make of
    ambulance give the petrol consumption as 16
    miles per gallon.
    How many miles per litre is this?

6   One type of loft insulation has a thickness of 6 in,
    a width of 370 mm and a length of 5.33 m. Find:

    a the thickness in millimetres

    b the width in inches

    c the length in feet.

7   When you tow a caravan or trailer, the maximum
    permitted speed is 50 miles per hour.
    What is this speed in kilometres per hour?

8   The luggage allowance when travelling by air is
    20 kg per person. A passenger weighs his case on
    scales at home and finds the weight is 3 stones.

    a What is the weight of his case in pounds?

    b By how many pounds is he under the
    allowance?

9   Gary is designing a storage unit for a collection
    of CDs.
    What is the minimum width of shelving, to the
    nearest inch, he can use to accommodate CDs
    which are 14.1 cm wide?

10 Pottery clay is generally sold in lumps of 56 lb.
    What is this weight in kilograms?

11 An advertisement for cabin crew requires
    applicants to:

    a have a height 5 ft 3 in–6 ft

    b be capable of swimming 25 yd.

    Convert these imperial measures to suitable
    metric measures.

12 Precious metals and gems are weighed in troy
    ounces. 1 troy ounce = 31.104 g.

    a What is the weight in grams of a gold
    necklace weighing 2.5 troy ounces?

    b What is the weight in troy ounces of a silver
    bracelet weighing 18 g?

13 Lengths of nails used to be measured in inches.
    What are the metric equivalents (to the nearest
    millimetre) for the following lengths?

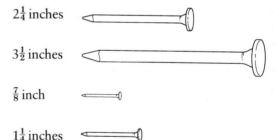

$2\frac{1}{4}$ inches

$3\frac{1}{2}$ inches

$\frac{7}{8}$ inch

$1\frac{1}{4}$ inches

14 A medicine spoon holds 5 ml.
    How many doses of medicine can be measured
    out from a quarter-pint bottle?

Measurements are found by using an appropriate measuring device, such as a thermometer or expanding tape, or by reading from a scale, as on a speedometer, weighing machine or voltmeter. In the following exercise, you are required to read measurements from the diagrams.

EXERCISE 5.4

1 What length has been measured on the rule?

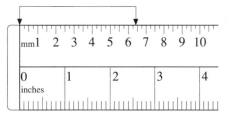

2 What is the depth of field when the camera aperture is set to f8?

30	15	10	7	5
10	5	3	2	1.5

22 16 11 8 4 ♦ 4 8 11 16 22

22	16	11	8	5.6	4	2.8

3 What is the weight of the parcel?

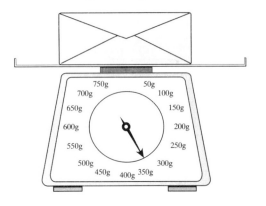

4 What temperature is shown on the clinical thermometer?

5 What time is recorded on the stopwatch?

6 A vehicle's speedometer is shown below. At what speed is it travelling:

a in miles per hour

b in kilometres per hour?

7 A lorry's tyres should have an air pressure of 75 psi (pounds per square inch). By how much should the pressure be increased if the present pressure is shown on the gauge below?

6 *Percentages*

'Inflation now stands at 7.3%.' 'Ford have given their workforce a 21.3% rise.' 'Unemployment in Winchester is less than 2%.'

Percentages are a part of our everyday lives. They are often quoted in the media, particularly in connection with money matters.

Percentages often help us make comparisons between numbers, but we must know exactly what a 'percentage' is.

6.1 *Percentages*

A percentage is a fraction with a particular number divided by 100:

$$20\% \text{ means } \frac{20}{100}$$

A decrease of 20% would be a decrease of $\frac{20}{100}$, which is the same thing as a decrease of $\frac{1}{5}$, a fifth.

$$\frac{1}{4} = \frac{1}{4} \times \frac{25}{25} = \frac{25}{100} \text{ which is } 25\%$$

To convert a fraction to a percentage multiply by 100.
To convert a percentage to a fraction, divide by 100.

EXAMPLE 1

Convert **a** $\frac{3}{5}$, **b** $\frac{9}{11}$ to percentages.

a $\frac{3}{5}$ as a percentage $= \frac{3}{5} \times 100 = 60\%$

b $\frac{9}{11}$ as a percentage $= \frac{9}{11} \times 100 = 81.82\%$ (to 2 d.p.)

EXAMPLE 2

Convert 65% to a fraction in its lowest terms.

$$65\% = \frac{65}{100} = \frac{13}{20}$$

Exercise 6.1

1 Convert the following fractions to percentages:

a $\dfrac{1}{5}$ **b** $\dfrac{1}{8}$ **c** $\dfrac{7}{10}$ **d** $\dfrac{13}{20}$

e $\dfrac{2}{3}$ **f** $\dfrac{9}{25}$ **g** $1\dfrac{3}{4}$ **h** $2\dfrac{1}{2}$

2 Convert the following percentages to fractions:

a 60% **b** 25% **c** 10% **d** 85%

e 15% **f** 130% **g** $37\dfrac{1}{2}\%$ **h** $33\dfrac{1}{3}\%$

3 Copy and complete the following table to give each quantity in its fractional, decimal and percentage form.

	Fraction	Decimal	Percentage
a	$\frac{3}{4}$		
b		0.5	
c	$\frac{1}{8}$		
d			$33\frac{1}{3}$
e		0.375	
f	$\frac{7}{10}$		
g			35
h		$0.\dot{6}$	
i	$\frac{3}{5}$		
j			62.5

6.2 *Finding a percentage of an amount*

EXAMPLE

Julian reads in the newspaper that the average pocket money for 12-year-olds has increased nationally by 14% in the last year. Julian's 12-year-old daughter Gilly has been given £1.60 per week for the last two years. How much more per week should he provide for a 14% increase?

$$14\% = \frac{14}{100}$$

$$14\% \text{ of } £1.60 = \frac{14}{100} \times £1.60$$

$$= 0.14 \times £1.60$$

Increase in pocket money = 22.4p = 22p (to the nearest 1p)
Note. See Section 2.1 for a further explanation of approximations.

EXERCISE 6.2

1   Calculate the following percentages to the nearest 1p.

   a   10% of £13.75   e   123% of £4.20

   b   50% of £637.24   f   12½% of £69.80

   c   7% of £316   g   10.80% of £900

   d   15% of £92.72   h   34.4% of £128.50

6.3 *Increasing an amount by a given percentage*

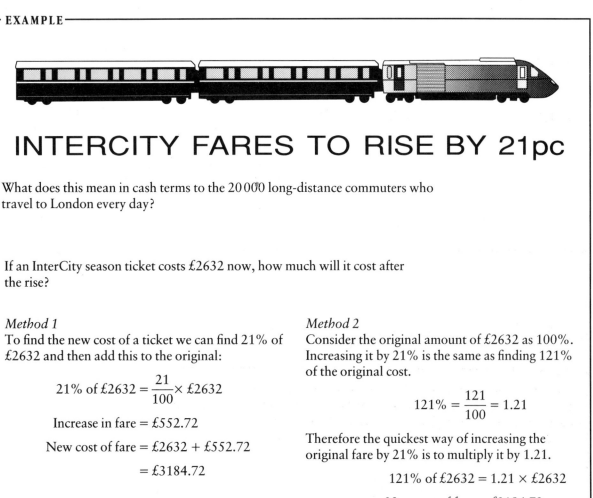

— **EXAMPLE** —

INTERCITY FARES TO RISE BY 21pc

What does this mean in cash terms to the 20 000 long-distance commuters who travel to London every day?

If an InterCity season ticket costs £2632 now, how much will it cost after the rise?

Method 1
To find the new cost of a ticket we can find 21% of £2632 and then add this to the original:

$$21\% \text{ of } £2632 = \frac{21}{100} \times £2632$$

Increase in fare = £552.72

New cost of fare = £2632 + £552.72

$$= £3184.72$$

Method 2
Consider the original amount of £2632 as 100%. Increasing it by 21% is the same as finding 121% of the original cost.

$$121\% = \frac{121}{100} = 1.21$$

Therefore the quickest way of increasing the original fare by 21% is to multiply it by 1.21.

$$121\% \text{ of } £2632 = 1.21 \times £2632$$

New cost of fare = £3184.72

EXERCISE 6.3

Give all answers to the nearest 1p.

1   Increase the following rail fares by 10%.

     a £9.20   **d** £9.81

     b £3.70   **e** £9.13

     c £5.00

2   Increase the given amount by the required percentage.

     a £72.12 by 50%   **d** £220 by $6\frac{1}{4}$%

     b 95p by 10%   **e** £124.80 by 25%

     c £360 by 120%   **f** £19.99 by $8\frac{1}{2}$%

6.4 *Decreasing an amount by a given percentage*

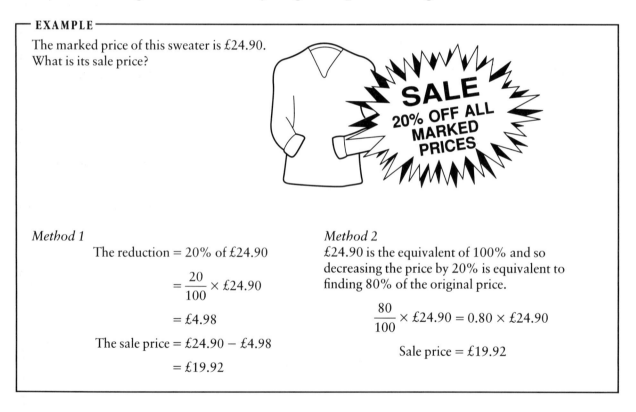

EXAMPLE

The marked price of this sweater is £24.90.
What is its sale price?

SALE
20% OFF ALL
MARKED
PRICES

Method 1

$$\text{The reduction} = 20\% \text{ of } £24.90$$

$$= \frac{20}{100} \times £24.90$$

$$= £4.98$$

$$\text{The sale price} = £24.90 - £4.98$$

$$= £19.92$$

Method 2

£24.90 is the equivalent of 100% and so decreasing the price by 20% is equivalent to finding 80% of the original price.

$$\frac{80}{100} \times £24.90 = 0.80 \times £24.90$$

$$\text{Sale price} = £19.92$$

EXERCISE 6.4

Give all answers to the nearest 1p.

1   Reduce the following marked prices by 20% to find the sale prices:

     a £30.00   **d** 45p

     b £10.50   **e** £12.99

     c £17.60

2   Decrease the given amount by the required percentage:

     a £54.10 by 8%   **d** £27.15 by $12\frac{1}{2}$%

     b 84p by 30%   **e** £99.05 by 40%

     c £128 by 60%   **f** £1.62 by 33%

6.5 *Expressing one quantity as a percentage of another*

In a survey of insurance companies it was found that the most common type of car accident was one car running into the back of another.

Out of 35 000 claims, 6280 were for this type of accident.

Information of this type is usually quoted as a percentage.

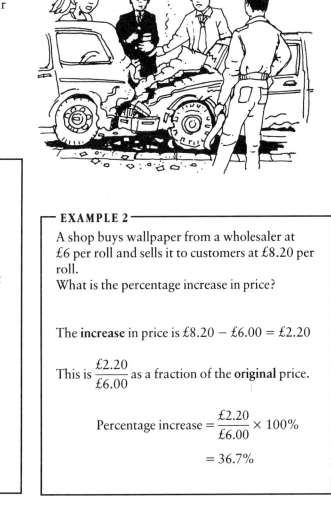

EXAMPLE 1

Find 6280 as a percentage of 35 000.

First express 6280 as a fraction of 35 000:

$$\frac{6280}{35\,000}$$

Then multiply this fraction by 100 to express it as a percentage:

6280 as a percentage of 35 000

$$= \frac{6280}{35\,000} \times 100\%$$

$$= 17.9\%$$

This means that almost 18% of car accidents are caused by cars running into the backs of other vehicles.

Note. See Unit 2 for a further explanation of significant figures.

EXAMPLE 2

A shop buys wallpaper from a wholesaler at £6 per roll and sells it to customers at £8.20 per roll.
What is the percentage increase in price?

The **increase** in price is £8.20 − £6.00 = £2.20

This is $\dfrac{£2.20}{£6.00}$ as a fraction of the **original** price.

$$\text{Percentage increase} = \frac{£2.20}{£6.00} \times 100\%$$

$$= 36.7\%$$

EXAMPLE 3

By what percentage has the marked price of £4.70 been decreased to give a sale price of £3.80?

The **decrease** in price is expressed as a fraction of the **original** price and then multiplied by 100.

$$\text{Decrease in price} = 90\text{p}$$

$$\text{Percentage decrease} = \frac{90\text{p}}{£4.70} \times 100\%$$

$$= \frac{£0.90}{£4.70} \times 100\% \quad \text{(both quantities must be in the same units)}$$

$$= 19.1\%$$

EXERCISE 6.5

Give all answers correct to 3 significant figures.

1 Express the first quantity as a percentage of the second:

  a 20, 25

  b 3, 87

  c 140, 80

  d 54, 108

  e 60p, £1.10

  f £16.25, £12.50

2 Find the percentage by which the first amount is increased or decreased to give the second amount:

  a £65, £80

  b £250, £300

  c 20p, 95p

  d £499, £399

  e £1.23, 67p

  f £24.50, £138.20

EXERCISE 6.6

1 A dress made by a Paris Fashion House has a recommended retail price of £870. A London shop advertises it at £710.
By what percentage has the shop reduced the price? Give your answer to the nearest integer.

2 Linda and Mario are discussing the students at their Art College.

  a Linda says that 60% of the students are female and Mario says that there are 52 more females than males.
How many students are there at the college?

  b Linda says that $\frac{2}{5}$ of the students attend on Wednesday only in the morning and Mario knows that 30% of the students attend all day on Wednesday.
How many students do not go into college on Wednesday?

3 A watch has a MRRP (maker's recommended retail price) of £32.99, but a jeweller's shop advertises it for £28.99.
By what percentage has the shop reduced the price? (to the nearest whole number)?

4 In a town of 25 000 inhabitants, 80% are over 18 years of age.

  a How many of the inhabitants are over 18?

Of these, $37\frac{1}{2}$% usually shop in the town's supermarket.

  b How many shop in the supermarket?

7240 people over 18 living in the town use hypermarkets regularly.

  c What percentage of people over 18 shop in hypermarkets?

5 A survey on teenage smoking found that 70% of girls of secondary school age tried smoking and that 36% of those who tried it became addicted.

In a secondary school with 580 female students:

  a how many girls would you expect to find had tried smoking?

  b how many girls would you expect to find had become addicted to smoking?

6 The residents in a rest-home each pay £231 per week. 28% of the total income of the home is spent on nursing care. The rest-home employs its nurses for a total of 588 hours per week.
What is the hourly rate of pay for each nurse?

7 Restaurants often add a service charge of 12% to your bill. A meal for two costs £28.60.
How much service charge will be added?

8 'Sunny Tours' offers a 5% discount on all holidays booked before 31 December the previous year.

How much will a family of 2 adults and 2 children aged 11 and 15 pay for a holiday whose advertised price is £380 each with a 30% reduction for children under 14 years of age?

9 In the survey of 3500 accidents at work, 17.6% happened on a Friday.
How many of the accidents occurred on a Friday?

10 Mr Robinson invested £32 000, together with money raised from a loan from his bank, in a manufacturing enterprise. He spent 65% on buildings, with an additional 28% on equipment.
How much did he have left to spend on materials?

7 *Wages and Salaries*

7.1 *Basic pay*

All employees receive a wage or salary as payment for their labour.

A **wage** is paid weekly and is calculated on a fixed hourly rate.
A **salary** is paid monthly and is calculated on a fixed annual amount.

Many wage earners are required to work a fixed number of hours in a week, and they are paid for these hours at the basic hourly rate.

EXAMPLE 1

Simon works in a hairdressers. His basic pay is £3.75 per hour for a 40-hour week. Calculate his weekly wage.

Weekly wage = Rate of pay × Hours worked

$$= £3.75 × 40$$

$$= £150$$

EXAMPLE 2

Layla's gross weekly wage (i.e. her wage before deductions) is £166.95. She works a 35-hour week.
What is her hourly rate of pay?

$$\text{Hourly rate of pay} = \frac{\text{Weekly wage}}{\text{Hours worked}}$$

$$= \frac{£166.95}{35}$$

$$= £4.77$$

EXERCISE 7.1

1 Calculate Donna's gross weekly wage if she works for 42 hours per week at a rate of pay of £4.10 per hour.

2 Daniel's yearly salary is £5756.
How much is he paid per month?

3 A basic working week is 36 hours and the weekly wage is £231.48.
What is the basic hourly rate?

4 An employee's gross monthly pay is £965.20.
What is his annual salary?

5 Carrie is an outworker and is paid £2.73 per hour to produce a wall-hanging tapestry.
When Carrie works 36 hours, how much is she paid?

6 Calculate how much Phillipa is paid per year if her monthly pay as a graphics designer is £1975 per month.

7 In one month, Mustafa earns £610 as a secretary.
What is Mustafa's annual income?

8 A shop assistant, Kayley, usually works 48½ hours a week and is paid £221. One week Kayley attends a family wedding and can work only 41 hours.
How much is Kayley paid for that week?

9 As a nurse, Annabel earns £437 per month.
What is Annabel's annual income?

10 Annabel's brother James works as a porter at the same hospital. He is paid £3.52 per hour. How much is James paid for a week in which he works 43 hours?

11 For her work as a travel courier, Morag is paid £210 per week. She normally works a 38-hour week.
What is Morag's hourly rate of pay?

12 As a maintenance worker at Stonehenge, Nicholas is paid £3.89 per hour.
How much is Nicholas's gross pay when he works $9\frac{1}{2}$ hours in a day?

13 The basic week in a factory is 35 hours. Find the weekly wage of the following employees whose basic hourly rate of pay is:

a a machine operator, basic rate £7.42 per hour

b a trainee, basic rate £4.45 per hour

c a supervisor, basic rate £12.60 per hour.

14 Derek is paid £192 when he works a 45-hour week in a factory making parts for a shipyard. How much is Derek paid per hour?

7.2 *Overtime rates*

An employee can increase a basic wage by working longer than the basic week, i.e. by doing overtime.
A higher hourly rate is usually paid for these additional hours.
The most common rates are **time and a half** and **double time**.

EXAMPLE

Mr Arkwright works a basic 36-hour week for which he is paid a basic rate of £5.84 per hour. In addition, he works 5 hours overtime at time and a half and 3 hours overtime at double time.

Calculate his gross weekly wage.

36 hours basic pay	$= £5.84 \times 36$	$= £210.24$
5 hours overtime at time and a half	$= (£5.84 \times 1.5) \times 5$	$= £43.80$
3 hours overtime at double time	$= (£5.84 \times 2) \times 3$	$= £35.04$
	$\therefore$ Gross pay	$= £289.08$

EXERCISE 7.2

1 Jim Cooper's basic wage is £6.20 per hour, and he works a basic 5-day, 40-hour week. If he works overtime during the week, he is paid at time and a half. Overtime during the weekend is paid at double time.
Calculate Jim's gross wage for the week when he worked five hours overtime during the week and four hours overtime on Saturday.

2 The number of hours worked by an employee is often calculated from a clock card similar to the one shown below. Harold Meyer works a basic eight-hour day, five days a week and his basic hourly rate is £4.15.

DAY	IN	OUT	IN	OUT	CLOCK HOURS	O/T HOURS
SAT	0730	1200	1230	1400	6	6
SUN	0800	1200				
MON	0730	1200	1300	1700		
TUES	0730	1200	1300	1730		
WED	0800	1230	1300	1730		
THURS	0730	1200	1245	1815		
FRI	0730	1200	1230	1600		

Overtime is paid at the following rates:
Time and a quarter for Monday to Friday
Time and a half for Saturday
Double time for Sunday
Calculate Harold's gross pay for this week.

3 a The basic weekly wage of employees in a small firm is £133 for a 38-hour week.
       What is the basic hourly rate?

   b All overtime is paid at time and a half.
       Calculate the number of hours of overtime worked by Ms Wiley during a week when her gross pay was £154.

4 Jenny, a machinist for a dressmaker, receives £3.41 per hour for her basic pay. One week she works a basic week of 36 hours, together with 8 hours overtime at time and a half.
   What is her gross pay for this week?

5 Collette normally works 38 hours per week helping to restore 'old masters'. One week she works five hours overtime at double time and receives a gross pay of £269.76.
   What is her hourly rate of pay for a weekday evening when Collette is paid time and a half?

6 Janine, a hotel receptionist, is paid £3.70 per hour for her basic 38-hour week. Overtime on Sundays is paid at double time, while other overtime is paid at time and a half.
   How much is Janine's gross pay when she works 47 hours in a week, 5 hours of which are on a Sunday?

7 Samantha is an assistant in a personnel section, earning £224 when she works a basic 36-hour week. One week she has to produce a summary of last year's appointments and works six hours overtime paid at time and a half.
   Calculate Samantha's gross pay for that week.

8   Emily, an assistant in a convalescent home, is paid £2.90 per hour for her basic 38-hour week. During a particularly busy week she does four hours overtime at time and a half and six hours overtime at double time.
    Calculate Emily's gross weekly pay.

9   Joanna, a dental assistant, earns £184 when she works her basic 36-hour week. In a week after the holidays she also worked 8 hours overtime at time and a half.
    Calculate Joanna's gross pay during that week.

10 A swimming pool attendant is paid £2.70 per hour for his basic 36-hour week. He is paid overtime at time and a half.
    How much does he earn in a week in which he does 6 hours overtime?

11 Ruth is a waitress who earns £211 when she works a basic 38-hour week. In one week, she had to work five hours overtime (paid at double time) as the restaurant was hosting a wedding reception.
    Calculate Ruth's gross pay that week.

12 The basic working week in a small factory is 35 hours (i.e. 7 hours per day) and the basic rate of pay is £3.98 per hour. The overtime rate is time and a half from Monday to Friday and double time on Saturdays. The table shown below shows the hours worked by five employees.
    For each employee, calculate the gross weekly pay.

	MON	TUES	WED	THUR	FRI	SAT
Andrews A J	7	7	8	9	8	0
Collins F	8	8	9	9	7	5
Hammond C	9	9	9	10	10	0
Jali Y	8	10	11	11	9	4
Longman B H	9	10	10	9	7	6

13 Carol works on a production line making televisions. When she works her basic week of 38 hours together with 4 hours overtime at double time, Carol receives a gross pay of £204.70.
    What is Carol's basic pay?

7.3 *Commission*

People who are employed as salespersons or representatives and some shop assistants are paid a basic wage plus a percentage of the value of the goods they have sold.

Their basic wage is often small, or non-existent, and the **commission** on their sales forms the largest part or all of their gross pay.

EXAMPLE

A salesman earns a basic salary of £690 per month plus a commission of 5% on all sales over £5000.
Find his gross income for a month in which he sold goods to the value of £9400.

He earns commission on (£9400 − £5000) worth of sales

$$\text{Commission} = 5\% \text{ of } (£9400 - £5000)$$
$$= 0.05 \times £4400$$
$$= £220$$

$$\text{Gross salary} = \text{Basic salary} + \text{Commission}$$
$$= £690 + £220$$
$$= £910$$

EXERCISE 7.3

1   An estate agent charges a commission of $1\frac{1}{2}\%$ of the value of each house he sells.

How much commission is earned by selling a house for £104 000?

2   Calculate the commission earned by a shop assistant who sold goods to the value of £824 if her rate of commission is 3%.

3   Find the gross monthly pay of Jasmine, who has a basic salary of £855 per month plus a commission of 2% of her monthly sales. She sells £51 410 of goods during the month.

4   A sculptor agrees to pay a studio 6% commission on all sales of her work.

How much commission does the sculptor pay the studio when it sells a sculpture for £8220.

5   Andrina is paid a basic wage of £50 per week by a group of knitters to sell their hand-knitted jumpers. She is also paid 17% commission on all her sales. In one week she sells 160 jumpers at £40 each.
How much is Andrina paid for that week?

6   An insurance representative is paid a commission of 8% on all insurance sold up to a value of £4000 per week. If the value of insurance sold exceeds £4000 per week, he is paid a commission of 18% on the excess. Calculate his gross pay for the 4 weeks in which his sales were £3900, £4500, £5100 and £2700.

7   Two firms place advertisements for an insurance representative:
Firm A offers an annual salary of £5000 plus a company car (worth £2500 per year) and 4% commission on sales over £200 000 per annum.
Firm B offers an annual salary of £7000 and 3.5% commission on sales over £150 000 per annum.

   a   Which is the better job if sales of £350 000 per year can be expected?

   b   If, in a good year, sales rose to £500 000 per year, which job would pay the higher amount and by how much?

8   A nurse at a doctor's surgery is paid a basic wage of £170 per week plus a commission of £2.05 for every vaccination she gives. In one week she gives 31 vaccinations. What is her gross pay for that week?

9   A dentist pays his technician Rachel commission for sealing the teeth of children to prevent tooth decay. Rachel is paid £4 per child up to the first 10 in that week and £3 for each child thereafter. How much commission does Rachel receive in a week in which she seals the teeth of 28 children?

10 Collette, a hairdresser, is paid 12% commission on her work. In one day, her clients pay £400. How much is Collette paid on that day?

11 An agent is paid 5% commission on all tickets sold for shows, and 8% for all coach trips. The agent sells tickets for shows to the value of £900 and £680 worth of coach trips.

Find his commission.

12 A car salesman is paid $2\frac{1}{2}$% commission on his weekly sales over £6000. In one particular week he sold two cars for £7520 and £10 640.

What was his commission for that week?

13 In addition to his basic salary of £210 per week, a double-glazing salesman is paid $1\frac{1}{2}$% commission on his sales. In one week he negotiates 4 sales of £1250, £180, £3850 and £6100 respectively.

Find his gross income for that week.

7.4 *Piecework*

Some employees, particularly in the manufacturing and building industries, are paid a fixed amount for each article or piece of work they complete. This is known as **piecework**.

They may also receive a small basic wage and, in addition, some are paid a bonus if production exceeds a stipulated amount.

EXAMPLE

Workers in a pottery firm who hand-paint the plates are paid a basic weekly wage of £120 and a piecework rate of 80p for every plate over 30 which they paint in a day.

Calculate the weekly wage of an employee whose daily output was as follows:

Day 1 35 plates   Day 2 38 plates   Day 3 40 plates
Day 4 45 plates   Day 5 39 plates

No. of plates over 30 painted = 5 + 8 + 10 + 15 + 9
                              = 47

Piecework bonus = 80p × 47   Weekly gross pay = £120 + £37.60
                = £37.60   = £157.60

EXERCISE 7.4

1 A firm employs casual labour to deliver advertising leaflets door to door. The rate of pay is £4.80 for every 100 leaflets delivered.
How much is earned by someone who delivers 1230 leaflets?

2 Karl is paid £3.60 per hour plus a bonus of 80 pence for every sack of rubbish collected. In one day Karl collects 30 sacks when he works 9 hours.
How much is his gross pay for that day?

3 A seamstress receives a bonus of 57 pence for every 2 fashion waistcoats made in excess of 15 per day.
What bonus is received if she makes 30 waistcoats in a day?

4   Mr Ansell, a picture framer, works a basic 40-hour week at £3.78 per hour, plus a bonus of £1.25 for every picture framed. In five successive days he frames 10, 11, 16, 17 and 8 pictures. What is Mr Ansell's gross wage?

5   A freelance computer operator is paid £7 for each page of Basic program which is converted into MAC Basic. In one day she completes 26 pages. How much is she paid for that day?

6   To prepare and complete a tax return, an accountant, Francine, charges a basic £70 plus £4, for every letter sent or received, and £5 for every phone call. In dealing with one client's return, Francine sends 25 letters, receives 18 letters in return and handles 24 phone calls. What is Francine's charge?

7   In addition to his basic salary, a doctor is paid £11.50 for each daytime home visit and £28 for each night call.
How much extra does he receive during a weekend when he makes 14 visits of which 5 are during the night?

8   Anya is paid by a charity to deliver lunches to housebound pensioners. Her rate of pay is £1.50 per lunch delivered plus £5 per day.
Calculate her pay on a day when she delivers 14 lunches.

9   A timeshare tout is paid £20 for each person she persuades to visit a development. In one week she sends 22 people to the development. How much does the tout receive?

10 Pierre is a guide showing tourists around the Roman amphitheatre in Arles. He is paid 100 francs per group plus a bonus of 10 francs per person. On one day there are 23, 18, 11, 17 and 21 tourists in the six groups he takes on guided tours of the amphitheatre. How much does Pierre earn that day?

11 A bricklayers receives a bonus of 54 pence for every 10 bricks laid in excess of 350 per day. What bonus does he receive if he lays 3070 bricks in a six-day week?

12 The Rapid Fix Tyre Company pays its fitters £3.60 per hour plus 80p for each tyre fitted. In one day Ahmed works 9 hours and fits 71 tyres. What is Ahmed's gross pay for that day?

7.5 *Deductions from pay*

Employees do not usually receive all the money they have earned.

Certain amounts of money are **deducted** from the gross pay and the pay the employee receives is the **net pay** or **take-home pay**.

The main deductions are:
- **Income Tax**
- **National Insurance**
- **Pension** (also called **Superannuation**)

Income tax (lowest rate)

Income tax is used to finance government expenditure.

It is a tax based on the amount a person earns in a tax year that begins on 6 April and ends on 5 April the following year.

Most people have income tax deducted from their pay before they receive it, by their employer, who then pays the tax to the Government. This method of paying income tax is called **PAYE** (Pay As You Earn).

Certain amounts of each person's income are not taxed. These amounts are called **tax allowances**.

The Tax Office sends the employee and the employer a PAYE Code which tells them the value of the allowances. For example, a tax code of 0342L would be given to a single person who has allowances of £342 × 10 = £3420.

$$\text{Gross income} - \text{Tax allowances} = \text{Taxable income}$$

The **lowest** rate of income tax in 1994–95 was 20p in the pound on taxable income up to £3000.
The allowances were: Personal, £3445; Married Couple, £1720.

The married couple's allowance is initially awarded to the husband, but it can be transferred to the wife if his earnings are less than £5165.

(In the year of marriage the amount awarded will be proportional to the number of months they have been married.)

EXAMPLE

Mr Browne earns £7000 per annum (per year), which is his only source of income. He is married.

Find **a** his total tax allowance, **b** his taxable income, **c** the tax paid per annum.

a Personal allowance $= £3445$ **b** Taxable income = Gross income − Allowances
    Married couple's allowance $= £1720$ $= £7000$ $- £5165$

    Total tax allowance $= £5165$ $= £1835$

    c Tax paid $= \dfrac{20}{100} \times £1835 = £367$

EXERCISE 7.5

Assume that the earnings stated in the following questions are the only source of income.

1   Find:

  (i)   the total tax allowance

  (ii) the taxable income

  (iii) the yearly tax paid, for:

  a a single man earning £4500 per annum

  b a married man earning £6950 per annum

  c a married woman earning £67 per week.

2   Find the yearly income tax payable by Mrs Bailey, who earns £5705 per annum and has a total tax allowance of £3725.

3   Miss Davis earns £6462 per year. She is entitled to the personal allowance plus an allowance of £960 per year for expenses necessary in her work. Calculate her monthly tax bill.

4   Find the yearly income tax payable by:
  a Ulrika, a single art gallery attendant, who earns £6243 per annum and has a total tax allowance of £3565

  b Ashley, a married graphics artist, who earns £105 per week and has a total tax allowance of £3595.

5 A trainee in a design studio is paid £473 per month. His personal allowance is £3445. Calculate the tax paid per month.

6 Zoe's husband is unemployed. Zoe works in a county council office and earns £7950 per year. Calculate her annual tax bill.

7 Jason, an unmarried office junior, earns £630 per month. He has a personal allowance of £5165. Calculate Jason's monthly tax bill.

8 Find:

  (i) the total tax allowance

  (ii) the taxable income

  (iii) the yearly tax paid, for:

  a Sanjay, a married care assistant earning £6200 per annum

  b Francesca, a single nurse, earning £111 per week.

9 Ben, a charity worker, earns £802 per month. He has a personal allowance of £7260. Calculate his monthly tax bill.

10 A travel consultant is paid £555 per month and has a tax-free allowance of £3714. How much tax does he pay per month?

11 A waitress is paid £130 per week. Her personal allowance is £5165. How much tax does she pay per week?

12 Find the annual income tax payable by Malcolm, a single apprentice, working in a steel plant, who earns £6800 per year and has a total tax allowance of £3825.

13 Anna is a trainee machine operator who earns £590 per month. If her personal allowance is £5250, calculate Anna's monthly tax bill.

Income tax (lowest rate and basic rate)

Most people who pay income tax earn more than £8165, and hence have a taxable income in excess of £3000.

Taxable income between £3000 and £23700 is taxed at 25p in the pound. Since most people pay the majority of their income tax at this rate, the 25p rate is known as the basic rate. If you are allowed tax relief (for example on mortgages, covenants, educational courses), the relief is usually given at 20% regardless of the rate at which you pay income tax.

If you pay tax at the highest rate of 40%, this reduced tax relief is obtained by halving the tax allowance you should receive. This produces the 'net tax allowance' which the Inland Revenue uses.

A similar adjustment is made for those who pay tax at 25%.

EXAMPLE

Graham is an engineer and earns £21 250 per year. His personal tax allowance is £5165. How much income tax does he pay per year?

Annual taxable income = Annual gross pay − Total allowance
$$= £21\,250 - £5165$$
$$= £16\,085$$

Income taxable at basic rate = Taxable income − £3000 (maximum at
$$= £13\,085 \qquad \text{lowest rate)}$$

Income tax at lowest rate = 20p × 3000 = £600
Income tax at basic rate = 25p × 13 085 = £3271.25
∴ Total annual income tax = £3871.25

EXERCISE 7.6

1 Find the yearly tax paid by:

   a Andrea, a single girl, earning £12050 a year

   b Philip, a single man, earning £182 per week

   c Sarah and John, a married couple, earning £21470 between them. Both earn more than £8000.

2 Jane and Denis live together. Denis earns £13185 per annum and Jane earns £10585 per annum.

   a What was their total tax bill for the year 1993–94, if they claimed only the standard allowances?

   b How much tax would they have paid if they had been married?

3 If, in the next budget, the Chancellor changes the basic rate of tax from 25% to 23%, but wages remain the same, how much less tax would be paid by the employees in question 1 above?

4 Sally is a design artist earning £27850 per annum. Her tax allowance is £3445. How much is Sally's annual tax bill?

5 Julian, an advertising agent, is paid a basic annual wage of £21500. She also receives £325 per month in commission. How much is Julian's monthly tax bill?

6 Mark, an accountant, earns £26500 per year. His tax allowance is £5248. How much tax does he pay each year?

7 Find the monthly tax bill payable by Ingrid, who has a company car and is therefore taxed as if she had an additional income of £2700. Ingrid earns £1890 per month and her tax allowance is £3445.

8 Find the monthly income tax paid by Asif, a staff nurse, who has a tax allowance of £3920 and earns £14500.

9 Asif's brother Salman is a porter in the same hospital. His basic wage is £320 per week, and he has a second income of £120 per month. Salman's tax allowance is £3445. How much tax does he pay each month?

10 Marcel, a restaurant owner, has an income of £2310 per month. His tax allowance is £5255. How much is Marcel's annual tax bill?

11 Ross, the manager of a health club in an hotel, earns £18500 per year plus £7450 in bonuses. His tax allowance is £3855. How much is Ross's monthly tax bill?

12 Richard, a window fitter, is paid £285 per week. He also works on Saturdays and admits to an income of £210 per month from this extra work. His tax allowance is £3452. How much tax does Richard pay each month?

13 As the manager of the 'Exhausts in an Instant' agency, Alf earns a basic salary of £21150 per year. He is also paid a commission which averages £96 per week. Alf's tax allowance is £3445. How much tax does Alf pay per year?

8 *Travel*

8.1 *Foreign currency*

Currency exchange

If you plan a trip abroad for business or holiday, you must work out the money you will need and the form in which you will take it.

Most people take a limited amount of cash in the currency of each country to be visited. They take the remainder in the more secure form of traveller's cheques. Alternatively, they use Eurocheques or credit cards to obtain cash.

In the UK British currency (pounds sterling) is usually exchanged for foreign currency at a bank or travel agency. Exchange rates between one currency and other currencies change frequently and are published daily in newspapers and displayed where money is exchanged.

By consulting the **selling price** you can calculate the amount of foreign currency you will be sold for your pounds and from the **buying price** you can calculate the amount of pounds you will receive in return for your foreign currency.

EXAMPLE

Mr Oztürk is to travel on a business trip to Turkey. He changes £350 into Turkish lira on a day when the bank selling price is 3750.

On returning home he changes his remaining 262 500 lira into sterling. The bank buying price is 4150 to £1.

Calculate:

a the amount of lira he receives
b the amount of pounds he receives on his return.

a The bank pays 3750 lira for every £1 it buys.
   For £350 he will receive 3750 × 350 lira
                              = 1 312 500 lira

b The bank charges 4150 lira for every £1 it sells
   For 262 500 lira he will receive $£\dfrac{262\,500}{4150}$

                              = £63.25

EXERCISE 8.1

1 Using the bank selling price, change:

   a £12 to Austrian schillings

   b £140 to Spanish pesetas

   c £96.50 to American dollars.

2 Using the bank buying price, calculate the sterling equivalent of:

   a 200 French francs

   b 11 100 Italian lira

   c 650 Japanese yen.

EXCHANGE RATES		
	Bank Buys	Bank Sells
Australia $	2.33	2.18
Austria Sch	20.85	19.65
Belgium Fr	62.40	58.50
Canada $	2.08	1.98
Denmark Kr	11.38	10.78
Finland MKK	7.00	6.60
France Fr	10.05	9.45
Germany Dm	2.978	2.798
Greece Dr	292	266
Italy Lira	2205	2275
Japan Yen	266	250
Netherlands Gld	3.33	3.15
Norway Kr	11.48	10.82
Portugal Esc	262.5	246.50
Spain Pta	190	178
Swedan Kr	10.86	10.20
Switzerland Fr	2.618	2.458
USA $	1.77	1.67

3 Geraldine and Peter ate a meal in a restaurant while on holiday in Rhodes.
The meal for two cost 4256 drachma. Use the bank selling price to calculate the cost of the meal in pounds.

4 The Andersons spent a holiday touring in Yugoslavia. While travelling they used 200 litres of petrol which cost 1236 dinar per litre.
The exchange rate was 4330 dinar to £1.

  a How much did the petrol cost them in pounds?

  b What was the price per litre of the petrol in pence?

5 Before going on holiday to Germany and Austria, the Williams family changed £600 into German marks. While in Germany they spent 824 DM and then changed their remaining marks into Austrian schillings as they crossed the border. The exchange rate was 7.047 Sch to 1 DM. Calculate:

  a the number of marks they received

  b the number of schillings they bought.

6 If Mr Oztürk (in the example on p.59) had postponed his trip to Turkey until the following week the bank selling price would have been 3915 lira to the pound.
On his return, the buying price would have been 4515 lira to the pound.

  a How many lira would he have received?

  b How many lira would he have had left on his return to Britain (assuming that he would have spent the same amount)?

  c How many pounds would he have received on his return?

  d How much money would he have saved by travelling the following week?

7 **a** Mr Elton changed £100 into French francs for a day trip to France. How many francs did he receive?

  b Unfortunately the excursion was cancelled and so he changed all his francs back to pounds. How many pounds did he receive?

  c How much money did he lose because of the cancellation?

Commission

In practice, the banks also charge commission for each currency exchange.

The commission is £1 on currency exchanges up to the value of £200 and 0.5% of the value above £200.

On traveller's cheques the commission is £2 for up to £200 in value and 1% of the value above £200.

EXERCISE 8.2

Questions 1 and 2 refer to Exercise 8.1.

1 **a** How much commission did Mr Elton pay when changing pounds to francs?

   b How much commission did he pay when changing the francs back to pounds?

   c How much did his cancelled trip cost him, including commission charges?

2 **a** How much commission did the Williams family pay for their Deutschmarks?

   b How much commission would they have paid if they had taken the £600 in traveller's cheques?

3 **a** For a three-week holiday, touring Germany, Switzerland and Austria, a group of four friends decided to take the equivalent of £900 abroad.

At the bank they changed £110 into Deutschmarks, £100 into Swiss francs and £120 into Austrian schillings. How much of each currency did they receive (after commission was deducted)?

   b After buying the foreign currencies, they changed as much as possible of the remaining money into traveller's cheques.

The smallest value of traveller's cheque which can be bought is £10.

   (i) How much did they exchange for traveller's cheques?
   (ii) How much commission did they pay for the cheques?

   c What was the total cost per person of the foreign currencies and cheques?

8.2 *Time*

There are two methods in general use for showing the time:

  (i) the 12-hour clock   (ii) the 24-hour clock.

With the 12-hour clock the day is divided into two periods, from midnight to noon (am) and noon to midnight (pm).

The 24-hour clock uses a single period of 24 hours, starting at midnight. The time is written as a four-digit number, without a decimal point, and there is no need to specify morning (am) or afternoon (pm).

This method is always used for timetables and is in common use on video recorders and digital clocks.

EXAMPLE

Write the times
a ten to nine in the evening,
b twenty past seven in the morning, using both the 12-hour and 24-hour clocks.

a The 12-hour clock time is 8.50 pm.
    The 24-hour clock time is 2050 (i.e. 8.50 + 12 hours).

b The 12-hour clock time is 7.20 am.
    The 24-hour clock time is 0720 (note the zero at the beginning to make a four-digit number).

EXERCISE 8.3

In the following exercise the time is written using words, the 12-hour clock or the 24-hour clock.
For each question, give the time using the other two methods.

1   Six fifteen in the morning

2   11.10 pm

3   0930

4   1.40 am

5   1350

6   2220

7   Ten to ten in the evening

8   10.45 am

9   Twenty-five past midnight

10   1656

EXAMPLE

The 0745 train from Newcastle is scheduled to arrive in Southampton at 1516.
How long is the journey?

Method 1

From 0745 to 0800	= 15 mins
From 0800 to 1500	= 7 hours
From 1500 to 1516	= 16 mins
Total journey time	= 7 hours + 15 mins + 16 mins
	= 7 hours 31 mins

Method 2

	Hours	Mins		Hours	Mins	
Train arrives	15	16	=	14	76	(76 = 16 + 60)
Train departs	7	45		−7	45	
Time taken			=	7	31	

The journey time is 7 hours 31 minutes.

EXERCISE 8.4

1   Mr Little catches the 0654 train to London.
If he arrives at the station at twenty to seven, how long does he wait?

2   Miss Brothers travels on the 0704 train. She arrives at the station nine minutes before the train is due.
At what time does she arrive at the station?

3   Mr Ghosh arrives at the airport at 8.35 am and his plane takes off 55 minutes later.
At what time does the plane take off?

4   At what time does the 0929 train at Coventry arrive if it is 13 minutes late?

5   **a** Mrs Richardson's afternoon train is scheduled to arrive in Birmingham at eight minutes past four, but it is 15 minutes late.
At what time, on the 24-hour clock, does she arrive?

   b Her connecting train leaves at 1651.
How long does she have to wait?

6   Chris has an appointment in London at 2.15 pm. The train journey from his local station takes 1 hour and 10 minutes. He allows a further 20 minutes to travel on the underground to his place of appointment. In case there are any delays on the journey, he allows an extra 15 minutes travelling time.
What length of time should Chris allow from his local station?

7   a   The boat from Dover to Calais departs at 1715. The crossing takes $1\frac{1}{2}$ hours and French time is 1 hour ahead.
At what time does the boat dock in France, French time?

   b   The same boat leaves Calais for Dover at 2000. At what time does it arrive in England, British time?

8.3 *Timetables*

All timetables use the 24-hour clock.

EXERCISE 8.5

Mondays to Saturdays

BASINGSTOKE (Bus Station) ⇌	....	....	....	....	0730	....	....	0840	0935	....	1035	1135	....	1235	1335	....	1435	1535
Basingstoke (Winton Square)	....	....	....	....	0735	....	....	0845	0940	....	1040	1140	....	1240	1340	....	1440	1540
Worting Road (South Ham)	....	....	....	....	0739	....	....	0849	0944	....	1044	1144	....	1244	1344	....	1444	1544
Worting (White Hart)	....	....	....	....	0743	....	....	0853	0948	....	1048	1148	....	1248	1348	....	1448	1548
Newfound (Fox Inn)	....	....	....	....	0747	....	....	0857	0952	....	1052	1152	....	1252	1352	....	1452	1552
Deane Gate	....	....	....	....	0753	....	....	0903	0958	....	1058	1158	....	1258	1358	....	1458	1558
Overton (Post Office) ⇌	....	....	....	0758	0756	....	....	0908	1003	....	1103	1203	....	1303	1403	....	1503	1603
Laverstoke (Mill)	....	....	....	0802	0802	....	....	0912	1007	....	1107	1207	....	1307	1407	....	1507	1607
Whitchurch (Square)	....	....	....	0809	0809	....	....	0919	1014	....	1114	1214	....	1314	1414	....	1514	1614
Whitchurch (Bere Hill Estate)	....	....	0650	....	....	0813	....	0923	....	....	1118	....	....	1318	....	....	1518	....
Whitchurch (Square)	....	....	0654	0809	0817	....	....	0927	1014	....	1122	1214	....	1322	1414	....	1522	1614
Hurstbournre Priors (Portsmouth Arms)	....	....	0659	0814	0822	....	....	0932	1019	....	1127	1219	....	1327	1419	....	1527	1619
The Middleway	....	....	....	0821	....	....	....	....	1026	....	....	1226	....	....	1426	....	....	1626
Longparish (Plough Inn)	....	....	0708	....	0831	....	....	0941	....	....	1136	....	....	1336	....	....	1536	....
Longparish (Station Hill)	....	....	0712	....	0835	....	....	0945	....	....	1140	....	....	1340	....	....	1540	....
London Road (Admirals Way)	....	....	0723*	0825	0843	....	....	0953	1030	....	1148	1230	....	1348	1430	....	1548	1630
ANDOVER (Bridge Street) arr.	....	....	0727	0829	0847	....	....	0957	1034	....	1152	1234	....	1352	1434	....	1552	1634
ANDOVER (West Street) ⇌ arr.	....	....	0729C	....	....	....	....	0959C	....	....	1154C	....	....	1354C	....	....		

ANDOVER (West Street) ⇌ dep.	0624	....	0734	....	....	....	0911	....	1111	....	....	1311	....	....	1511	....	....	....
ANDOVER (Bridge Street) dep.	0626	....	0736	....	0831	....	0913	1031	1113	....	1231	1313	....	1431	1513	....	1631	1735
London Road (Admirals Way)	0630	....	0740	....	0835	....	0917	1035	1117	....	1235	1317	....	1435	1517	....	1635	1739
Longparish (Station Hill)	....	....	....	....	....	....	0925	....	1125	....	....	1325	....	....	1525	....	....	1747
Longparish (Plough Inn)	....	....	....	....	....	....	0929	....	1129	....	....	1329	....	....	1529	....	....	1751
The Middleway	0634	....	0744	....	0839	....	....	1039	....	....	1239	....	....	1439	....	....	1639	....
Hurstborne Priors (Portsmouth Arms)	0641	....	0751	....	0846	....	0938	1046	1138	....	1246	1338	....	1446	1538	....	1646	1800
Whitchurch (Square)	0646	....	0756	....	0851	....	0943	1051	1143	....	1251	1343	....	1451	1543	....	1651	1805
Whitchurch (Bere Hill Estate) ⇌	....	....	....	....	....	....	0947	....	1147	....	....	1347	....	....	1547	....	....	1809
Whitchurch (Square)	0646	....	0756	....	0851	0851	0951	1051	1151	....	1251	1351	....	1451	1551	....	1651	1813
Laverstoke (Mill)	0653	....	0803	....	0858	0858	0958	1058	1158	....	1258	1358	....	1458	1558	....	1658	1820
Overton (Post Office) ⇌	0657	....	0807	....	0902	0902	1002	1102	1202	....	1302	1402	....	1502	1602	....	1702	1824
Deane Gate	0702	....	0812	....	0907	0907	1007	1107	1207	....	1307	1407	....	1507	1607	....	1707	1829
Newfound (Fox Inn)	0708	....	0818	....	0913	0913	1013	1113	1213	....	1313	1413	....	1513	1613	....	1713	1835
Worting (White Hart)	0712	....	0822	....	0917	0917	1017	1117	1217	....	1317	1417	....	1517	1617	....	1717	1839
Worting Road (South Ham)	0716	....	0826	....	0921	0921	1021	1121	1221	....	1321	1421	....	1521	1621	....	1721	1843
Basingstoke (Winton Square)	0720	....	0830	....	0925	0925	1025	1125	1225	....	1325	1425	....	1525	1625	....	1725	1847
BASINGSTOKE (Bus Station) ⇌	0725	....	0835	....	0930	0930	1030	1130	1230	....	1330	1430	....	1530	1630	....	1730	1852

1   Use the bus timetable to answer the following questions.

   a   Mr Tully arrives at Basingstoke bus station at 10.15 am. How long does he have to wait for a bus?

   b   How many buses from Basingstoke stop at Longparish?

   c   Miss Dawes catches the 0908 bus at Overton. To get to Salisbury she must change buses at Andover. The Salisbury bus leaves Andover at 1038.

   How long does she have to wait at Andover?

   d   Mrs Goff lives in South Ham and visits her mother in Whitchurch for at least 3 hours every Wednesday. If she catches the 1044 bus from Worting Road, which buses can she catch from The Square in order to be home before 5 o'clock?

2 Assume that the time in France and Belgium is 1 hour ahead of British time.

Dover/Boulogne [1¾ hours]	0030		0330		0630		0930	1230	1530	1830	2130	
Boulogne/Dover		0130		0430		0730	1030	1330	1630	1930	2230	2359
Dover/Calais [1¼ hours]	0200	0400	0600 0730	0900 1030	1200 1330	1500 1630	1800 1930	2100 2230				
Calais/Dover	0015 0200	0400	0600 0730	0915 1045	1215 1345	1515 1645	1815 1945	2115 2245				
Dover/Ostend [4 hours]	0115	0430	1000	1400	1630	1930	2130					
Ostend/Dover		0600	0945	1145	1345	1745	2100	2345				

a How many ferries leave Dover in the evening between 7 o'clock and 10 o'clock?

b At what time does the 7.30 pm boat arrive in Ostend?

c The 1330 ferry from Dover arrives in Calais at 1610.
How many minutes late is it?

d The Carmichael family have hired a chalet in Boulogne, but it is not available until after 12 noon.
Assuming it takes 45 minutes to pass through customs and drive to the chalet, what is the earliest ferry they should catch from Dover?

e Mr and Mrs Davenport plan to return to England on the 0130 ferry from Boulogne but arrive just as the boat is leaving.
How much time will they save if they catch the next available ferry from Calais?
(Assume that it will take more than half an hour, but less than 2 hours to drive from Boulogne to Calais.)

f The 1215 ferry from Calais to Dover leaves 20 minutes late.
Because of heavy seas, the crossing takes 45 minutes longer than usual.
At what time does the ferry arrive in Dover?

EXERCISE 8.6

1 Paul and Catherine go to Portugal to buy cotton material for their company. The material costs 147 escudos per metre and the cost of printing the pattern is 74 escudos per pattern which is $66\frac{2}{3}$ cm in length.
If the exchange rate is 261 escudos to the pound, how much are Paul and Catherine charged for 120 metres of the cotton material?

2 Paul and Catherine live in Southampton and decide to fly on the afternoon British Airways flight from Heathrow. The journey to Heathrow from Southampton takes 1 hour. Paul and Catherine want to allow 30 minutes to park their car, and intend to check in 50 minutes before the flight takes off. The flight timetable from Heathrow to Lisbon is shown below:

Heathrow	0825	1025	1350	1415	1830
Lisbon	1105	1305	1630	1650	2205
Airline	TAP	BA	TAP	BA	BA

Find:

a the latest time they should leave Southampton

b their time of arrival in Lisbon.

3 Enzo and Lucinda are going to a marketing conference in Naples, Florida. They consider two flights:
   - American Airlines
     departing London Heathrow at 0955, arriving Miami at 1440
   - Virgin Atlantic
     departing London Gatwick at 1115, arriving Miami at 1545.

   The time in Miami is 5 hours behind Britain. Naples is a two-hour drive from Miami.

   a Give two factors which could determine which airline Enzo and Lucinda use.

   b Assuming that to pass through immigration control in Miami would take $1\frac{1}{4}$ hours and that collection of their hire car would take a further 40 minutes, what would be the time in Britain when they arrive in Naples if they use:

   (i) American Airlines

   (ii) Virgin Atlantic?

4 Enzo and Lucinda hire a 2-door full-size car in America. The cost is given in the table below. In addition, they must pay insurance (LDW) which is $11.95 per day. They arrive in Miami on Tuesday afternoon and, using the same airline, fly home on Friday afternoon. One day for the car hire is any 24-hour period. In addition they are charged $14.95 for a tank full of petrol. Using the exchange rate of $1.49 to the pound, calculate the total cost in pounds of hiring the car.

RENT A CAR RATES

	Economy		Compact		Intermediate				Full Size				Luxury		Minivan/Convertible	
	2-Door (EXAR)		4-Door (CCAR)		2-Door (ICAR)		4-Door (IDAR)		2-Door (SCAR)		4-Door (FCAR)		(LCAR)		(MVAR/STAR)	
EFFECTIVE 01 JAN 94-31 DEC 94	D	W	D	W	D	W	D	W	D	W	D	W	D	W	D	W
FLORIDA	£8	£29	£16	£55	£17	£59	£18	£65	£20	£79	£25	£85	£40	£169	£42	£175
NEW YORK CITY	—	—	£25	£139	£27	£155	£29	£159	£32	£165	£33	£169	—	—	—	—
NEW YORK / ILLINOIS*	£18	£115	£24	£130	£25	£140	£26	£143	£27	£155	£29	£159	£35	£200	£37	£209
CALIFORNIA	£12	£49	£13	£65	£15	£75	£17	£79	£18	£89	£19	£95	£22	£135	£25	£139
REST OF USA	£13	£63	£17	£79	£18	£89	£19	£95	£20	£105	£20	£109	£21	£155	£22	£159

5 A rest-home organises a day trip for its residents to France. The coach leaves Salisbury at 9 am and takes $3\frac{1}{4}$ hours to travel to the Channel Tunnel. The shuttles leave at 5, 20, 35 and 55 minutes past each hour and 53 minutes after arriving at the terminal at Folkestone the coach is driven on to the French motorway.
   At what time does this coach go on to the French motorway?

6 Six helpers and 34 residents have lunch and tea in France. Lunch with wine costs 44.2 francs each, and tea costs 500 francs for the whole party. At an exchange rate of 8.85 francs to the pound, find the total cost in pounds of their meals.

7 A travel company is pricing a holiday package to the Canary Islands. The flight will cost £11 000 and the company expects to fill 120 of the 150 seats on the plane. The hotel will charge 5400 pesetas per person per night. The travel company adds on 20% of the total costs for its profit and agent's commission. At 215 pesetas to the pound, what cost should the company price a one-week (7-night) holiday?

8 The data below shows the timetable of an airline between Boston and Dallas/Fort Worth and between Dallas/Fort Worth and Corpus Christi. Edward arrives at Boston at 10.30 am and catches the next flight. At what time should he arrive at Corpus Christi?

Boston Departure	Dallas/Fort Worth Arrival	Dallas/Fort Worth Departure	Corpus Christi Arrival
6.44 am	9.59 am	6.53 am	8.06 am
8.30 am	12.01 pm	8.10 am	9.45 am
11.48 am	3.15 pm	10.57 am	12.15 pm
2.10 pm	5.46 pm	12.52 pm	2.08 pm
		3.50 pm	5.09 pm
5.20 pm	9.03 pm	5.12 pm	6.50 pm
6.45 pm	11.49 pm	9.51 pm	11.05 pm

9 A manufacturer of navigational instruments sells instruments for cruisers. One instrument measuring sea depth is sold in the Caribbean for $84. In England it is sold for £34.
What is the percentage increase in cost in the Caribbean?
(Use $1.49 to the pound.)

10 A company exports its goods using the Portsmouth–Caen ferry. Frank knows that he must allow $3\frac{1}{4}$ hours to drive to Portsmouth and an additional hour for customs.

 a What time must he leave to catch the afternoon ferry on Tuesday 27 July?

JUL	T 1	F 2	S 3	S 4	M 5	T 6	W 7	T 8	F 9	S 10	S 11	M 12	T 13	W 14	T 15	F 16	S 17	S 18	M 19	T 20	W 21	T 22	F 23	S 24	S 25	M 26	T 27	W 28	T 29	F 30	S 31
0800	E	E	D	E	E	E	E	E	E	D	E	E	E	E	E	C	C	D	E	E	D	D	C	C	D	D	D	D	D	C	C
1500	E	E	E	E	E	E		E	E	E	E	E		E	D	D	D	E	E		D	D	D	D	E	E		D	D	D	
2330	E	D	E	E	E	E	E	E	D	E	E	E	E	E	E	C	C	D	E	E	D	D	C	C	D	D	D	D	D	C	C

 C, D, E identify the tariff operating on that ferry.

The crossing time is 6 hours, except for the 2330 from Portsmouth which takes 7 hours.

 b When does he expect to arrive in Caen?
 Give your answer in British time.

9 *Statistical Terms*

In 1834, the Royal Statistical Society was founded, and defined statistics as 'using figures and tabular exhibitions to illustrate the conditions and prospects of society'. Statistics is now used to deal with the collection, classification, tabulation and analysis of information and opinions.

Data. Data is the information which has been collected or researched. The word 'data' is a plural and the singular is 'datum' (a single piece of information).

Variables. Information is collected about *variables* such as weights, numbers of clients, types of disease.
A *variable* is something which can change from one item to the next. It can be either **quantitative** (i.e. numerical like weight or number of clients) or **qualitative** (i.e. an attribute like car colour or type of disease).

There are two types of quantitative variables:

(i) *Continuous.* A continuous variable is a variable which could take all possible values within a given range, e.g. the height of a tree.

(ii) *Discrete.* A discrete variable is a variable which increases in steps (often whole numbers), e.g. the number of rooms in a building.

A discrete variable does not have to consist only of whole numbers. For example, the size of shoes is also a discrete variable, and the sizes go up in steps of a half ($5, 5\frac{1}{2}, 6, 6\frac{1}{2}$, etc.).

The number of steps climbed is a *discrete* variable.

The distance travelled on the escalator is a *continuous* variable.

Observation. An observation is the value taken by a variable. For example, an age of 17 years is an observation when the variable is age.

Population. The term '*population*' means everything (or everybody) in the category you are considering. For example, if you were making a study of cathedrals, the population could be all the cathedrals in Britain. If you were investigating what attracts people to certain types of holiday, the population would be all holiday-makers.

EXERCISE 9.1

For each population below, state whether the variable given is qualitative, discrete or continuous:

1 the numbers of employees in a county's factories

2 the weights of new born babies in Britain

3 the age at death in 1994 of a town's inhabitants

4 the lengths of bolts coming off a factory production line

5 the colour preferences of customers in a city's clothes shops

6 the acceleration rates of new models of motorbike in a given year

7 the time taken to complete a job by each employee of a firm

8 the brands of toothpaste sold by chemists

9 the number of passengers on flights to the Continent during one summer

10 the newspapers on sale at station kiosks

11 the number of cars parked each morning in a firm's car park over a period of time

12 the type of holiday accommodation available in a resort.

10 *Sampling, Surveys, Questionnaires*

One of the problems with statistical surveys involving people is that, whatever your opinion, there are likely to be many other people with the same opinion. If you ask only these people, your opinion will be seen to be that of the whole population. If you ask only people with the opposite opinion, you will be seen to be in a minority. Therefore, you must ask a variety of people, so that you have a true picture of the population.

Remember, however, that in statistics, the term **population** does not necessarily refer to people. If you wished to survey the ages of cars on the road, your population might be all the cars in Britain.

10.1 *Surveys*

When you record any information – for example, about other people's opinions or numbers of surviving African elephants or types of road accidents – you are carrying out a **survey**. The survey results may be obtained by asking questions, by observation or by research.

To obtain completely accurate information, you would have to ask *everybody* (in your town or country or whatever), and receive answers from everybody, or observe *all* the elephants in Africa.

10.2 *Censuses*

When information is gathered about all the members of a population, the survey is called a **census**.

A national census is carried out every ten years. The last one was in 1991. Every adult in Britain is asked a large number of questions on mainly factual matters, for example the number of rooms in their house, their age, and the number of cars they possess.

A national census is a very large undertaking, and the results, though accurate, take a substantial length of time to be produced. Apart from the vast number of people to be asked, and the placing of their answers in computers, it is very difficult to ensure that every adult has in fact replied. It costs the country a great deal of money to complete a national census.

10.3 *Samples*

It is usually impossible for firms, newspapers, biologists, medical researchers, etc., to obtain information about the whole population, because the survey:

- may be expensive
- may take a long time
- may involve testing to destruction – e.g. if you wish to find out how long batteries last, you test them until they run out
- may be impossible to carry out for every member of the population – e.g. a survey to find the weights of trout in Scottish rivers.

A small part of the population is chosen for the survey and this is called a **sample.**

The statistician then assumes that the results for the sample are representative of the population as a whole. The larger the number of people asked, the more likely their response is to be a valid result for the whole population.

Clearly it is vital that for the survey to be accurate the sample you choose must be representative of the whole population.

To achieve this, every member of the population must have an equal chance of being chosen.

10.4 *Sampling methods*

Random sampling

A random sample is one in which every member has an equal chance of being selected.

Campaign groups for or against a particular issue (such as the possible siting of a new supermarket near a park) can often obtain a large majority for their point of view simply by selecting which passers-by to question (perhaps the people living near the park who will be worried about the possibility of noise). By careful selection, majorities as high as 70% can easily be obtained both for and against the same issue! (Some people may well want a supermarket behind their back garden.)

The simplest way to obtain a random sample is to give every member a number, and to select numbers from tickets in a box (as in a raffle), or (if there are too many for this method) select numbers by computer. (Random numbers can also be obtained by using the RAN button on some calculators.)

It is common to use the electoral roll of a suitably sized area (on which every adult is listed) to obtain a numbered list from which to select a sample.

Periodic sampling

With periodic or systematic sampling, a regular pattern is used to pick the sample, for example, every hundredth firework on a production line. This can give a unrepresentative sample if there is a pattern to the list which is echoed by the sample.

Stratified random sampling

A stratified sample is more accurate than a random sample, and is used in opinion polls, when 1 or 2% accuracy is important. A stratified sample (or **strata sample**) is one in which the population is divided into categories. The sample should then be constructed to have the same categories in the same proportions.

Random sampling is then used to select the required numbers in each category.

For example, if you wished to find out about the earnings of students in a sixth-form college, it would be sensible to have both lower sixth and upper sixth students represented. You may also wish to make sure that one-year students, males and females, are fairly represented. Suppose there are 1000 students in college, of whom 220 are lower sixth one-year students, 420 are lower sixth two-year students and 360 are upper sixth students.

A sample of 50 would contain the following numbers:

$$\text{LVI one-year students} = \frac{220}{1000} \times 50 = 11$$

$$\text{LVI two-year students} = \frac{420}{1000} \times 50 = 21$$

$$\text{UVI students} \qquad = \frac{360}{1000} \times 50 = 18$$

The eleven LVI one-year students would be randomly chosen from the 220 students in college. The other two strata would be chosen in the same way.

Quota sampling

For a quota sample, a manufacturer may determine the proportions of each group to interview.

For example, if a manufacturer wishes to launch a new chocolate bar on the market, it may be more important to canvass the opinions of children and those who do the shopping than any other sector of the market.

A market researcher paid to survey a sample of 100 people could be instructed to ask, say, 20 people under the age of 18, 30 in the age range 19 – 40 who do the family shopping, 10 in the same age range who don't, 30 in the age range over 40 who do the family shopping, and 10 in this age range who don't. The researcher will probably use convenience sampling (see below) to choose who to ask, but once one of the quotas is filled, no more people in that category may be asked. The researcher will continue to ask people in the other categories until the sample of 100 has been surveyed.

This is a common method used for market research, but inexperienced (or lazy!) researchers may choose an unrepresentative sample.

Convenience sampling

The most convenient sample is chosen, which, for a sample of size fifty, usually means the first fifty people you meet. There is obviously no guarantee that this sample will be representative. In fact it is highly likely that it won't be.

10.5 *Bias*

The results of a survey are biased if the sample is not representative of the whole population.

Bias can be introduced if:

- the sample is unrepresentative. Even when using random sampling an unusual sample may be chosen, and this is just bad luck.
- an incorrect sampling method is used. Sampling methods, other than random, or stratified random sampling, are very likely to produce biased samples.

If you wanted to know people's views on drinking, a survey held outside a public house at closing time would clearly produce a different response from one held outside the office of the 'Teetotallers' League'! Neither would be representative of the complete population. Both of these samples would be biased.

- the questions asked in the survey are not clear or are leading questions (see section 10.6).

EXERCISE 10.1

In questions 1 to 8:

a identify the population

b criticise the method of obtaining the sample

c recommend an alternative way of obtaining a sample.

1 A journalist at a local newspaper wants to canvass popular opinion about plans for a new shopping centre in town. He goes into the High Street, and asks people, until he has asked 50.

2 Stephanie wishes to find out the earnings of college students. She goes into a college common room, and asks 40 girls.

3 The police wish to ascertain how many cars have a valid tax disc. One day, they set up a survey point on a road out of a town, between 5pm and 6pm. They stop a car, and check its tax disc. As soon as it has left, they stop the next car.

4 A geography student needs to collect five soil samples from his garden for a project. He stands in the middle, and throws a coin in the air. Where it lands, he takes a sample.

5 For a survey into the smoking habits of teenagers, Carol went to a tobacconist's near a school at 3.30pm, which was when the school day ended. She asked everyone entering the shop how much they spent on cigarettes in a week.

6 To find out how many homes in a telephone area have central heating, a salesgirl telephones 100 people, picked at random from a telephone directory.

7 To find out the make of car that people in an area of town use, Peter went out after lunch and knocked on doors until he had one hundred responses. He was pleased with his efficiency, as he had finished by 4pm.

8 To investigate what influenced people in their decision on mode of transport to work, John went to the station just before the 8.15 train departed, and asked as many people as he could.

10.6 *Questionnaires*

If your questions are written down and given to people to complete, the list of questions is called a **questionnaire**. The questions you ask must be chosen with care. They must:

(i) **not give offence**. Some people do not wish to give their precise age, or social class, so you *either*: (*a*) find an alternative question, (e.g. 'Which of these age ranges applies to you?'), *or* (*b*) fill in the information by using your own judgement.

(ii) **not be leading**. 'What do you think of the superb new facilities at . . .' will *lead* most people to agree they are better than the old facilities. People do not usually want to contradict the questioner. However, the point of the survey should not be to obtain agreement with your view, but to obtain other people's opinions.

(iii) **be able to be answered quickly**. The person answering the questions will often have only a small amount of time to spare and will not want you to write long sentences on their point of view. To obtain information easily from the survey it is helpful to have Yes/No answers or 'boxes' for the answers which are ticked. Here is an example:

How many different television sets does your household possess?
0   1   2   3   4   5   More
☐ ☐ ☐ ☐ ☐ ☐ ☐

A questionnaire must also be easy for anyone to understand. The questions themselves must also be designed carefully. The question 'How much do you watch TV?' could result in the following types of response:

'A lot', 'Not much'
'Every night', 'twice a week'
'For two hours a night'
'Whenever there's sport, a film, . . .'

A better question is 'How many hours do you spend watching TV?', but this may encourage wild guesses because of poor memory.

An even better question to ask is 'How many hours did you watch TV *last* night?'. You can then offer a range of possible answers such as:

'Not at all'
'Up to $\frac{1}{2}$ hour'
'$\frac{1}{2}$ to 1 hour'
'1 to 2 hours'

and so on.

If you suspect different times are spent on different days, it is up to you, as a statistician, to ask a few people each day over a period of a week.

All surveys are open to error. The larger the sample, the more accurate the result.

10.7 *Pilot surveys*

It is common for companies to carry out an initial survey on a small area of the country in order to identify potential problems with the questions and to identify typical responses. This limits the errors in expensive large-scale surveys.

EXERCISE 10.2

Criticise the questions asked in this exercise and suggest questions which should be asked to find the information required.

1   What do you think of the improved checkout facilities?

2   Do you agree that BBC2 programmes are the best on TV?

3   What is your date of birth?

4   Sheepskin coats are made from sheep. Do you wear a sheepskin coat?

5   Dolphins are wild animals. Do you enjoy watching dolphins perform?

6   Sunbathing causes skin cancer. Do you sunbathe?

7   Vitamin D is obtained from sunlight. Do you sunbathe?

8   Is the new decor a major improvement on the old?

9   Would you rather use your local shops than a major supermarket miles away?

*10.8 *Hypothesis testing*

A statistical survey should have a purpose. It may be used to find out people's opinions (e.g. an opinion poll) or to discover what the population requires of a new product (consumer research), but often it is used to test a theory. A statement is made about a population, or populations, which can be tested statistically. This statement is called a **hypothesis.**

For example:

1   'Women live longer than men.'

2   'You can't tell margarine from butter.'

3   'A new leisure centre would benefit the town.'

4   'The most popular colour of car is red.'

are four statements which are **hypotheses** (plural of 'hypothesis'). Each of these hypotheses can be investigated statistically.

To test the truth of the hypothesis someone must devise an appropriate method to collect data. This must then be analysed before a conclusion can be made, based on the results of the analysis.

The hypothesis can be tested by carrying out a survey or experiment, by observation, or by using published data (which is the result of someone else's survey).

For the four examples above:

1   To test the hypothesis that women live longer than men, government statistics published over several years could be used. Averages and measures of spread could be calculated (see Unit 13) and compared.

2   An experiment could test whether or not it was possible to tell the difference in taste between margarine and butter, perhaps by blindfolding people and seeing whether they can identify which is which.

3 A method for deciding if a new leisure centre is needed could be to devise a suitable questionnaire and survey a sample of the town population.

Among other things, the questionnaire would need to find out what facilities people required for sports, how their needs were being met at the present time, and whether they would consider using a new local leisure centre.

4 One method of testing the hypothesis that 'the most popular colour of car is red' would be to carry out a survey of cars on a busy stretch of road and record results taken at different times on different days on a survey sheet.

You will understand more about analysing data when you have worked through Units 13 (Averages) and *14 (Cumulative Frequency).

EXERCISE 10.3

1 State an appropriate method which could be used to test the following hypotheses:

   a If it rains on St Swithun's day, it will rain for the next forty days and forty nights.

   b Consumers prefer . . .

   (Choose any product or set of products which interests you).

2 Devise an experiment to test the hypothesis: 'Students studying Leisure and Tourism have quicker reactions than those studying Art and Design.'

3 An artist wants to find out the preferences of potential customers in their choice of paintings. How would he carry out a survey to discover these preferences?

4 A potter in Cornwall considers whether to produce coffee mugs or cups and saucers for his new hand-made range.
How would he carry out a survey to test opinion on which holiday-makers would prefer to buy?

5 Design a questionnaire to test the hypothesis that most burglar alarms are sold to victims of a recent burglary.

6 An estate agent wants to carry out a survey to discover what incentives would make house sellers use his agency in preference to others. How would he do this?

7 One village has a high incidence of childhood leukaemia.
How would you test the hypothesis that this is due to natural causes?

8 A student nurse decides to investigate differences in the occurrence of breast cancer in Europe. The rate in Southern France is very low. Design a questionnaire to test the hypothesis that this difference is due to diet rather than lifestyle.

9 A tour operator wonders whether it would be profitable to arrange flights between Exeter, the local airport, and Malaga, Spain.
Construct three questions for a questionnaire designed to discover whether this would be profitable.

10 A doctor analyses sporting injuries in two neighbouring villages, Hartington and Easeham. Hartington shows a greater number than Easeham. The doctor believes that this is because the residents of Hartington are younger than those in Easeham.
How would you design a questionnaire to test this hypothesis?

11 A company considers producing a cabriolet (open-top) version of a small car.
Design a questionnaire to survey opinion and discover whether this would be a sensible decision.

12 A manufacturer makes fittings for front doors. The fittings are made in brass and chrome and the manufacturer is wondering whether to introduce a range in black matt finish.
How would the company carry out a survey to find out whether the new range would be successful?

11 *Classification and Tabulation of Data*

11.1 *Tabulation*

The purpose of tabulation is to arrange information, after collection and classification, into a compact space so that it can be read easily and quickly. It then may be represented pictorially to enable relevant facts to be seen readily, as explained in the next chapter.

Tabulation consists of entering the data found in columns or rows.

> **EXAMPLE**
>
> The numbers of pensioners living in certain villages were:
>
> | Village | Number of pensioners |
> | --- | --- |
> | Ashurst | 31 |
> | Botleigh | 17 |
> | Crow | 28 |
> | Downton | 24 |
> | Eaglecliffe | 19 |
> | Fillingdales | 33 |
> | Total | 152 |
>
> It is important that the tables produced are neat, all rows and columns are clearly identified, and that units (where appropriate) are given.

11.2 *Classification of data*

Assuming that additional data had been collected, more detailed information could be given by subdividing the rows and/or columns.

> **EXAMPLE**
>
> Using the data from the Example above and subdividing the columns into male and female gives more information about the pensioners:
>
> | Village | Number of pensioners | |
> | --- | --- | --- |
> | | Male | Female |
> | Ashurst | 12 | 19 |
> | Botleigh | 5 | 12 |
> | Crow | 10 | 18 |
> | Downton | 11 | 13 |
> | Eaglecliffe | 9 | 10 |
> | Fillingdales | 15 | 18 |
> | Total | 62 | 90 |

Note: It is essential that all the relevant information is collected during the survey.

It is not possible, for example, to determine a person's sex after the survey has been completed.

11.3 *Tally charts*

It is common to record the data by means of a **tally chart**.

Suppose a survey was being carried out to determine the popularity of the various activities offered at a local leisure centre. First a list would be drawn up of possible activities: swimming, badminton, fitness training, etc. Then each person entering the leisure centre would be asked which activity they were paying for and a tally mark (*l*) would be recorded against the chosen activity.

To enable the results to be totalled quickly, it is usual to tally in groups of five, the fifth stroke being drawn diagonally across the previous four: *JHT* .

A section of the results for this survey could look like this:

Activity	Tally	Total
Archery	JHT JHT I	11
Badminton	JHT JHT JHT JHT III	23
Bowls	JHT III	8
Fitness room	JHT JHT JHT IIII	19
Judo	JHT JHT JHT JHT	20

11.4 *Frequency tables*

A table which shows a set of variables and the number of times each variable occurs (its **frequency**) is called a **frequency table** or **frequency distribution table**.

If a large amount of quantitative data has been collected, it is generally convenient to record the information in a more compact form by combining variables into **groups** or **classes**. Continuous variables, such as time, length, speed, will normally be grouped before the information is collected.

Suppose the leisure centre survey is extended to find the amount of time people spend in the centre.

First the size of each class is decided (say 15 minutes).

Then a table is drawn up of all the classes. The time each person in the survey has spent in the centre is tallied against the appropriate class and hence the frequencies are found.

Time spent (minutes)	Tally	Frequency
Less than 15	JHT I	6
15 – 29	JHT JHT	10
30 – 44	JHT JHT III	13
45 – 59	JHT JHT II	12
60 – 74	JHT JHT JHT I	16
75 – 89	JHT JHT JHT JHT	20
90 – 104	JHT JHT JHT JHT I	21
105 – 119	JHT JHT JHT II	17
120 – 134	JHT JHT IIII	14

EXERCISE 11.1

1 During a survey to find how knowledgeable the general public is about art, 40 people were asked to name as many artists as possible in one minute. The responses were:

```
 1    5    3    5    1    8   15    1
 2    2    1    3    4    4    1    2
13   11    8    6    1    2    5    2
 3    4    9    2    3   10    1    6
 2    7    1    4    6    4    5    3
```

Use a tally chart to draw up a frequency table for this data.

2 A textile mill spins yarn. The thickness of the yarn is measured at intervals, and the measurements, in millimetres, of a sample of 50 are given below.

```
0.72   0.98   0.81   0.96   0.91   0.90   0.76
0.92   0.95   0.91   0.83   0.91   0.89   0.86
0.93   0.94   0.78   0.93   0.83   0.86   0.91
0.78   0.92   0.88   1.03   1.04   1.01   0.94
1.03   0.90   0.85   0.85   0.91   0.82   0.88
0.95   1.02   0.99   0.97   0.92   0.82   0.90
1.03   0.93   0.94   0.86   0.87   0.93   0.89
0.92
```

Using intervals of 0.70–0.74, 0.75–0.79, 0.80–0.84, etc., draw up a tally chart to obtain the frequency distribution.

3 A small business carried out a survey to find the number of days absence of the employees over one year. The results were:

```
 3    1    4    2    1    5   20    5   15
 0   17   26    0   11    1    3   10    8
15   10   17   10    6   13   12   10   14
 5    8    3   21    0    3   18    3   18
 3   42    9   18   10   21   10    5    6
14    1    5    5    0    5    7   30    9
 0    5    6   25   23    6    4   11   12
```

Collect the information on a frequency table using intervals 0–4, 5–9, 10–14, 15–19, etc.

4 During a survey into changes in the conditions of work of clerical staff, 50 workers gave their present salaries (in £) as:

```
14030   12670   10180   11320    9870
10120   10130   15460   13680    9920
13830   11610   11880   14280   12200
11020   11570   10990    9700   11810
10880   11370   12090    9800    9670
12230   11680    8590    9680   10280
10420   12120    9330   10540    7490
 9240    8990    7630   11010    9180
 8320    8640   15200    8680   12040
 8680    7480    7720    8290    8470
```

Organize the data on a frequency table using intervals £7000–£7999, £8000–£8999, etc.

5 The staff in a medical practice monitored the waiting times of patients from the time the patient sat down until called to see the doctor.
The times, in minutes and seconds, were:

```
10:03   12:05    7:15    9:44   11:15
10:02   14:23   12:15   12:42   15:00
 5:43    9:08    9:53    9:03   14:21
 7:24   10:57   12:26    7:13   15:30
10:53   12:26   10:57   13:48    8:00
 9:24   12:48   10:17   11:02    7:48
 9:56   14:09    7:23    9:03    9:59
 9:32    8:05    7:53   14:23   13:03
```

a Write each waiting time to the nearest minute and use a tally chart to obtain the frequencies.

b Summarise the given waiting times in a frequency table using intervals $5.00 \le T < 7.00$, $7.00 \le T < 9.00$, etc., where T is the waiting time.

6 The weights (in kg) of 63 male patients admitted to a ward were recorded as:

```
72.4   68.2   69.3   71.1   66.8   67.2   65.4
68.0   78.9   76.0   70.8   64.3   82.3   70.2
74.2   76.7   65.5   71.6   74.1   68.7   66.8
83.3   74.9   71.5   75.7   71.6   73.2   82.5
73.8   78.2   65.6   76.9   76.8   81.5   77.2
75.8   75.4   80.3   78.0   68.3   76.0   78.5
78.8   71.7   74.4   69.8   77.6   73.4   77.3
74.9   72.4   66.9   73.7   74.4   68.8   82.6
73.7   79.8   74.0   71.8   73.4   76.0   79.2
```

Using intervals 60–, 65–, 70–, etc., summarise the information in a frequency table.

7 An increasing number of couples are choosing to celebrate their wedding in an exotic location. A survey to find the most popular destinations produced the following data (A = Antigua, B = Barbados, F = Florida, J = Jamaica, K = Kenya, L = St Lucia, M = Mauritius, S = Seychelles):

B J L S S L K A K B
M A A J L L L L B S
K J F F B L K K L A
M K J J K L B S J K
L B J K K L M A L J

Record the data on a frequency table.

8 The number of unoccupied seats on 80 transatlantic flights in one day were:

32	8	9	6	12	30	9	11	5	39
6	25	26	42	33	16	13	30	5	29
43	34	11	26	2	39	35	19	20	40
15	11	20	34	31	17	23	2	17	15
32	3	44	6	1	7	26	35	18	25
37	4	39	37	34	26	33	7	21	16
18	15	29	35	21	6	40	39	13	12
4	4	38	39	12	0	4	33	34	18

Summarise the information on a frequency table using class intervals 0–4, 5–9, 10–14, 15–19, etc.

9 The following data are the weights (w), in kilograms, of the luggage of 50 passengers boarding a charter flight to Europe. The luggage allowance was 20 kg per person.

18.04	22.32	18.02	20.16	20.50	15.18
13.48	19.90	17.98	19.76	17.12	22.00
21.44	20.04	17.30	16.30	20.24	18.76
17.24	19.96	16.72	15.92	19.66	17.94
18.70	19.94	15.02	17.58	16.80	17.52
17.10	19.82	22.44	15.80	19.02	18.82
15.76	19.46	18.29	20.23	17.78	15.82
15.90	16.46	16.72	18.22	19.00	20.50
17.62	20.44

oup the information into classes of width 2 kg using intervals $12.00 < w \le 14.00$, $14.00 < w \le 16.00$, $16.00 < w \le 18.00$ etc and display in a frequency table.

10 The number of faults found in a sample of 50 micro chips was:

1	0	0	0	2	0	0	0	1	0
0	0	1	1	0	1	0	0	2	0
0	0	0	0	1	0	0	0	0	0
2	0	0	1	0	1	1	0	3	0
1	1	0	0	2	0	2	1	0	1

Summarise the data on a frequency table.

11 A firm manufactures ball bearings for the motor and motorbike industries. In order to monitor accuracy, samples are taken at intervals from five machines and the diameters (d) of those bearings are measured in millimetres.

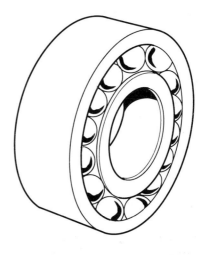

The results of one set of samples are given below:

49.46	50.15	51.15	51.36	49.72
50.41	50.03	48.16	50.26	49.43
49.66	49.31	50.32	49.76	46.78
50.16	50.98	51.15	49.40	48.88
48.90	50.47	49.33	50.08	48.20
49.76	49.67	50.05	50.70	49.46
50.14	49.39	52.63	49.93	49.19
50.09	49.27	49.63	51.09	48.21

Summarise the data on a frequency table using class intervals of 1 mm:

$46.00 \le d < 47.00$, $47.00 \le d < 48.00$, ..., $52.00 \le d < 53.00$.

12 People leaving a department store were asked to take part in a survey on shopping habits. A section of the results is shown below:

Customer	Sex	Under 20	Age 20–40	Over 40	Under 5 min	Time in shop 5–20 min	Over 20 min	Nil	Amount spent Up to £20	Over £20
1	M		✓			✓				✓
2	F			✓			✓			✓
3	M	✓			✓			✓		
4	F	✓				✓			✓	
5	F		✓			✓			✓	
6	F	✓			✓			✓		
7	M			✓			✓		✓	
8	F			✓			✓			✓
9	M		✓			✓			✓	
10	M	✓			✓				✓	
11	F			✓		✓				✓
12	F		✓				✓		✓	
13	M		✓		✓				✓	
14	M	✓				✓				✓
15	F		✓			✓		✓		
16	M			✓		✓			✓	
17	F			✓	✓			✓		
18	F		✓				✓			✓
19	F	✓				✓		✓		
20	F	✓				✓			✓	

a Suggest a number of ways in which the data could be divided into two or more groups.

b Using two of your suggestions, display the relevant data on frequency tables.

12 *Statistics on Display*

12.1 *Pictorial representation of data*

The presentation of data in the form of tables has been considered in Unit 11. However, most people find that the presentation of data is more effective, and easier to understand, if the data is presented in a pictorial or diagrammatic form.

The pictorial presentation used must enable the data to be more effectively displayed and more easily understood. The diagrams must be fully labelled, clear and should not be capable of visual misrepresentation. Types of pictorial representation in common use are the pictogram, bar chart, pie chart and frequency polygon.

Statistical packages may also be used to present data in a variety of ways. You cannot, however, rely completely on a computer to produce your pie charts, pictographs, etc. You must also be able to carry out the necessary calculations yourself and draw the most appropriate diagrams for the given data.

There are many ways of presenting data in pictorial form. It is clearly necessary to be able to interpret correctly any diagrams given.

The general interpretation of statistical pictures and graphs is that the bigger the representation, the larger the population in that group. However, it is also possible to interpret statistical diagrams so as to be able to calculate the population of each group.

12.2 *Pictograms*

In a **pictogram** data is represented by the repeated use of a pictorial symbol. The example below shows how a pictogram works.

> **EXAMPLE**
>
> A survey of 1000 people living in Freeton was taken, to see what colour of cars they owned.
>
> Represent this data in the form of a pictogram. The results of the survey were:
>
> | Colour of cars | Number of cars |
> |---|---|
> | Red | 60 |
> | White | 200 |
> | Blue | 100 |
> | Grey | 50 |
> | Gold | 80 |
> | Black | 30 |

Here is one possibility. A full car symbol represents 20 cars; half a car represents 10 cars. It is not possible to show small fractions of a symbol accurately, and the detail required should not normally be to more than half of a symbol (but certain symbols may allow for a quarter).

Colour of car

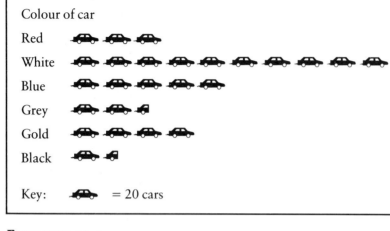

Key: = 20 cars

Exercise 12.1

1 The numbers of bottles of champagne sold in five villages is shown on the following pictogram:

Abbotshurst

East Lynne

Marlinsby

Tobbenham

Westering

a In which village were the most bottles sold?

b How many bottles were sold in Martinsby?

c How many bottles were sold in total?

2 The contents of a fruit bowl comprised:

Apples	7	Bananas	3
Pears	5	Peaches	7
Kiwi fruit	6	Oranges	2

Illustrate this data by means of a pictogram.

3 Students in a department of a college were asked about the type of accommodation in which they lived. The data was:

Flat	25	Semi-detached house	40
Maisonette	5	Detached house	30

Illustrate this data by means of a pictogram.

4 In a survey to find the most popular design on Christmas cards, 600 people were asked which animal they preferred. The results are shown on the pictogram.

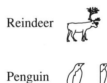

Reindeer

Penguin

Robin

Polar bear

(A full picture represents 50 voters.)

a How many people chose the polar bears design?

b What percentage of people chose the reindeer?

c Find the ratio of the votes for robins to the votes for penguins.

5 The number of people present in a Paris fashion show were:

Individual buyers	54
Store buyers	18
Celebrities	27
Photographers	45
Journalists	36

Illustrate this data by means of a pictogram.

6 The numbers of employees in four solicitors' offices were:

Archibald and Archibald	8
Dugdale, Wynne and Luff	10
JSC Weston-Hough	6
Mordecai and Sons	12

Draw a pictogram to represent this data.

7 A college canteen carried out a survey to decide which type of bread roll to serve. The answers are shown in the pictogram.

Crusty White

Soft White Baps

Granary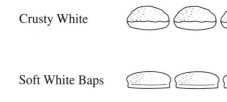

Brown Wholemeal

(One roll represents 4 votes.)

a Which was the favourite type of roll?

b How many customers preferred wholemeal rolls?

c What percentage preferred white bread?

8 The number of patients on a register of six doctors in a group practice is:

Dr Smith	2400
Dr Rawlings	1800
Dr Wong	3000
Dr Payne	2700
Dr Williams	2100
Dr Fisher	1500

Show this information on a pictogram.

9 The number of residents in five rest-homes is shown on the pictogram.

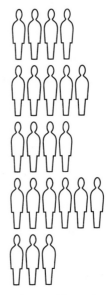

Candlelight	
Indian Summer	
Tranquillity	
Concordance	
Evensong	

(Each picture represents five residents.)

a How many residents are there in Candlelight?

b Which rest-home has the smallest number of residents?

c What is the total number of residents?

10 The number of flights for each airline out of Gatwick in a one-hour period was:

British Airways	8	Aer Lingus	2
Swissair	1	Britannia	6
Virgin Atlantic	1	Monarch	3

Illustrate this data on a pictogram.

11 One clock represents one hour on the following pictogram, which shows the time taken to cross the English Channel by different routes.

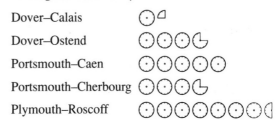

Dover–Calais	
Dover–Ostend	
Portsmouth–Caen	
Portsmouth–Cherbourg	
Plymouth–Roscoff	

a Which route takes the longest time?

b How long does it take to go from Portsmouth to Cherbourg?

c What is the difference in the time taken to cross the Channel between the Dover-to-Calais route and the Dover-to-Ostend route?

12 The management of a car plant wanted to know how many of the workers used the cars produced by their company. They decided to carry out a survey of the cars parked in the factory's car park one day. The results were:

Ford	35	Citroen	20
Rover	30	Renault	10
BMW	5	Vauxhall	25

Construct a pictogram to illustrate the results.

13 The workforce of a factory were asked by which mode of transport they came to work. The results are shown in the following pictogram, each figure representing 10 workers:

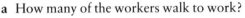

a How many of the workers walk to work?

b Which form of transport is used least to get to work?

c What is the total work force of the factory?

12.3 *Bar charts*

A **bar chart** is a diagram consisting of columns (i.e. bars), the heights of which indicate the frequencies. Bar charts may be used to display discrete or qualitative data.

EXAMPLE

Fifty households were surveyed, and the number of children in each family was recorded as follows:

Children in family	Frequency
0	8
1	11
2	17
3	8
4	5
5	1

Represent this data by means of a bar chart.

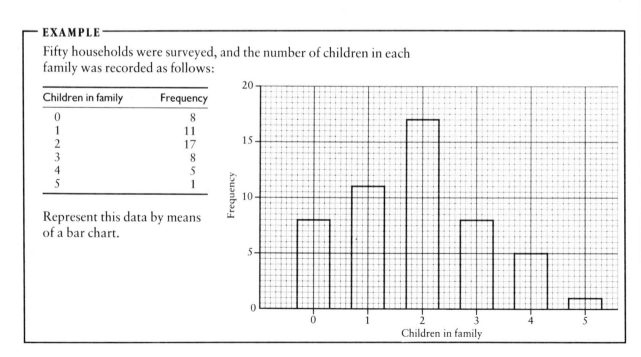

Dual bar charts

Dual bar charts are used when two different sets of information are given on connected topics.

EXAMPLE

The number of people over 17 years old, and the number of people holding driving licences in a particular street were found over a period of years.

These are as shown below.

Year	1986	1987	1988	1989	1990	1991
No. of people over 17	32	27	29	31	33	39
No. of people with driving licence	12	17	19	11	24	28

Represent this data by means of a dual bar chart.

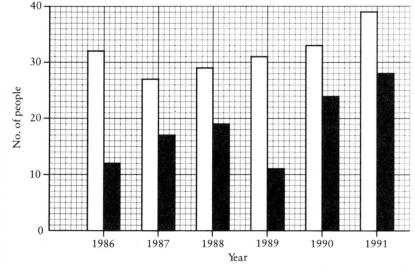

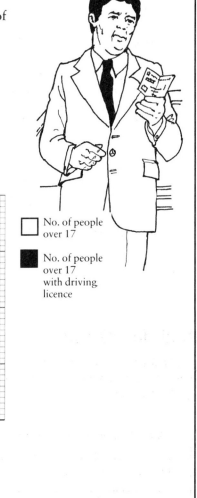

No. of people over 17

No. of people over 17 with driving licence

Sectional bar charts

Sectional bar charts, or **component bar charts**, are used when two, or more, different sets of information are given on the same topics. They are particularly useful when the *total* of the two or more bars is also of interest.

EXAMPLE

The numbers of saloons and hatchbacks sold by a garage were recorded.

Month	Jan	Feb	Mar	Apr	May	Jun
Saloons	18	7	8	12	10	13
Hatchbacks	16	12	9	7	9	8

Represent this data by means of a sectional bar chart.

Note that each column gives:

  (i) the number of saloons sold,

 (ii) the number of hatchbacks sold, and

(iii) the total number of cars sold during that month.

All three sets of information can rapidly be compared by using the same diagram.

EXERCISE 12.2

1 The bar chart shows the type of trees
   recorded during a survey of a section
   of a forest.

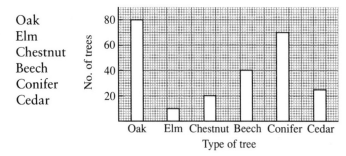

Oak
Elm
Chestnut
Beech
Conifer
Cedar

  a Which tree was seen most frequently?

  b Reconstruct the frequency table.

  c What was the total number of trees growing in this area?

2 Twenty people noted the television channel they were watching at 8.15 pm on two successive nights. The results were:

	First night	Second night
BBC 1	6	7
BBC 2	4	1
ITV	6	6
CHANNEL 4	3	4
SATELLITE	1	2

Draw a suitable bar chart to illustrate this data.

3 Thirty students designed ball gowns. The colours of the gowns were 12 black, 5 gold, 10 red, 2 blue, and 1 green.

Illustrate this information by means of a bar chart.

4 A graphics company investigated how many hours their employees actually worked on a computer during a week in January 1993 and again in 1994. The results were:

Time per week (hours):	0	0–1	1–2	2–4	4–10	10–20	20–40
1993	32	17	4	10	2	1	25
1994	17	2	5	11	12	21	34

Represent this data by means of a dual bar chart.

5 The number of students in an art class on six successive evenings were:

	Eve 1	Eve 2	Eve 3	Eve 4	Eve 5	Eve 6
Male	11	9	8	9	7	6
Female	7	8	9	10	11	13

Illustrate this information by means of a sectional bar chart.

6 In a three-month period, the number of days in which different products were advertised on two hoardings were compared. These are shown in the dual bar charts below.

a One hoarding was in an inner city, and the other one was in a suburban area. Which hoarding was in the inner city?
Give a reason for your answer.

b How many more days did Hoarding A advertise alcohol than Hoarding B?

c Which products were advertised only on Hoarding A?

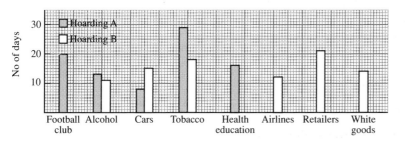

7   The numbers of large appliances sold by an electrical retailer during one day were:

Washing machines	35	Cookers	28
Televisions	38	Video Recorders	12
Refrigerators	21		

Illustrate this data by means of a bar chart.

8   An insurance company keeps records of life endowment policies sold by its representatives. In a six-month period the number of policies sold by their top salesmen were:

	With Profits	Without Profits
January	11	21
February	15	12
March	28	13
April	21	20
May	18	27
June	16	30

Represent this data by means of a sectional bar chart.

9   The number of houses sold by four agents in the first six months of 1993 and 1994 were:

	1993	1994
John	27	29
Mary	15	24
Carl	28	19
Latha	22	32

Represent this data by means of a dual bar chart.

10 Peter and Frances Mead decide to apply for a franchise. They investigate the possible companies selling fast food and the results of their investigations are shown on the bar chart below.

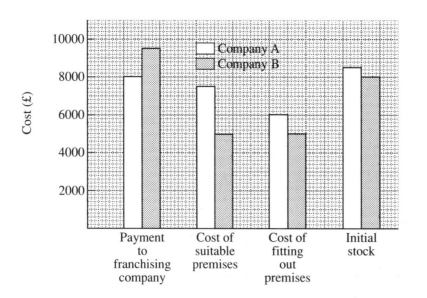

a What is the total cost of franchising with Company A?

b What is the total cost for franchising with Company B?

c How much greater is the payment to franchising Company A than to Company B?

d If Peter and Frances franchise with Company A, they would expect to have double the profits than if they had franchised with Company B. What other information would they need to know before they chose which company to franchise with?

11   The numbers of patients in six wards of a general hospital were:

Children	32	Cardiac	16
Orthopaedic	17	Surgical	28
Gynaecological	24	Geriatric	36

Represent this data by means of a bar chart.

12   The numbers of residents, and the numbers of staff employed at nursing homes in a small town were:

Nursing home	Residents	Staff
Golden Memories	45	28
Peacehaven	21	16
Autumn Leaves	41	24
Silver Threads	31	19

Represent this data by means of a sectional bar chart.

13   The birth rate per 1000 of population and the infant mortality rate per 1000 live births were found for a number of countries:

	The Gambia	Hungary	Italy	Samoa	UK
Birth rate	47.5	12.2	10.1	39.1	13.3
Infant mortality rate	174	20.4	10.9	4.4	9.4

Construct a dual bar chart to represent this data.

14   The goals scored in 38 football league matches on Saturday 24 February 1990 were:

Number of goals in match	0	1	2	3	4	5
Number of matches	3	6	10	12	5	2

Illustrate this information by means of a bar chart.

15   Jean-Paul and Michelle noted how the cost of their summer holiday had varied in the last two years. The money had been spent as shown:

	Travel	Rent of Villa	Food	Drink	Entertainment	Insurance
Cost 1993 (£)	720	820	550	140	250	110
Cost 1994 (£)	650	920	480	160	150	120

Represent this data by means of a dual bar chart.

16 The holiday destinations of 100 people entering an airport were:

	France	Spain	Greece	Italy	Morocco	USA
Male passengers	3	18	9	8	5	9
Female passengers	4	11	15	2	6	10

Draw a sectional bar chart to illustrate this data.

17 The bar chart below shows the results of a survey of socio-economic groups which was conducted in two housing estates in the same town. For each household, the occupation of the head of the house was used to determine the appropriate group.

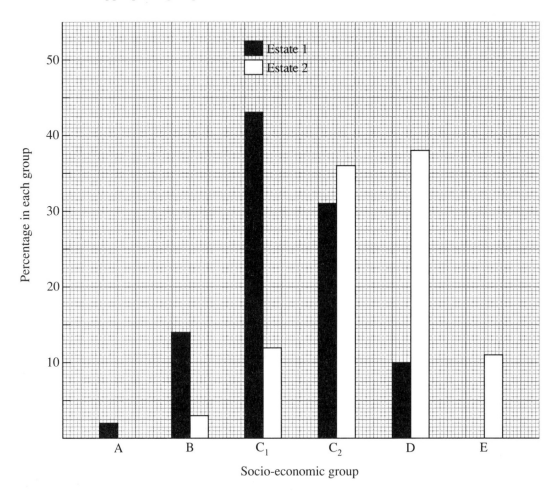

a What can you deduce about the two housing estates?

b What percentage of households belong to group D in:
   (i) Estate 1,   (ii) Estate 2?

c If 215 households were surveyed in Estate 1, how many are in Group B?
   (Give your answer to the nearest whole number.)

18   A researcher for a guide to good, small hotels collects data on the facilities offered by each establishment. The data obtained is represented in the sectional bar chart shown.

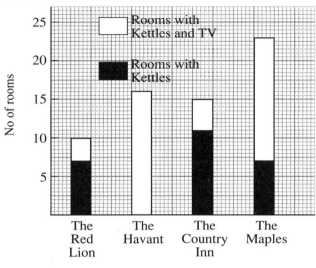

a   How many (i) kettles, (ii) TVs are provided by the Country Inn?

b   What percentage of rooms at the Red Lion have not a TV?

c   Which hotel has the largest number of rooms with both a kettle and a TV?

19   The numbers of kitchen units produced each day by one workman were:

Monday   38   Tuesday   29   Wednesday   41
Thursday   35   Friday   27

Show this information by means of a bar chart.

20   The number of employees in five tailoring establishments is shown on the sectional bar chart below.

a   Which firm employs most salespersons?

b   How many tailors are employed by the largest establishment?

c   What is the ratio of salespersons to tailors at Chandler?

d   What percentage of Jones's staff are tailors?

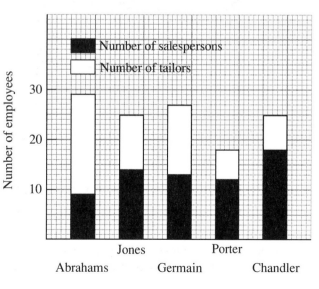

21 The percentage of trade of certain countries with the EC and the USA was calculated in 1985 to be as follows:

	Barbados	Falklands	Israel	Ireland	France	UK
% trade with E.C.	8.3	100	34.2	69.1	53.7	48.8
% trade with USA	52.8	0	28.2	9.8	8.7	14.7

Illustrate this information by means of a dual bar chart.

22 The number of employees in five small printing companies were:

Firm A   6 secretaries   and 17 other staff
Firm B   8 secretaries   and 14 other staff
Firm C 11 secretaries   and 10 other staff
Firm D   5 secretaries   and 12 other staff
Firm E   7 secretaries   and 6 other staff

Represent this data by means of a sectional bar chart.

12.4 *Pie charts*

A **pie chart** is another type of diagram for displaying information. It is particularly suitable if you want to illustrate how a population is divided up into different parts and what proportion of the whole each part represents. The bigger the proportion, the bigger the slice (or 'sector').

EXAMPLE

Represent by a pie chart the following data.

The mode of transport of 90 students into college was found to be:

Walking	12
Cycling	8
Bus	26
Train	33
Car	11
Total	**90**

Represent this data by means of a pie chart.

A circle has 360°. Divide this by 90 to give 4°. This is then the angle of the pie chart that represents each individual person.

Since 12 people walk to college, they will be represented by $12 \times 4° = 48°$.

Similarly for the others:

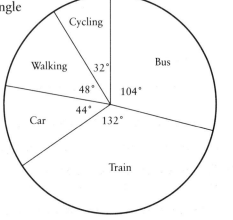

	Angle in pie chart
Walking	$12 \times 4 = 48°$
Cycling	$8 \times 4 = 32°$
Bus	$26 \times 4 = 104°$
Train	$33 \times 4 = 132°$
Car	$11 \times 4 = 44°$
	Total = 360°

Method for calculating the angles on a pie chart

Here is a summary of how to work out the size of each bit of 'pie'.

(i) Add up the frequencies. This will give you the total population (call it p) to be represented by the pie.

(ii) Divide this number into 360.

(iii) Multiply each individual frequency by this result. This will give you the angle for each section of the pie chart.

Interpreting pie charts

The initial interpretation is the fact that the largest portion of a pie chart relates to the largest group, and the smallest portion to the smallest group. However, if any of the data is known, the rest of the data can be calculated.

EXAMPLE 1

The pie chart below shows the number of students in different sections of a college. 220 students are in the Construction department.

a How many students are there in the college?

b How many students are there in Catering?

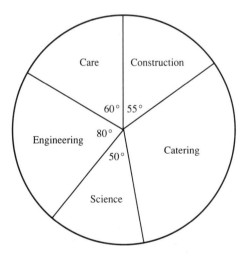

a 55° represents 220 students.

$$\therefore 1° \text{ represents } \frac{220}{55} = 4 \text{ students.}$$

The complete circle (360°) represents $4 \times 360 = 1440$ students.

∴ There are 1440 students in the college.

b The angle representing Catering is
$360 - (80 + 55 + 60 + 50) = 115°$.

∴ The number of students in Catering is $4 \times 115 = 460$.

EXERCISE 12.3

Illustrate the data given in questions 1, 2 and 3 below by means of a pie chart.

1 The types of central heating used by households in a village were:

Solid fuel	14
Gas	105
Electricity	41
None	20

2 240 students were asked what they were intending to do during next year. The results were:

80 going to university
86 staying at college
64 going into employment
10 with no firm intention.

3 The numbers of bedrooms in 720 houses recorded as:

1 bedroom	80
2 bedrooms	235
3 bedrooms	364
4 bedrooms	39
5 bedrooms	2

4 The pie chart shows the different drinks sold at lunchtime in a college. 720 drinks were sold in total.
Find the number of each different drink sold during lunchtime:

a Coke

b Orange

c Coffee

d Chocolate

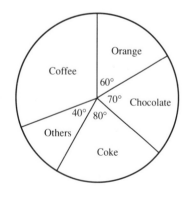

5 The number of special birthday cards sold by a newsagents in a week were:

Mum	42
Dad	34
Grandad	18
Granny	16
Brother	25
Sister	17
Son	15
Daughter	13

Illustrate this information on a pie chart.

6 An artist designed book jackets for 225 books during a five-year period with one publishing house. The books were classified as Thriller, Romance, Travel, Hobby and Science.

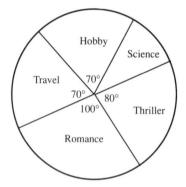

a What size angle represents science books?

b How many jacket designs did the artist create for science books?

c How many jacket designs were created for thrillers?

d What fraction of the designs were for romances? (Give your answer in its lowest terms.)

7 Each pound spent at the Winchester Theatre Royal box-office is used to meet the theatre's expenses as follows:

Performance fees	60p
Salaries	17p
Premises and depreciation	10p
Administration	5p
Publicity	5p
Equipment	3p

Draw a pie chart to show how each pound is spent.

8   The number of clients of each of the partners in a business were:

Kerry   43
Michell   22
Owen   18
Richard   7

Illustrate this information on a pie chart.

9   The proportion of the cost of manufacturing a dinner service was:

Raw material   5%
Manufacture cost   28%
Hand painting cost   51%
Overheads   5%
Profit   11%

Represent this data on a pie chart.

10 The pie chart shows the different types of petrol which a garage sold in one week.
The garage sold 25 000 gallons of diesel.

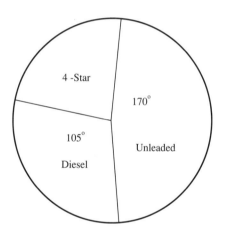

a   How much unleaded petrol was sold?

b   How much 4-star petrol was sold?

c   What were the total sales?

11 A health centre calculated the distance patients from one practice lived from their GP's surgery:

Under 1 mile: 510 patients
Between 1 and 2 miles: 1230 patients
Between 2 and 3 miles: 140 patients
Over 3 miles: 280 patients.

Illustrate this information on a pie chart.

12 The pie chart shows the type of dwellings in which people in a village live. There are 720 dwellings in the village. By measuring the angles, find how many are:

a   detached houses

b   bungalows

c   semi-detached houses.

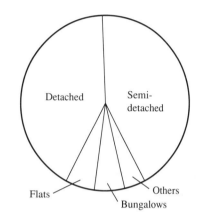

13 The number of villagers undertaking activity to ensure 'active living' were:

Swimming   1020
Walking   3580
Jogging   105
Keep fit centre   85
Other   610

Draw a pie chart to illustrate this data.

14 The holiday destinations of 60 people were:

France	Spain	Greece	Tunisia	USA	Caribbean	Portugal
21	15	6	3	8	5	2

Represent this information by means of a pie chart.

15 At a sports centre, the ages of 100 people were recorded as follows:

Under 20 years   30
20 to 29 years   15
30 to 39 years   12
40 to 59 years   14
60 years and over   29

Construct a pie chart to illustrate this data.

16 The pie chart shows the number of passengers flying from London to Miami on one afternoon. 1800 passengers in total flew this route on that afternoon.

Find the number flying:

a Virgin

b American Airlines

c British Airways

The plane used by Virgin is a Boeing 747 seating 370 passengers.

d What percentage of the Virgin seats was occupied?

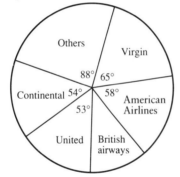

17 Out of 90 employees in a manufacturing company, there were 10 managers, 15 salesmen, 52 production line workers, 4 typists, and 9 quality controllers.
Illustrate this information on a pie chart.

18 A manufacturer of combined harvesters commissioned a survey on the use of agricultural

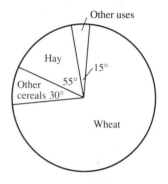

land in South Australia. The result is shown in the pie chart.

a Find the percentage of land use for wheat.

b The total acreage is 3 000 000 acres. What area was used for hay?

19 In 1984, in the UK, there were 4 500 000 people employed in manufacturing. Of these, 600 000 were in the food industry, 650 000 were in mechanical engineering, 500 000 in electronic engineering and 400 000 in printing.
Identify the remainder as 'other industries', and draw a pie chart to represent this information.

12.5 *Line graphs*

A bar chart can be replaced by a line graph, provided that the quantity on the horizontal axis is continuous, e.g. age, temperature or time.

In this case the data is plotted as a series of points which are joined by straight lines.

Line graphs associated with time are called **time-series graphs.**

They are used, for example, by geographers to illustrate monthly rainfall or yearly crop yield, etc., and by businesses to display information about profits or production over a period of time.

They show trends and have the advantage that they can be easily extended.

EXAMPLE

The numbers of cars sold by a garage during the first nine months of 1990 were:

Month	Jan	Feb	Mar	Apr	May	Jun	Jul	Aug	Sep
Number sold	32	25	17	10	14	5	4	48	27

Represent this data by means of a line graph.

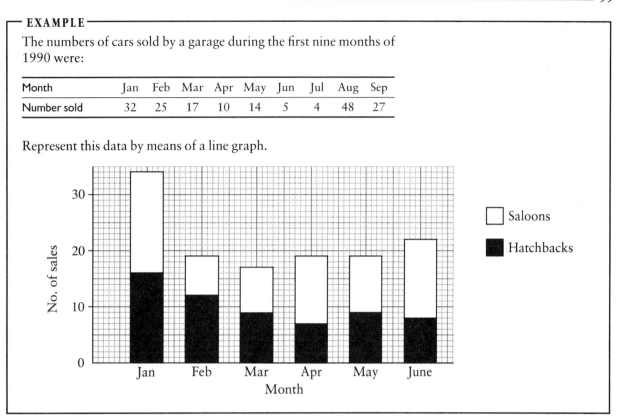

EXERCISE 12.4

Illustrate the data given in questions 1, 2 and 3, using a line graph.

1 The rainfall during a period of six months was:

Month	Jan	Feb	Mar	Apr	May	Jun
Rainfall (mm)	75	192	86	89	25	19

2 The maximum temperatures for six successive months at Sunbourne were:

Month	Apr	May	Jun	Jul	Aug	Sep
Temperature (°C)	61	74	72	91	85	56

3 The girth of a tree was:

Age (years)	10	20	30	40	50	60
Girth (cm)	25	63	98	135	170	210

4 In an art class, students were asked to draw a bowl of fruit. The number of grapes drawn by the students were:

Number of grapes	0	1	2	3	4	5
Number of students	2	7	6	3	2	1

Construct a line to show this information.

5 The graph below shows the number of births (measured along a vertical axis) in a given year (measured along a horizontal axis).
Answer the questions below by reading off the values from the graph.

a Estimate the number of children born in 1915.

b In which years were approximately 825 000 children born?

c Which year had the lowest number of births?

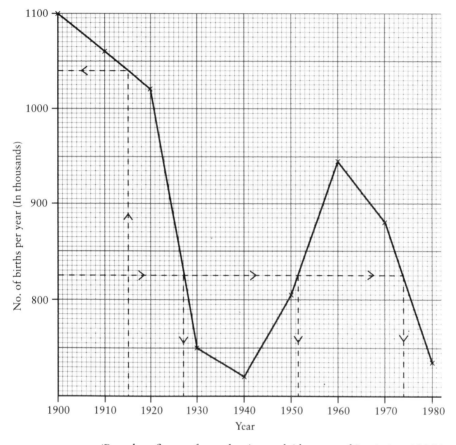

(Based on figures from the *Annual Abstract of Statistics*, 1988.)

6 Mordecai makes cuddly toys. The number of koala he made in one week is shown on the line graph below:

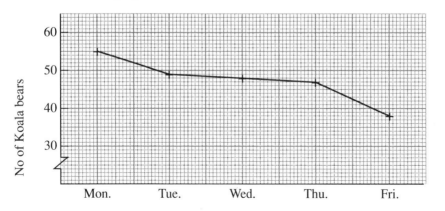

a The trend of this graph is downwards. Give a possible reason for this.

b During the following week, Mordecai's production of koala bears was:

Mon	Tue	Wed	Thur	Fri
41	46	49	48	42

What was the total production for each week?

7 The graph shows the average gross weekly earnings of men from 1970 to 1986.

   a Estimate the average weekly earnings in 1974.

   b Estimate the average weekly earnings in 1984.

   c Why is the answer to **b** a better estimate than the answer to **a**?

   d In which year did the average weekly wage reach £100?

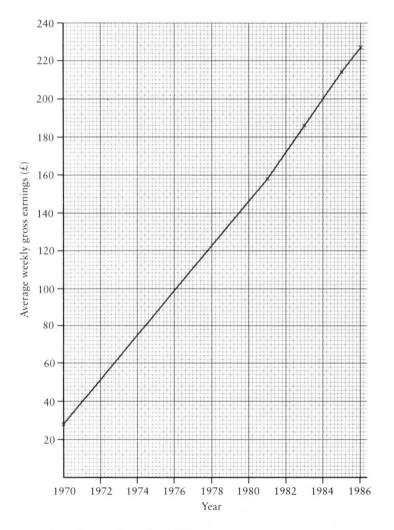

(Based on figures from *Social Trends*, 1988.)

8   The temperature of an office in degrees Fahrenheit, was recorded on a day
    in winter as:

8 a.m.	9 a.m.	10 a.m.	11 a.m.	12 noon	1 p.m.	2 p.m.	3 p.m.
56	66	68	69	70	71	70	69

a   Draw the information on a line graph.

b   Between which times was the temperature
    change greatest?
    Give a possible reason for this change.

c   The recommended temperature for an office is
    between 61 and 80.
    Estimate for how long the temperature was at
    the recommended level.

9   Mark's height was recorded each year on his birthday; the result for every
    second year is shown on the line graph.

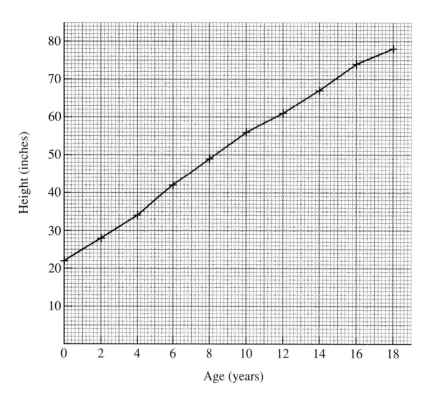

a   Estimate Mark's height on his ninth birthday.

b   During which two years was his rate of growth the greatest?

c   What do you think will happen to his growth rate after his eighteenth
    birthday?

10 The numbers of children with mumps registering at a health centre were:

Monday	Tuesday	Wednesday	Thursday	Friday
18	7	8	9	6

Show this information on a line graph.

11 The line graphs below compare the number of wet days during the year in London and Nice.

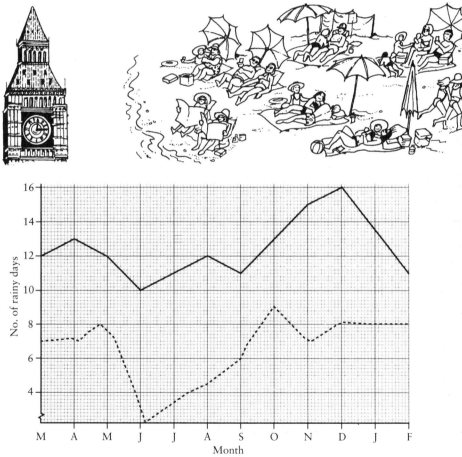

a Which graph represents the number of rainy days in London?

b Which is the wettest month for each city?

c Which month is the driest for each city?

d In which month does the smallest difference in the number of wet days occur?

12 The numbers of passengers carried by an airline (in thousands) were as follows (Sp = spring, Su = summer, etc.):

	1988				1989				1990		
Sp	Su	Au	Wı	Sp	Su	Au	Wi	Sp	Su	Au	Wi
21	48	31	17	22	49	29	18	23	41	24	25

  a Plot this information on a line graph.

  b State any trends which the data suggests.

13 The numbers (in thousands) of steel pipes made by a company were:

Jan	Feb	Mar	Apr	May
24	23	18	14	27

Illustrate this information by means of a line graph.

14 The graph below shows the number of cars supplied per month by a car manufacturer to a garage's sales section:

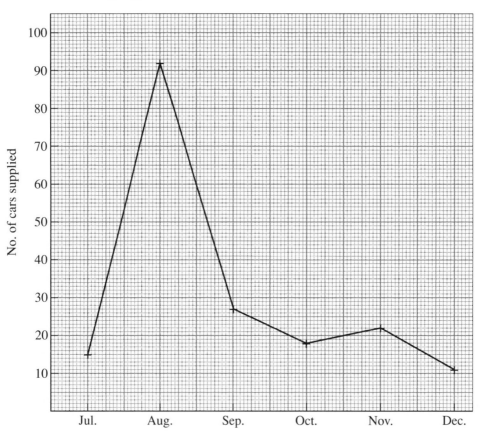

  a In which month were most cars supplied?
Give a possible reason for this large amount.

  b How many cars were supplied in November?

  c What was the total number of cars supplied during the six months?

  d What was the average number of cars supplied per month during this period?

12.6 *Frequency polygons*

A method of presenting data which is an alternative to a histogram is the **frequency polygon**. They are often used to compare frequency distributions, i.e. to compare the 'shapes' of the histograms, because it is possible to draw more than one frequency polygon on the same graph. It is easier to make comparisons using frequency polygons than using histograms.

For ungrouped data, the frequencies are plotted as points. For grouped data, which is more usual, the frequencies are plotted against the mid-point of the class interval. In both cases the points are joined with straight lines.

EXAMPLE 1

The heights of 80 students were recorded. The data was:

Height (cm)	150–160	160–170	170–180	180–190	190–200	200–210
No. of students	4	7	15	47	6	1

Represent this data by means of a frequency polygon.

The new table is:

Mid-point of class	155	165	175	185	195	205
Frequency density	4	7	15	47	6	1

Frequency polygon

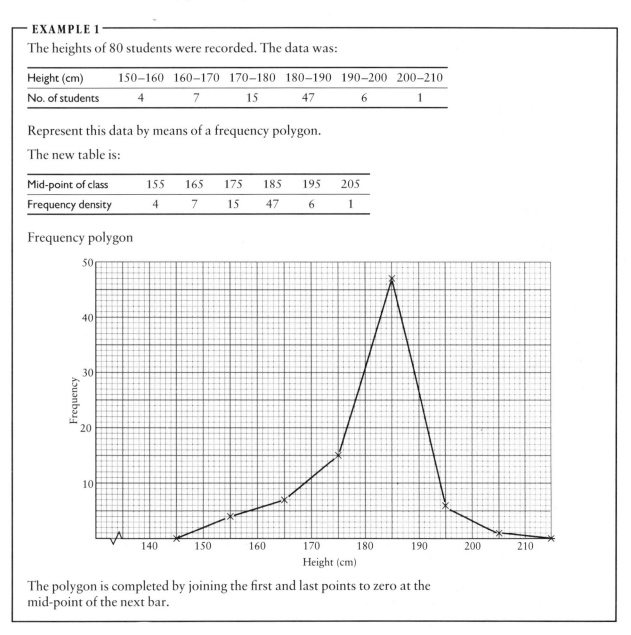

The polygon is completed by joining the first and last points to zero at the mid-point of the next bar.

When frequency polygons are used to compare two sets of data, it is the shapes of the distributions which are important. For this reason, the mid-points of the classes are often plotted against the actual frequencies, rather than the frequency densities which would be used for a histogram.

--- EXAMPLE 2 ---

The mock examinations results in Mathematics for two successive GCSE groups are recorded on the table below.

Mark	1–20	21–40	41–60	61–80	81–100
Group 1 % frequency	5	12	35	28	20
Group 2 % frequency	7	26	48	9	10

a Draw the frequency polygon for each group.

b Assuming the ability of the pupils was the same in each year, comment on the mock examination papers.

a In this example, the percentage frequencies are plotted against the class mid-points, which are 10.5, 30.5, 50.5, 70.5 and 90.5.

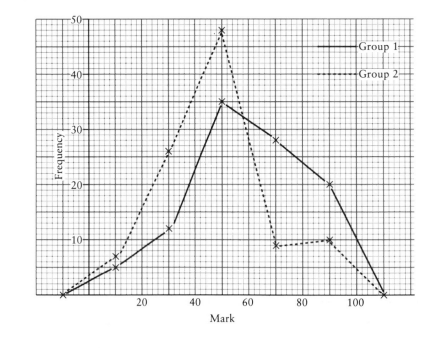

b Group 2 appear to have been given a more difficult examination paper than Group 1.

EXERCISE 12.5

1 Draw the frequency polygon for the data given below.
The speeds of 100 cars on a motorway were recorded. The data found was:

Speed (mph)	30–40	40–50	50–60	60–70	70–80	80–90
Number of cars	2	11	35	42	9	1

2 A teacher noted the rates of absence from her Maths class on Mondays and Fridays. The results are given on the table below.

No. absent from class	0	1	2	3	4	5	6	7	8	9	10	11
Monday frequency	3	6	6	7	4	4	3	0	0	0	0	0
Friday frequency	0	2	2	3	4	5	2	0	6	3	2	1

a Draw the frequency polygon for each day, using the same axes.

b Comment on the absence rates for the two days.

3 The table below shows the number of letters per word in 100 words of two books.

No. of letters	1	2	3	4	5	6	7	8	9	10	11	12
Frequency, Book A	3	12	28	7	14	11	6	6	7	4	1	1
Frequency, Book B	6	8	37	22	7	11	6	0	1	2	0	0

a Draw the frequency polygons using the same axes.

b One extract was taken from a child's story and the other from an adult science fiction story.
State which is which, giving reasons for your decision.

4 The number of new designs being introduced by two furniture manufacturers was:

	1989	1990	1991	1992	1993	1994
Danish Design	8	7	8	5	2	1
Ultimate Style	4	4	3	4	6	7

Draw the frequency polygons and comment on your results.

5 Choose two daily newspapers, one full size and the other a tabloid. Compare them by drawing frequency polygons of the number of words per sentence in one hundred sentences taken from similar sections in each newspaper.
(If you keep these results, they could be used in future work to calculate means, medians, and standard deviations.)

6 The table below shows the adult population of males and females in 1986.

Age	16–24	25–34	35–44	45–54	55–64	65–74	75–84
Male population (millions)	4.1	3.9	3.8	3.1	2.8	2.1	1.2
Female population (millions)	4.0	3.9	3.8	3.2	2.9	2.7	2.4

(Source: *The Office of Population Censuses and Surveys*)

Draw the frequency polygons and comment on your results.

7   A casino carried out an experiment using eight dice to find the number of sixes in each throw of the dice.
The objective was to see if the experimental results matched the expected theoretical calculations.
The frequency polygon shows the expected results.

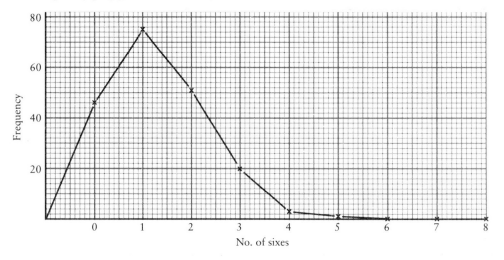

The experimental results were:

Number of sixes	0	1	2	3	4	5	6	7	8
Frequency	50	75	51	20	3	1	0	0	0

a   Copy the given graph and plot the frequency polygon for the experimental results on the same axes.

b   Comment on the two sets of results.

8   The number of faults on a car production line in two successive months, before and after a new model was introduced, was:

Number of faults	0	1	2	3	4	5	6	7	8	9	10
Frequency (old models)	0	0	1	4	5	8	8	2	1	0	2
Frequency (new model)	4	8	5	11	1	0	2	0	1	0	0

Draw the frequency polygons and comment on your results.

12.7 *Drawing inferences from diagrams*

When you can readily transfer data to pictorial form, and can convert pictorial representation back into numerical data, you can start to draw inferences from the data given in either form.

Drawing inferences from statistical data is not an exact science. There is rarely a correct, precise answer. If some of the data does not fit the overall pattern, this should be noted. Then, the reasons for the apparent contradiction should be considered.

We can illustrate this by an example.

┌─ **EXAMPLE** ───┐

The number of people each day visiting an open-air swimming pool in
August were:

341, 352, 347, 355, 361, 341, 344, 352, 344, 360, 371, 347, 329, 351, 621, 357,
348, 359, 354, 372, ...

What can be inferred from this data?

The 15 August figure of 621 is clearly exceptional and should be easily
identified.

The reasons why this figure is exceptional would be unlikely to be found
without further questioning – for example:

  (i) was an alternative swimming facility closed for the day?

 (ii) was the weather on the 15th substantially hotter than on the other
      days?

(iii) does the data refer to a country with a Bank Holiday on 15 August
      (e.g. France)?

These are all possible reasons and you may be able to suggest others.

└───┘

Some data gives results from which suitable inferences can be fairly quickly
drawn. Here is an example.

┌─ **EXAMPLE** ───┐

A men's clothes shop has two branches: one in a city centre, and one at an
out-of-town shopping complex. The weekly sales of the two shops over a
period of three months are given below:

Date (week commencing)		December				January				February			March	
		7	14	21	28	5	12	19	26	2	9	16	23	2	9
Sales in	City shop	18	21	23	14	29	31	28	7	5	8	6	4	5	8
thousands	Out-of-town	22	27	52	15	4	5	6	8	9	8	10	9	7	8
of pounds	shop														

What can be inferred from this data?

From the above data, the following inferences could be made:

  (i) Sales immediately prior to Christmas are higher than at other times in the
      three-month period.

 (ii) Sales in the out-of-town complex are generally higher than those in the
      city shop.

(iii) The city shop had a 'sale' during the first three weeks of January.

(iv) During the 'sale' the trade at the out-of-town shop was reduced.

In reality, the firm could well investigate the types of garments sold over the
year to decide whether or not to promote the same articles in both shops at the
same or different times. Computerisation of sales enables shops to keep far
better checks on stock sold. This enables them to react more quickly to
consumer demand and to supply each individual shop with the goods which its
specific customers require.

└───┘

13 *Averages and Range*

Frequency distributions and graphs, such as dual bar charts and frequency polygons may be used to compare sets of data. It is also very useful to be able to compare a single, 'typical', statistic from one set of data with a single, 'typical', statistic from another set of data.

This statistic must be representative of the distribution. For this reason it is usually located at or near the centre of the distribution and is called a **measure of central location** or **average**.

The most commonly used averages are the **mean, mode** and **median**.

13.1 *The arithmetic mean*

The **arithmetic mean**, which is usually just referred to as the mean, is the most widely used average.

To calculate the mean, the total of the values is found and this is 'shared out' equally by dividing by the total number of values.

EXAMPLE

A company owns five nursing homes. The number of residents in the five homes is 45, 21, 41, 31 and 38.
What is the mean number of residents per home?

$$\text{Total number of residents} = 45 + 21 + 41 + 31 + 38$$
$$= 176$$
$$\text{Number of homes} = 5$$
$$\therefore \text{Mean number of residents} = \frac{176}{5} = 35.2$$

This means that, if the five homes had the same number of residents, each home would cater for approximately 35.

Note. Although it is impossible to have 35.2 residents, it is usual to leave a mean as a decimal answer to show that it is a calculated value and to allow more accurate comparisons to be made.

The mean is often denoted by the symbol $\bar{x}$ and given in formula form as

$$\text{Mean} = \frac{\Sigma x}{n}$$

Σ is a capital Greek letter (sigma). Σx means the sum of all the terms and n is the number of terms.

EXERCISE 13.1

1 The weekly wages of ten workers were:

£110, £115, £135, £141, £119, £152, £144, £128, £117, £139.

Find the mean wage.

2 The wind speed (in mph) at 8 am on a particular day, was recorded at a number of measuring stations as:

88, 74, 61, 92, 48, 59, 71, 80, 70, 51, 48, 45, 75, 80, 82.

Find the mean wind speed.

3 A rugby team scores 37, 21, 64, 0, 18, 7, 35, 49, 28, 51, 82, 71 points in 12 successive matches. What is its mean score?

4 Eight people were asked their ages, and the replies were 37, 41, 29, 17, 15, 21, 32, 38. John claims that their average age is over 29.
Why is he correct?

5 Five men have a mean height of 1.95 m.

Four women have a mean height of 1.72 m.

What is the mean height of the nine people?

6 The attendances at an art exhibition on six successive days were 130, 97, 110, 78, 64 and 150.

What was the mean daily attendance?

7 A quilter bought eight odd lengths of material from the ends of rolls to use for patchwork. She was charged for eight metres.

The actual lengths of the pieces were 1.50 m, 0.75 m, 1.20 m, 0.90 m, 1.30 m, 1.25 m, 1.55 m and 1.90 m.

a What was the mean length of a piece of material?

b Did she make a 'good buy'?

8 A secretary typed four documents in one hour. The numbers of words (to the nearest 10 words) were 1200, 850, 1570 and 880.

a What was the average number of words per document?

b What was the secretary's average typing speed in words per minute (w.p.m.)?

9 A canteen's food bills for one week were £498, £529, £384, £366, £620, £591, £485.

a What was the mean cost per day?

The number of employees served on each day was 109, 110, 84, 88, 122, 94, 82.

b What was the average cost per head?

10 In six successive weeks, the number of cases dealt with by a probation officer was 12, 15, 13, 11, 14, 16.

What was the mean number of cases per week?

11 Five overweight people volunteered to go on a sponsored diet. Their initial weights were 183 lb, 227 lb, 138 lb, 199 lb and 150 lb.

After three months, their weights were 141 lb, 180 lb, 126 lb, 146 lb and 140 lb.

a What was the total weight loss?

b What was the mean weight loss per person?

c What was the mean weight loss per week? (Assume 1 month = 4 weeks.)

12 The map shows the temperatures in various parts of Britain on a given day.

a What was the mean temperature?

b What was the mean temperature for:
(i) the North?
(ii) the South?

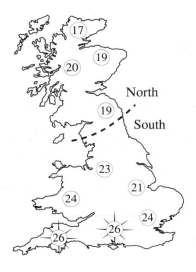

13 In 1948 the winning distances for the discus were 52.78 m, 51.78 m, 50.77 m.

In 1988 the winning distances were 68.82 m, 67.48 m, 67.38 m.

a What was the mean distance in 1948?

b What was the mean distance in 1988?

c Comment on the results.

14 Twelve cars of the same model were fuelled with exactly one gallon of petrol. The cars were then driven over the same course at a steady speed of 56 mph until the petrol ran out. The number of miles travelled by each car was recorded:

38, 41, 44, 38, 35, 42, 41, 39, 44, 43, 46 and 40.

Is the manufacturer justified in claiming that the number of miles per gallon, at 56 mph, is 41 for this model of car?

15 A time study was carried out at a factory to find the times taken for each process. Six fitters were timed assembling a piece of machinery. Their times (in minutes and seconds) were:

6:50, 5:35, 7:05, 5:10, 6:20 and 5:30.

What was the mean time for the job?

13.2 *The mode*

The **mode** is the number which occurs most frequently. Suppose seven students scored as follows in a test:

$$2, 3, 6, 7, 7, 8, 9$$

The mean score here is $\dfrac{42}{7} = 6$.

The **mode**, the number which occurs most frequently, is 7.

Some distributions can have more than one mode. For example, the numbers of people hiring a firm's mini bus were:

3, 3, 4, 5, 7, 8, 8, 8, 10, 11, 13, 13, 14, 15, 15, 15.

Both 8 and 15 are modes.

This distribution is said to be **bimodal**.

EXAMPLE 1

The number of days spent in hospital by patients on a surgical ward were
2, 3, 3, 2, 4, 4, 3, 5, 10, 3, 2, 4, 3, 4.
Find the mode.

When the numbers of days are written in ascending order:
2, 2, 2, 3, 3, 3, 3, 3, 4, 4, 4, 4, 5, 10
it can be seen that the number occurring most often is 3.
This means that the mode or modal number of days is 3.

Modal class

When the values are grouped the mode is replaced by a **modal class**, which is the group of values occurring most frequently.

EXAMPLE 2

What is the modal class in the following table, which shows the time spent by customers in a leisure centre.

Time spent (minutes)	Frequency
Less than 15	6
15 –	10
30 –	13
45 –	12
60 –	16
75 –	20
90 –	21
105 –	17
120 – 135	14

There are 21 people who spent between 90 and 104 minutes in the leisure centre.
This is the highest frequency.
∴ The class 90 – 104 is the modal class.

13.3 *The median*

The **median** is the value of the 'middle' observation when the observations are placed in numerical order.

To calculate the median, list all the observations given in numerical order (usually ascending), and the median is the value of the middle one.

A median cannot, therefore, be found for qualitative data.

EXAMPLE 1

The cost of diesel fuel (per litre) at five garages is 46.8p, 44.2p, 52.9p, 53.7p and 48.9p.
What is the median cost?

Write the costs in ascending order:

$$44.2 \quad 46.8 \quad 48.9 \quad 52.9 \quad 53.7$$

Find the cost in the middle position:

$$44.2 \quad 46.8 \quad (48.9) \quad 52.9 \quad 53.7$$

∴ The median cost is 48.9p per litre.

EXAMPLE 2

A sixth garage charges 46.9p per litre for diesel. The costs are now 46.8p, 44.2p, 52.9p, 53.7p, 48.9p and 46.9p.
What is the median cost?

Because there is an even number of costs, there are *two* costs in the 'middle':

44.2   46.8   (46.9   48.9)   52.9   53.7

The convention is to average these two 'middle' values.

The average (mean) of 46.9 and 48.9 $= \dfrac{46.9 + 48.9}{2} = 47.9$

∴ The median cost is 47.9p per litre.

EXERCISE 13.2

1 A die was thrown 12 times, and the scores were 2, 4, 1, 3, 4, 1, 5, 6, 6, 4, 2, 5.

  a What was the modal score?

  b What was the median score?

2 Eleven cars have the following colours:
blue, black, red, white, silver, blue, red, grey, black, blue, green.

  What is the modal colour?

3 The IQs of 70 students were recorded, to the nearest integer, as:

IQ	Frequency
95–99	5
100–104	7
105–109	18
110–114	21
115–119	7
120–124	4
125–129	5
130–134	1
135–140	2

What is the modal class?

4 The numbers of cars per hour on a country road during the hours of daylight were recorded as 11, 13, 15, 11, 17, 12, 18, 14, 7, 9, 14, 16, 7, 11.

  a Find the mean number of cars.

  b Find the modal number of cars.

5 The weights of parcels (in kg) delivered to a library were:

7.4, 8.2, 11.1, 7.8, 2.5, 5.6, 7.1, 8.9, 2.3, 2.7, 2.9, 4.1.

Find the median weight.

6 What was the modal number of artists named by the general public in question 1 of Exercise 11.1 (p. 80)?

7 A photographer arranges a family group with the tallest members of the family in the centre and the smallest on the outside:

Mrs Lee   Mr Lee
Alec   James   Linda   Eric

4' 6"   5' 1"   5' 8"   5' 11"   5' 4"   4' 6"

For his next photograph, he arranges the family in ascending order of height.

  a Who are now in the centre of the line?

  b What is the median height of the family?

  c Which average is not a representative value?

8 The price of a loaf of bread (in pence) at 10 shops was found to be:

44, 49, 51, 68, 62, 44, 69, 51, 44, 47.

 a What was the median price?

 b What was the modal price?

9 Five managerial staff have car allowances of £35 000, £23 000, £21 000, £18 000, £28 000. Six office staff each have a car allowance of £10 000.

 a What is the median allowance?

 b What is the modal allowance?

 c What is the mean allowance?

 d Which average best represents the allowances?

10 What was the modal class in:

 a Question 5

 b Question 6

 of Exercise 11.1 (p. 80)?

11 The ages at which eleven patients were first diagnosed as diabetic were:

5, 12, 16, 18, 25, 16, 17, 57, 32, 60, 61

 a What was the median age?

 b What was the modal age?

12 In question 7 of Exercise 11.1 (p. 80), what was the modal holiday destination for a wedding?

13 The cost of a ski lift pass in seven popular ski resorts is:

£112, £160, £134, £100, £88, £112, £120

 a What is the modal cost?

 b What is the median cost?

14 The number of missing parts in packs of kitchen units was recorded for a sample of 10 packs as:

4, 3, 6, 4, 1, 0, 1, 2, 0, 4

 a Find the modal number of missing parts.

 b Find the median number of missing parts.

15 The time taken (in minutes and seconds) to carry out the test on packs of kitchen units was recorded for six quality controllers as:

5:20, 6:40, 5:30, 4:24, 3:58, 4:30

Find the median time taken.

13.4 *The use of mean, mode and median*

The three averages are useful in different contexts.

- If you were an employer considering the production capacity of your works, it would be helpful to use the *mean* of past production, as this would give you a good idea of the number of goods you can produce.

- If you were a shopkeeper wanting to keep a minimum stock of shirts to sell, the *mode* would be the best to use, as this will tell you which shirts you are most likely to sell.

- If you were a union wage negotiator, the *median* salary would be appropriate to use, because the few high wage earners would not then affect your 'average' of the wages paid.

EXERCISE 13.3

In each of the following situations, decide which of the mode, the median and the mean would be the most appropriate to use. (You are not required to find any values.)

1   A group of artists working on a sculpture each suggested how it should be positioned.

A typical value is required.

2   Students in an art class were asked how long they had spent on their last project

The replies (in hours) were:
3, 4, 3, 5, 10, 4, 4, 3

3   Witnesses to a shoplifting incident were asked how many thieves were involved.

Their answers were:
1, 2, 2, 3, 3, 3, 3, 4

4   A student tries to decide if he is fairly paid for his part-time job.

He asks some friends how much per hour they are paid for similar work.

5   The electricity consumption for a dental practice is noted for the months from October to March.

A typical value is required.

6   Witnesses to a heart attack were asked to estimate how long the sufferer was unconscious. The answers (in minutes) were:
8   $8\frac{1}{2}$ $7\frac{1}{2}$ 9, $9\frac{1}{2}$

The time needs to be determined as accurately as possible.

7   Ten students were asked how much they spent on their last year's holiday.

The answers were:
£250, £162, £340, £140, £860, £300, £98, £380, £970 and £105

8   Caravaners returning from Europe on a cross-channel ferry were asked what distance they had travelled during their holiday.

A typical value was required.

9   A manager and his deputy managers were asked to estimate the cost of installing a new production process.

The average of the estimates is to be taken as a working value.

10 Matches are packed into boxes on which is written 'average contents 280 matches'.

---

*13.5 *The mean and median of a frequency distribution*

In this example the data is recorded in a frequency table:

EXAMPLE 1

Find the mean and mode of the following scores:

Score	Frequency
1	3
2	5
3	11
4	1
5	5

The score of 2, for example, occurred five times, but instead of totalling $2 + 2 + 2 + 2 + 2$, it is quicker to multiply 2 by 5. Similarly, instead of totalling $3 + 3 + 3 + \ldots$ eleven times, it is quicker to calculate 3×11.

The table can be extended like this:

Score x	Frequency f	Score × Frequency xf
1	3	3
2	5	10
3	11	33
4	1	4
5	5	25
Totals:	$\Sigma f = 25$ *(Total frequency)*	$\Sigma xf = 75$ *(Total of 25 scores)*

$$\text{Mean score} = \frac{\Sigma xf}{\Sigma f} \left(\text{i.e.} \frac{\text{Total of 25 scores}}{\text{Total frequency}} \right) = \frac{75}{25} = 3$$

The highest frequency is 11.
∴ The mode is 3.

EXAMPLE 2

Thirty households were surveyed, and the number of children in each household was recorded. Find the mean and the mode.

No. of children in each family	0	1	2	3	4	5
Frequency	4	6	13	4	2	1

No. of children in each family x	Frequency f	xf
0	4	0
1	6	6
2	13	26
3	4	12
4	2	8
5	1	5
Totals:	30	57

$$\text{Mean} = \frac{\Sigma xf}{\Sigma f}$$

$$= \frac{57}{30}$$

$$= 1.9 \text{ children}$$

There were 30 households. Therefore the median number of children is between the numbers in the 15th and 16th households. The cumulative frequencies (see Unit 14) are 4, 10, 23, . . ., i.e., both the 15th and 16th households contained 2 children.

∴ The median is 2 children.

EXERCISE 13.4

1 An agricultural researcher counted the numbers of peas in a pod in a certain strain as follows:

No. of peas	3	4	5	6	7	8
No. of pods	5	5	20	35	25	10

Find the mean number of peas per pod.

2 The Ace Bus Company went through a bad patch when its buses always left the city centre late. This grouped distribution table shows how late:

Minutes late	0–10	10–20	20–30	30–40	40–60
Frequency	5	8	21	14	5

Find the mean number of minutes late.

3 The numbers of words per sentence on a page of a book were:

No. of words	1–3	4–6	7–9	10–12	13–15
Frequency	3	38	59	27	4

Find the mean length of a sentence.

4 The numbers of faults found by a potter in glazed pots after being fired in the kiln were:

No of faults	0	1	2	3	4	5
Frequency	15	8	7	6	3	1

a What was the mean number of faults?

b What was the median number of faults?

c What was the modal number of faults?

d Which average best represents the data?

5 The number of weddings per week attended by a photographer was:

No of weddings	0	1	2	3	4	5	6	7	8
No. of weeks	2	8	3	5	10	7	9	5	3

a What was the mean number of weddings attended per week?

b What was the median number of weddings attended per week?

6 The numbers of times the photocopier was used on one day by the staff in an office were recorded:

No of times used	2	5	6	7	8	9	10
Frequency	1	3	3	2	4	4	1

Find a the median, b the mean number of times the photocopier was used on this day.

7 The manager of an electrical business recorded the number of TV sets brought in for repair each week day over a three-month period. The results of the survey were:

No. of TV sets	0	1	2	3	4	5	6
Frequency	5	7	12	15	19	16	4

a What was the median number of TV sets?

b What was the mean number of TV sets?

8 The numbers of children per family on a housing estate were recorded as follows:

No. of children	0	1	2	3	4
No. of families	12	15	5	2	1

Find a the mean, b the median number of children per family.

9 At a research centre for the common cold, 25 volunteers were exposed to the cold virus under controlled conditions. The time taken (in days) for the first symptoms of a cold to appear were (one person did not catch a cold):

No. of days	2	3	4	5	6
Frequency	2	5	8	7	2

a Find the mean number of days.

b Find the median number of days.

c If the person who did not catch cold were included in the data, which average would not be changed?

10 The goals scored in 38 football league matches on Saturday 24 February 1990 were:

No. of goals per match	0	1	2	3	4	5
No. of matches		3	6	10	12	5	2

a Find the mean number of goals per match.

b Find the median number of goals per match.

11 The numbers of injuries per week sustained at a dry-ski school were:

No. of injuries	0	1	2	3	4	5	6	7
No. of weeks		3	10	9	13	5	7	4	1

a Find the mean number of injuries per week.

b Find the median number of injuries per week.

12 Find **a** the mean, **b** the median number of faults in the micro chips (see question 10, Exercise 11.1, p. 81).

No. of faults	0	1	2	3
Frequency	31	13	5	1

c Which average should be used to compare this data with a similar set?

13 During a survey into the ages of employees in a factory, the ages of the apprentice tool makers were recorded as:

Age (years)	17	18	19	20	21	22	23
Frequency	4	4	5	2	3	2	1

a Find the median age.

b Find the mean age.

c Comment on your results.

13.6 *Range*

Averages are used to represent sets of data or to compare them, but an average on its own does not give sufficient information about the distributions.

Suppose we are comparing the climate of two places in Turkey. Town A has an average yearly temperature of about 12°C and town Z has an average yearly temperature of about 13°C. From this, we might suppose that the climates are similar and that town Z possibly lies south of town A.

In fact, town Z is Zonguldak, which is on the Black Sea coast, and town A is Ankara, which is further south in the interior of Turkey.

The monthly temperature distributions for the two towns are:

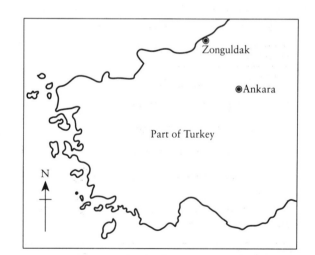

Month	J	F	M	A	M	J	J	A	S	O	N	D
Temperature in Ankara (°C)	−0.2	1.2	4.9	11.0	16.1	20.0	23.3	23.4	18.4	12.9	7.3	2.1
Temperature in Zonguldak (°C)	6.0	6.3	7.0	10.5	15.0	19.2	21.7	21.6	18.4	15.0	11.5	8.5

We can see that the climate in Ankara is more variable than in Zonguldak. There is a larger difference between summer and winter temperatures, whereas in Zonguldak there is a smaller spread of temperatures and a more equable climate.

We need a statistic which will measure this spread of values. The term we use to describe spread is **dispersion**, and there are several ways of measuring it.

The simplest measure of spread is the **range**, which is the difference between the lowest and the highest values.

The range of temperatures for each town is

Ankara: Range = 23.4 − (−0.2) = 23.6°C
Zonguldak: Range = 21.7 − 6.0 = 15.7°C

There is a problem with using the range because it uses only two values and so it can be distorted by a very high or low value.

EXERCISE 13.5

1 A fashion designer makes a particular style of skirt in various lengths:

19″, 24″, 28″, 32″, 34″ and 36″.

What is the range of lengths?

2 Five bank clerks took a 'tea break' at 10.30 am. They returned to their desks at the following times:

10.38, 10.40, 10.42, 10.45 and 10.48.

a Find the time taken for each 'tea break' and calculate the mean.

b Find the range of the times.

3 Eight patients suffering from lung cancer were asked how many cigarettes per day they smoked. The replies were:

40, 44, 25, 0, 50, 30, 35, 30.

Calculate (i) including the non-smoker, (ii) excluding the non-smoker:

a the mean number of cigarettes smoked per day.

b the range of the number of cigarettes smoked per day.

4 The numbers of cars on a hovercraft in one day were:

37, 28, 8, 5, 17, 39, 22, 10.

Find the range.

5 The number of cars produced per year per employee by nine manufacturers in England were:

7.1, 12.1, 8.1, 4.7, 11.6, 9.4, 3.6, 12.5, 3.9.

Find the range.

6 Two designers collect shells, fossils, small stones, etc., with which to make jewellery and to decorate their designs.

They collect from two beaches early in the morning. The numbers of items collected each day for a week are recorded below:

Day	Mon	Tue	Wed	Thu	Fri	Sat	Sun
Beach I	20	27	49	71	62	24	15
Beach 2	43	39	29	46	51	37	42

a Calculate the mean of each distribution.

b Calculate the range of each distribution.

c Which beach is the best for beach combing and why?

7   Two book clubs offer 'mystery parcels' of books for £8.50, stating that the minimum value of the contents is £15.

A survey of eight such parcels from each of the two clubs found that the actual value of the contents was:

Club 1 Value (£)	16.00	15.80	16.85	15.80	17.85	15.30	15.75	15.45
Club 2 Value (£)	15.95	16.90	16.85	17.85	15.25	17.50	17.00	17.25

a Calculate the mean and range of the data and comment on your results.

b Find the median value of the contents for each club.

c By comparing the mean and median, describe the distribution of each set of data.

8   A patient's blood pressures were recorded on 10 successive days.

Systolic blood pressure	118	126	119	125	127	126	120	136	120	106
Diastolic blood pressure	78	80	80	82	88	87	87	96	81	66

a Calculate the mean systolic and diastolic blood pressures.

b Find the range of:
  (i) the systolic blood pressures   (ii) the diastolic blood pressures.
  Normal levels are 110–140 for systolic and 70–90 for diastolic blood pressure.

c What can you conclude about this patient's blood pressure?

9   Two archers each shot six arrows at similar targets. The distance, in centimetres, of each shot from the centre of the target was measured and recorded:

Shot	1	2	3	4	5	6
1st archer	89	53	45	54	56	38
2nd archer	120	112	10	26	59	6

a Calculate the mean distance from the centre for each archer.

b Calculate the range for each archer.

c Which archer was the better shot?

10   The diameters (in millimetres) of ball bearings should be 50 mm.
Two samples of eight bearings, produced by two of the machines in question 11, Exercise 11.1 (p. 81), had diameters as given below:

Machine 3	51.15	48.16	50.32	51.15	49.33	50.05	52.63	49.63
Machine 5	49.72	49.43	46.78	48.88	48.20	49.46	49.19	48.21

a Calculate the mean diameter for each machine.

b Calculate the range for each machine.

c Comment on the performances of the two machines.

14 *Cumulative Frequency*

The cumulative frequency is the total frequency up to a particular class boundary. It is a 'running total', and the cumulative frequency is found by adding each frequency to the sum of the previous ones.

14.1 *The cumulative frequency curve (or ogive)*

Virtually all cumulative frequency curves (or ogives) have an 'S' shape. How an ogive is built up will be seen in the following example.

EXAMPLE

The marks obtained by 100 students in an examination were as shown below.

Marks	No. of students (frequency)
0–10	1
11–20	2
21–30	13
31–40	24
41–50	32
51–60	16
61–70	11
71–80	1

Draw the cumulative frequency curve for this data.

First, we construct a new table. This keeps a running total of the frequencies in the second column.

Marks	Cumulative frequency
0–10	1
0–20	1 + 2 = 3
0–30	3 + 13 = 16
0–40	16 + 24 = 40
0–50	40 + 32 = 72
0–60	72 + 16 = 88
0–70	88 + 11 = 99
0–80	99 + 1 = 100

From the cumulative frequency column we can see that one student has 10 marks or less, three students have 20 marks or less, sixteen students have 30 marks or less, and so on.

Next we plot the cumulative frequencies against the **upper class boundaries.** We plot 3 (students) against 20 (marks) and 16 (students) against 30 (marks). The graph then looks like this:

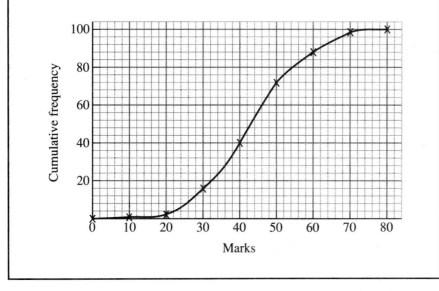

14.2 *The median*

The median mark is the mark obtained by the middle student. For example, if there are 100 students, the median student is the 50th (half-way point). (The strict definition would of course be the $50\frac{1}{2}$th student, but this accuracy cannot be obtained from a graph, and it is unnecessary at this stage.)

Suppose we wanted to find out the median mark in the example above. We would look across from the 50 on the cumulative frequency axis to the curve, then read down vertically to the number of marks. In this case the median is 43 marks. This is illustrated below:

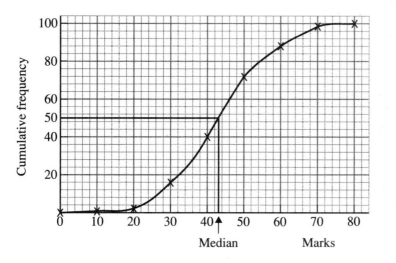

14.3 *The interquartile range*

(i) The **lower quartile** is the mark obtained by the student $\frac{1}{4}$ of the way along the distribution.

There are 100 students in the example on p. 122, so the 25th student is $\frac{1}{4}$ of the way up the cumulative frequency axis. From the graph, the 25th student has 35 marks, so the lower quartile is 35.

(ii) The **upper quartile** is the mark obtained by the student $\frac{3}{4}$ of the way up the cumulative frequency axis. This is the 75th student, whose mark is 52, so the upper quartile is 52.

The upper and lower quartiles are illustrated below:

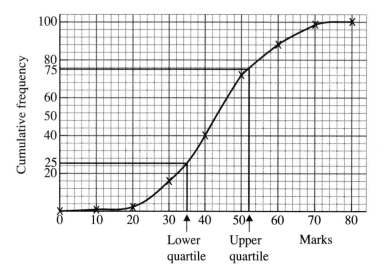

(iii) The **interquartile range** is the difference between the upper quartile and the lower quartile.
In our example, the interquartile range is:

$$52 - 35 = 17 \text{ marks.}$$

The **semi-interquartile range** is half the interquartile range, 8.5 in our example.

Note. Half the students have a mark between the lower and upper quartiles. Hence the interquartile range of 17 shows that half the marks obtained lie in an interval of 17. The semi-interquartile range of 8.5 shows that half the population lie (roughly) within 8.5 marks of the median mark.

Like the range (see p. 119), the interquartile range is used as a measure of spread.

14.4 *Percentiles*

We can use the example on p. 122 to define a **percentile**. As the name suggests, percentiles divide the cumulative frequency distribution into 100 parts, just as the quartiles divide it into quarters. The 70th percentile, for example, is the highest mark obtained by 70% of the entry. From the cumulative frequency curve this mark is 49, so the 70th percentile is 49 marks (as shown opposite).

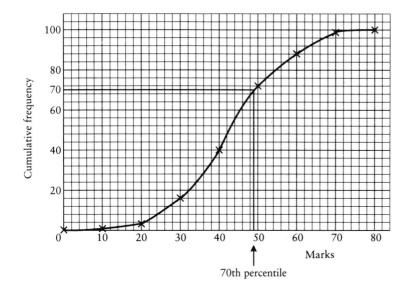

EXERCISE 14.1

In questions 1 – 12, calculate the cumulative frequencies, and draw the cumulative frequency curve. Hence find:

a the median
b the lower quartile
c the upper quartile
d the interquartile range.

Part **e** is given separately for each question.

1 The times taken for students to complete two questions were recorded as:

Time (in minutes)	0–20	20–25	25–30	30–35	35–40	40–45	45–50
No. of students	3	12	25	49	21	7	3

   e Estimate the number of students who took more than 41 minutes.

2 The marks gained by 90 students on a test (out of 100) were:

Marks	0–20	21–40	41–60	61–80	81–100
Frequency	2	15	32	33	8

   e (i) What percentage of students passed the exam if the lowest pass mark was 37?

      (ii) Six students are given a distinction.
         What was the lowest mark to obtain a distinction?

      (iii) Find the 90th percentile.

3 The number of tiles hand-painted by artists in a week were:

No. of tiles	50–	60–	70–	80–	90–	100–
No. of artists	3	12	25	32	15	2

   e Estimate the number of artists who painted less than 65 tiles in a week.

4 The time taken for designers to sketch a ball gown was recorded as:

Time (in minutes)	20–	30–	35–	40–	45–	50–60
No. of designers	1	3	15	28	7	1

e Estimate the number of designers who took less than 42 minutes to complete a sketch.

5 The annual charges made by an accountant for her services were:

Charge (£)	0–	1000–	1200–	1400–	1600–	1800–2000
No. of clients	3	14	28	15	5	1

e How many clients paid more than £1450 in that year?

6 The times taken for a secretary to type letters in a day were:

Time (minutes)	0–	3–	6–	9–	12–	15–18
No. of letters	8	9	12	11	5	1

e It took the secretary an additional 90 seconds to place the letter in an envelope ready for posting.

What percentage of letters took less than fourteen minutes to type and place in an envelope?

7 The weights of 100 men of height 5′ 8″ were recorded. The data found was:

Weights (kg)	48–56	56–64	64–72	72–80	80–88	88–96
Frequency	2	11	25	41	20	1

e (i) Estimate the number of men who weigh less than 62 kg.
(ii) Estimate the number of men who weigh more than 83 kg.

8 The weekly number of children developing chicken pox in a town was recorded over a period of four years.

No of cases of chicken pox	0–10	11–20	21–30	31–40	41–50	51–60
No. weeks	38	71	64	19	3	0

No of cases of chicken pox	61–70	71–80	81–90	91–100	100+
No. weeks	0	4	7	2	0

e An epidemic is declared when the number of cases reaches 87 per week. In how many weeks during the four year period is an epidemic declared?

9 The number of visitors to a theme park for 100 summer days was:

No of visitors	1000–	1500–	2000–	2500–	3000–	3500–	4000–
No. of days	6	21	34	20	12	5	2

e The theme park makes a profit when more than 1700 visit the park. On how many days was a profit made?

10 The time taken to travel down a flume at an aquapark was found for 100 successive visitors.

Time (seconds)	0–	130–	140–	150–	160–	170–	180–	190–	200–	210–	220–
No. of people	1	1	2	3	11	28	32	12	5	4	1

e The aquapark calculates the safe interval to allow between two people as the difference between the 90th percentile and the 10th percentile times plus 1 minute.
What is the interval required?

11 The waist measurements of 100 size 12 skirts were found to be:

Waist (inches)	22–	22.4–	22.8–	23.2–	23.6–	24–	24.4–	24.8–	25.2–	25.6–	26–
No. of skirts	1	2	3	7	21	32	26	4	2	1	1

e (i) Many shops would declare skirts of size 12 which are under 23″ and over 25″ mis-sized. How many skirts need re-sizing?
(ii) One store has a quality control which means that skirts of size 12 must be between 23.9″ and 24.6″. How many skirts would pass their quality control?

12 The number of staff employed by companies in an area was found to be:

No. of staff	1–5	6–10	11–15	16–20	21–25	26–30	31–35	Over 35
No. of companies	15	62	31	21	10	2	1	0

e Julia reports to a local business group that 90% of the companies employ less than 20 workers. Is she correct?

13 Potatoes are supplied to a greengrocer's shop in 50 kg bags. Each of the potatoes in one of these bags was weighed to the nearest gram, and the following table was drawn up:

Mass (g)	50–99	100–149	150–199	200–249	250–299	300–349
No. of potatoes	5	53	87	73	33	3

a (i) Complete the cumulative frequency for these potatoes.
(ii) Draw the cumulative frequency graph.

b From your graph, estimate:
(i) the median mass
(ii) the number of potatoes weighing at least 225 g each.

c For a party, Harry requires 50 baking potatoes, each weighing at least 225 g. The greengrocer sells the potatoes without special selection.
(i) Use your answer to **b**(ii) to estimate how many kilograms Harry will have to buy.
(ii) Taking the mean mass of the 50 baking potatoes to be 260 g, estimate how many kilograms of potatoes he will have left over.

15 *Probability*

15.1 *Introduction*

Probability is a measure of how likely something is to occur. What occurs is an **outcome**.

This likelihood or probability can be represented on a sliding scale from the probability when an event is certain to occur to the probability when the event cannot occur.

Suppose twenty children in class 2X are studied. It is found that 19 do not wear glasses, and 1 does wear glasses. 11 of the 20 children are girls and 9 are boys.

Suppose a child is picked at random. The likelihood of the following events occurring fits into the following pattern.

Event	Likelihood
The child studied is in class 2X	Certainty
The child does not wear glasses	Highly probable
The child is a girl	Just over half
The child is a boy	Just under half
The child wears glasses	Highly unlikely
The child's age is over 70	Impossible

Since 19 out of 20 children do not wear glasses, the likelihood that a child selected at random does not wear glasses is 19 out of 20, or $\frac{19}{20}$. Therefore, the probability that a child selected at random is not wearing glasses is $\frac{19}{20}$.

If all 20 children are wearing shoes, the likelihood that a child selected at random is wearing shoes is 20 out of 20, i.e. $\frac{20}{20}$, which is 1. Therefore, the probability is 1.

None of the children have green hair. The probability that a child selected at random has green hair is 0 out of 20, i.e. $\frac{0}{20}$, which is 0.

If an event is bound to occur, then its probability is 1.

If an event cannot occur, then its probability is 0.

The probability of a child not wearing glasses is $\frac{19}{20}$.

The probability of a child wearing glasses is $\frac{1}{20}$.

The probability of a child wearing glasses or not wearing glasses is 1 (i.e. a certainty).

Note that $\frac{19}{20}$ (not glasses) + $\frac{1}{20}$ (glasses) = $\frac{20}{20}$ = 1 (certainty).

From this we can work out that:

(i) **The total probability for all possible outcomes is 1.**
(ii) **Probability of event happening = 1 − Probability of it not happening**

The events in the initial example occur with the following probabilities:

Event	Likelihood	Probability
The child studied is in class 2X	Certainty	1
The child does not wear glasses	Highly probable	$\frac{19}{20}$
The child is a girl	Just over half	$\frac{11}{20}$
The child is a boy	Just under half	$\frac{9}{20}$
The child wears glasses	Highly unlikely	$\frac{1}{20}$
The child's age is over 70	Impossible	0

15.2 *Probability from theory and experiment*

Probability can be found either by theory or by experiment.

The theory method relies on logical thought; the experimental method relies on the result of repetition of the event producing results which are taken to be typical.

EXAMPLE

Find the probability of getting a head when tossing an unbiased coin.

Theory method

'Unbiased' means both events (head, tail) are equally likely to occur.

Heads and tails are the only outcomes,

∴ Probability of head + Probability of tail = 1

  (since total of all possible outcomes is 1)

Probability of head = Probability of tail

∴ Probability of tail = $\frac{1}{2}$.

Experimental method

Toss an unbiased coin 100 times, and count the number of tails you obtain. You might obtain 49 tails.

∴ The experimental probability of getting a tail is $\frac{49}{100}$.

If the event is repeated many times, it is usual for the experimental probability to be close to the theoretical probability, but not to be exactly the same.

For the probability of a person being right-handed, there is no theory to use. This would be found by experiment. For example, ask 100 people and see how many are right-handed. The more people you ask, the more likely it is that your probability is accurate, but it must be appreciated that the probabilities found by experiment are not exact. The result may also be different if the experiment is repeated.

EXERCISE 15.1

1 A jewellery designer has a stock of unpolished, semi-precious stones.
   The probability that a stone is flawed is $\frac{2}{15}$.

   What is the probability that a stone is perfect?

2 The probability that a new business fails within ten years is $\frac{7}{10}$.

   What is the probability that a new business succeeds?

3 The probability that a family has three or more children is $\frac{1}{9}$.

   What is the probability that a family has less than three children?

4 The probability that a plane is late is $\frac{2}{3}$.

   What is the probability that a plane is on time or early?

5 The probability that a car will have to be recalled to rectify a fault is $\frac{3}{5}$.

   What is the probability that a new car will not be recalled?

15.3 *Simple probabilities*

When n different events are equally likely to occur in an experiment, then the probability of each event occurring is $\frac{1}{n}$.

The general formula when results are equally likely is:

$$\text{Probability of event} = \frac{\textbf{Number of results giving event}}{\textbf{Number of possible results}}$$

EXAMPLE 1

An unbiased cubical die, marked 1 to 6, is thrown.
What is the probability of getting a 5?

There are 6 equally likely results.

∴ The probability of getting a 5 is $\frac{1}{6}$.

EXAMPLE 2

A bag contains seven balls, identical in shape and size. Three balls are white and four are blue. One ball is selected from the bag at random.
What is the probability that the ball is white?

There are seven balls. The probability that any one ball is selected is $\frac{1}{7}$.

There are three white balls.

∴ The probability of selecting a white ball

$= \dfrac{\text{No. of white balls}}{\text{Total no. of balls}}$

$= \dfrac{3}{7}$

EXERCISE 15.2

1 Jane has a bag containing only 7 oranges and 3 apples. She selects a fruit from the bag at random. What is the probability that it is an apple?

2 A die, numbered 1 to 6, is thrown.
   What is the probability of getting a 6?

3 A die, numbered 1 to 6, is thrown.
   What is the probability of getting an even number?

4 From a pack of cards, one card is drawn.
   What is the probability that it is:

   a red **b** a Jack **c** the Queen of Spades?

5 What is the probability of picking an even number from the numbers 10 to 20 (inclusive)?

6 A bag contains coloured beads for collage work. There are 6 green beads, 12 blue beads, 10 white beads and 8 red beads.

   If a bead is chosen at random, what is the probability that it is:

   a blue **b** not red?

7 In a survey of 60 commuters, it was found that 3 took more than one hour to travel to work and 12 took between half an hour and one hour.

   If a commuter is picked at random, what is the probability that the journey to work took less than half an hour?

8 Out of 20 patients seen by a doctor one morning, 2 were seriously ill and 10 required some treatment. The remainder did not require any medical attention.

   If a patient was chosen at random, what is the probability that the patient did not require any medical attention?

9 After a flight from Canada to the UK, 242 pieces of luggage arrived safely, but 6 were missing. Four of the missing cases were later found on other flights.

   What was the probability, on that flight, of a passenger's luggage being permanently lost?

10 Out of a sample of 20 lamp bulbs tested at a factory, 3 were found to be faulty and did not work.

   A bulb is selected at random, what is the probability that it works?

15.4 *Simple laws of addition*

Mutually exclusive events

Two events are said to be **mutually exclusive** when both cannot happen at the same time.

Suppose you toss a coin. The event 'obtain a head' and the event 'obtain a tail' are mutually exclusive, as you cannot obtain both a head and a tail at the same time.

Addition law for mutually exclusive events

If one event takes place, and you require the probability of A *or* B occurring (and *both* cannot occur), use the **addition law**:

Probability (A *or* B) = Probability (A) + Probability (B).

EXAMPLE

From a pack of cards, one card is drawn. What is the probability that it is an Ace or a Jack?

$$\text{Probability (Ace)} = \frac{4}{52}$$

$$\text{Probability (Jack)} = \frac{4}{52}$$

$$\therefore \text{Probability (Ace or Jack)} = \frac{4}{52} + \frac{4}{52}$$

$$= \frac{8}{52}$$

$$= \frac{2}{13}$$

EXERCISE 15.3

1 A card is selected from a pack of 52 cards.

What is the probability that it is

a a spade

b a red honour card (i.e. J, Q, K, A)

c a spade or a red honour card

d a 7 or a 10?

2 A man throws a die numbered from 1 to 6.

What is the probability that he throws a multiple of five or a multiple of three?

3 In a game of bingo there are 20 red, 3 black, 15 blue and 12 white balls left.

What is the probability that the next ball picked is either a red or a blue ball?

4 A set of ten cards has one of the digits 0 to 9 printed on each card. If a card is chosen at random, what is the probability that it is:

a an odd number

b a multiple of three or an even number

c a prime number or a multiple of four?

5 A biased die has probabilities $\frac{1}{5}$ of throwing a six, $\frac{1}{5}$ of throwing a three and $\frac{3}{20}$ of throwing any other number.

What is the probability of throwing a three or a four?

6 A textile artist has four blocked designs; a star, a large circle, a small circle and a crescent.

If he picks a design at random, what is the probability that he has chosen:

a a circle design

b a crescent

c a circle or a crescent?

7 The probability that a telephonist will receive a phone call in the next 5 minutes from a business in the UK is $\frac{3}{8}$.

The probability that she will receive a call in the next 5 minutes from abroad is $\frac{1}{4}$.

a What is the probability that she will receive a phone call either from the UK or from abroad in the next five minutes?

b What is the probability that she can take a 5-minute break without being interrupted by a phone call?

8 Of the patients seen in a casualty department, $\frac{3}{8}$ had been injured in road accidents, $\frac{1}{4}$ had been injured at home and $\frac{1}{8}$ had been injured at work. The remainder were suffering from other serious illnesses.

What is the probability that the next patient was:

a injured in the home or at work

b neither injured in a road accident nor at work?

9 In a survey at a leisure centre, it was found that 20 of the forty visitors questioned were going swimming, 8 were going to the fitness centre, 6 to play badminton and 4 to play squash. The remaining two were going to spectate.

What is the probability that a visitor was:

a going swimming

b going to play badminton or squash

c was neither going to swim nor to spectate?

10 A glassware factory produces a batch of glass bowls. On inspection it is found that $\frac{1}{9}$ are chipped and $\frac{1}{6}$ are flawed only by bubbles in the glass. The remaining bowls are perfect. Chipped bowls are rejected.

What is the probability that:

a a bowl is not perfect

b a bowl is offered for sale?

15.5 *Possibility space*

When more than one event takes place, you should write down every possible result.

The possibility space diagram is a means of identifying every possible result. It is used when two or more events occur, and where each of the outcomes is equally likely. Here is an example.

EXAMPLE

Two unbiased dice, numbered 1 to 6, are thrown, and the score is found by adding the scores on the two dice.
What is the probability of obtaining a total of 10?

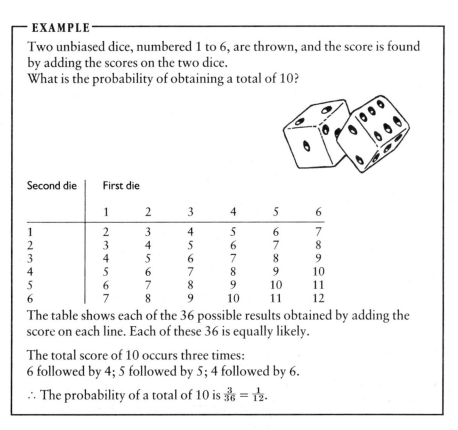

Second die	First die					
	1	2	3	4	5	6
1	2	3	4	5	6	7
2	3	4	5	6	7	8
3	4	5	6	7	8	9
4	5	6	7	8	9	10
5	6	7	8	9	10	11
6	7	8	9	10	11	12

The table shows each of the 36 possible results obtained by adding the score on each line. Each of these 36 is equally likely.

The total score of 10 occurs three times:
6 followed by 4; 5 followed by 5; 4 followed by 6.

∴ The probability of a total of 10 is $\frac{3}{36} = \frac{1}{12}$.

EXERCISE 15.4

1 Two dice, numbered from 1 to 6, are thrown, and the score is found by multiplying the scores on the two dice.
  What is the probability of a score of:

  a 12 **b** 20 **c** 30?

2 Two coins are thrown. What is the probability of obtaining:
  a two heads, **b** one head and one tail?

3 Two tetrahedral dice, with faces marked 2, 4, 6 and 8, are thrown together, and the score is found by adding the scores on the two dice. What is the probability of obtaining a score of:

  a 10 **b** 12?

4 A die, numbered from 1 to 6, and a coin are thrown. If a head is obtained, the score is double that shown on the die. If a tail is obtained, the score is that shown on the die. What is the probability of obtaining a score of:

  a 6 **b** 8?

5 A card is selected from a pack of 52 cards, and a die, numbered 1 to 6, is thrown. If the card is a heart, the score is twice that shown on the die. If the card is a diamond, the score is 5. If the card is black, the score is that shown on the die. What is the probability of obtaining a score of:

  a 5 **b** 6?

6 A pot goes through three stages: throwing, firing and decorating. At each stage an apprentice's pots are equally likely to come through perfectly or to be flawed.

  List all the possible outcomes for the three stages.

  What is the probability that the apprentice's pot:

  a is perfect

  b has two or more flaws?

7 A silversmith has a box containing a large number of silver bars. There are an equal number of bars of lengths 2 cm, 3 cm, 4 cm and 5 cm. Another box contains a large number of silver hearts with overall depths of 1 cm, 2 cm and 3 cm. There are equal numbers of hearts of each size.

  The silversmith randomly picks a bar from one box and a heart from the other and joins them to form a pendant as shown in the diagram.

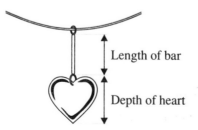

Length of bar

Depth of heart

Complete a possibility space diagram to show the possible lengths of the pendants. What is the probability that:

a a pendant is 5 cm long

b a pendant is more than 5 cm long

c the length of the bar and the heart are the same?

8 When an office clerk arrives at work the first thing she does is switch on the computers, laser printers, photocopiers and the fax machine. She does not always switch them on in the same order.

List all the possible orders of switching on the machines.

What is the probability that:

a she switches the photocopiers on first,

b she switches the laser printers on before the computers,

c she switches the fax machine on after the computers but before the photocopiers?

9 When I go to the bank, I have to wait in a queue for 5, 6, 7, 8 or 9 minutes with equal probability. My transaction is then equally likely to take 2, 3, 4 or 5 minutes.

Complete a possibility space diagram to show the total times I might spend in the bank.

What is the probability that:

a I spend more than 10 minutes in the bank

b I spend exactly 8 minutes in the bank

c I spend less than 7 minutes in the bank?

10 A new drug is being tested on a group of volunteers, one third of whom are children, one third female adults, and one third male adults. The volunteers are divided into three equal groups. Group X are given a placebo (a syrup containing no drug), Group Y are given a dose of strength 1 unit, and Group Z a dose of strength 2 units. The daily dosages are half for children, one for females, and one and a half for males.

Complete a possibility space diagram to show all the possible dosages.

Dose \ Group	X	Y	Z
Child: $\frac{1}{2}$			
Female: 1			
Male: $1\frac{1}{2}$			

a What is the probability that a dose of 2 units is taken?

b What is the probability that a dose of more than 1 unit is taken?

c What is the probability that no drug is taken?

11 Each person's blood contains two genes which are either rhesus positive (R$^+$) or rhesus negative (R$^-$). One gene is inherited from the father and one from the mother.

a Complete the table below to show all the possible gene combinations inherited by Hester whose father has one R$^+$ and one R$^-$ gene and whose mother has two R$^-$ genes.

Father: R$^+$ R$^-$ Mother: R$^+$ R$^-$

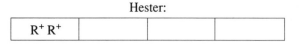

Hester: R$^+$ R$^+$

b If Hester marries and her husband's genes are R$^+$ R$^-$, write down all the possible gene combinations which their child could have.

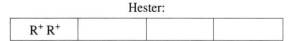

Father: R$^+$ R$^-$ Mother: R$^+$ R$^-$

Hester: R$^+$ R$^+$

Child:

c If a person inherits two rhesus negative genes, their blood is rhesus negative. Otherwise it is rhesus positive.

When a mother who is rhesus positive conceives a baby who is rhesus negative there are complications. The mother is given an injection to prevent the production of anti-bodies.

What is the probability that Hester is rhesus negative?
What is the probability that the baby is rhesus positive?

12 Three horses in a race have an equal chance of winning. If the horses are named Ace Accelerator, Best Bet and Champion's Choice, list all the possible results.

a What is the probability that Ace Accelerator wins?

b What is the probability that Best Bet comes in first or second?

c What is the probability that Champion's Choice beats Ace Accelerator?

13 A restaurant serves a choice of four main courses which cost £5.50, £6.50, £7.50 and £8.50. There is also a choice of three desserts. One costs £1.50 and the other two cost £2.

Complete the table below to show all possible price combinations:

	£5.50	£6.50	£7.50	£8.50
£1.50				
£2.00		£8.50		
£2.00				

If customers are equally likely to choose any combination of main course and dessert, what is the probability that a customer will pay:

a £8.50 **b** more than £8.50 **c** less than £10?

14 Four quality control operatives each take one spring from a batch and test it either for strength or for elasticity. They work independently and are equally likely to apply either test.
List all the possible outcomes.

What is the probability that:

a four springs are all given the same test

b two springs are tested for elasticity and two for strength?

15 A locksmith makes spring locks for doors.

The latches are equally likely to be 23 mm, 24 mm, 25 mm or 26 mm deep, and the striker-plate recesses to be 25 mm, 26 mm or 27 mm deep.

Complete the table below to show the difference in depth between the latch and the recess.

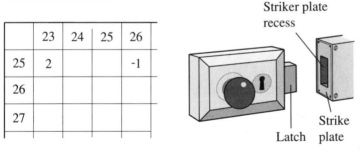

Striker plate recess

	23	24	25	26
25	2			-1
26				
27				

Latch   Strike plate

For the lock to work, the recess must be at least 1 mm deeper than the latch.

What is the probability that:

a the lock will not work

b the recess is more than 2 mm deeper than the latch

c the latch is more than 4 mm shorter than the recess?

16 *Networks and Decision Trees*

Critical path analysis, like linear programming, is a relatively recent development in mathematics. The techniques used today were first used by the Electricity Generating Board in the 1950s when they were trying to reduce the time taken to overhaul electricity generating equipment. It was also used around this time to design and develop the Polaris missile.

The procedure is to list all the jobs to be done, arrange them in a logical order on a diagram and then see what effect this has on the completion time.

The examples used in this unit are, of course, simple ones and could be solved by other methods, but the techniques used are the same as those used for a large, complex problem where a lot of things are happening at the same time.

16.1 *Networks*

A network diagram consists of **vertices** (or **nodes**) and lines which join them called **arcs**.

For example, consider the information on the map shown below:

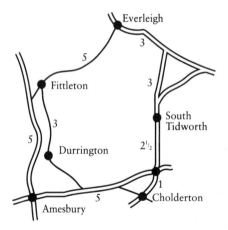

If the distance from Durrington to Cholderton is 5 miles, this can be drawn more simply as a network diagram:

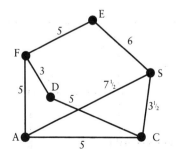

The **vertices** (A, C, D, etc.) represent towns or villages.
The **arcs** (CA, SE, EF, etc.) represent direct routes between places,
The **weight of an arc** (5, 1, 3½, etc.) represents the distance, in miles, between two places.

EXAMPLE

Hantconnect run a coach service
between the six towns Winchester, W,
Basingstoke, B, Southampton, S,
Portsmouth, P, Andover, A
and Farnborough, F.
The coach company connects the towns
B to P, S to P, A to F via B and each town
to W.

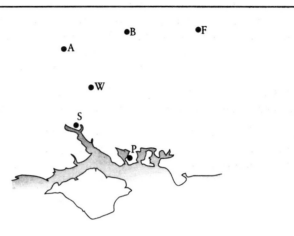

a Draw a network showing these routes.

b Angela wishes to travel from Basingstoke to Southampton. Assuming that she wishes to make as few changes as possible, along which routes could she travel?

a

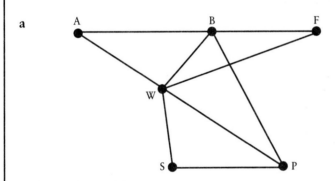

b She could travel by:
Basingstoke – Winchester – Southampton *or* Basingstoke – Portsmouth – Southampton.
In real life Angela would also consider the costs and travel times for each route before making a decision.

EXERCISE 16.1

1 A network diagram of a coach service
is shown alongside. Which routes would
Gerry travel to go from:
a A to C
b B to D
c C to D?

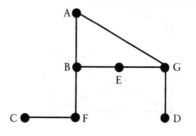

2   A designer needs to travel from Alton to Wimbledon where she has an exhibition of her work.
    The diagram below shows a network of the roads between Alton and Wimbledon and the estimated times, in minutes, to travel between towns.
    Plan a route which will enable her to get to the exhibition in the shortest possible time.

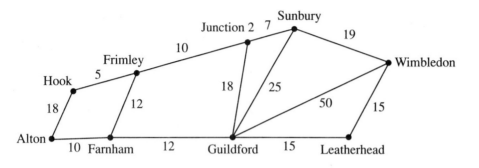

   a What is the shortest time for the journey?

   b What is the planned route?

3   An artist is planning a series of paintings of historical buildings in a town.
    Before starting painting, he intends to take photographs of all the buildings.
    The diagram below shows a sketch map of the town and the distances between the sites in metres.
    Plan a route for the artist which will enable him to start and finish at point S and visit each site in turn.

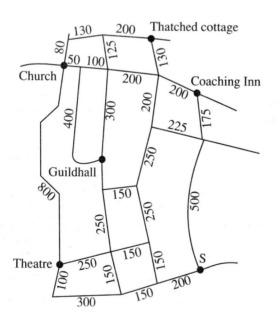

   a Draw a simplified network of the sites and the distances between them.

   b What is the planned route?

   c What will be the total distance covered on this route?

4 A retailer has shops in several towns, as shown on the network below. The delivery van picks up goods at the warehouse in Ashford, delivers to each shop and returns to the warehouse.
Plan a circular route which will visit each town and cover the shortest possible distance.
The distances are in miles.

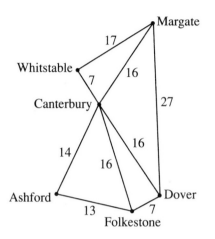

a What is the planned route?

b What is the distance covered?

The driver of the delivery van hears on the radio that the road between Dover and Margate is blocked by an accident.

c Replan the route to avoid this road.
What will be the extra distance travelled?

5 The diagram shows the site of a small printing business with distances in metres. The computers in each building are to be connected into a single network.
Each building must be connected to another building on the site, but it is not necessary for it to be connected to more than one other building.

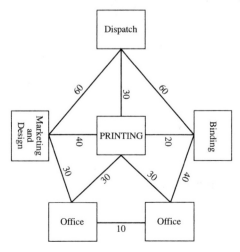

a Plan how the connections are to be made so that the least amount of digging up of the site for cables can be done. Draw a diagram to show your connections.

b What is the total length of the channels which will need to be dug for the cables?

6 A district nurse needs to visit certain families on her morning round.
Each of the letters A to E on the street map below indicates a family to be visited.

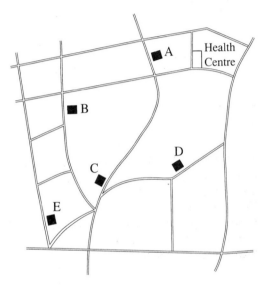

The distances between the houses and the Health Centre (H) are given on the table below in miles.

	H	A	B	C	D	E
H	–	0.2	–	0.6	0.6	–
A	0.2	–	0.6	0.6	–	–
B	–	0.6	–	0.5	–	0.5
C	0.6	0.6	0.5	–	0.3	0.4
D	0.6	–	–	0.3	–	0.7
E	–	–	0.5	0.4	0.7	–

a Draw a network based on this information.

b Find a route for the nurse which will take her from the Health Centre, to each house and back to the Health Centre covering the shortest possible distance.

c What is the length of the route?

7   A gentleman works voluntarily for 'Meals on Wheels'. He needs to make at least one delivery in each street which is shown in bold on the map below. The distances between junctions are given on the map in miles.

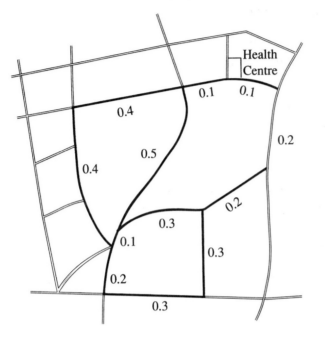

Below is a simplified network. The road junctions are labelled 1, 2, 3, 4 and 5.

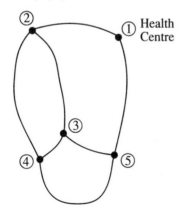

a   Copy the network and add to the diagram the distances between junctions

Plan a route for him which starts and finishes at the Health Centre and covers every street at least once. (He will need to go down some streets more than once.)

b   Which roads will need to be covered twice?

c   State the route which he should follow.

d   What distance will he travel?

8   American Airlines fly direct from Miami, M, to St Martin, S, and from New York, N, to each of Barbados, B, Kingston, K, Miami and St Martin. They also fly to all these airports from Puerto Rico, P. Draw a network diagram showing these routes and identify the possible routes from New York to St Martin with no more than two flights.

9   The diagram below shows the runway of a small, local airport.
    The runway and the approach roads have to be inspected regularly and any
    debris from the aircraft removed.
    An inspection crew leaving hangar A covers the runway and the approach
    roads which are marked with a dotted line, then returns to the hangar.

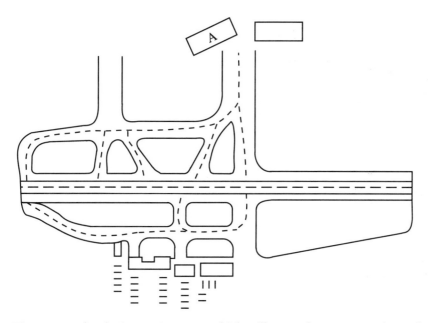

Plan a route for the inspection crew which will cover the runway twice and
the approach roads at least once.

A network diagram of the roads and runway is shown below.

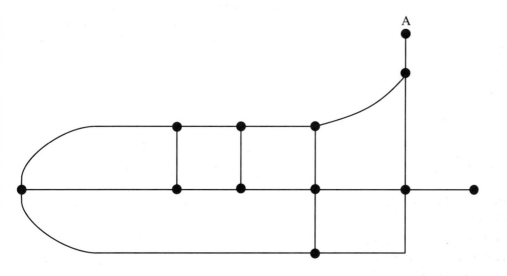

Draw the diagram and mark on it your suggested route.
Show clearly which roads have been covered twice.

10 In a chemical factory, liquids which have been fully processed are sent, by pipes, to holding vats.
The diagram below represents a system of pipes and the time taken to travel along each pipe is given in minutes.
A chemical solution is to be sent from point S_1 for storage in vat A.

Plan a route which will take it from S_1 to A in the shortest time.

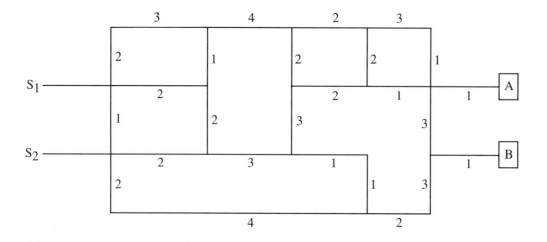

a What is the shortest time for the liquid to travel from S_1 to A?

b Draw a diagram to show the quickest route.

11 A forklift truck collects products from several points in a factory and delivers them to a central storage area. The delivery points are shown on the network below by vertices A, B, C, D and E, the storage area is S. Distances between delivery points and the storage area are given in metres.
The truck cannot carry products from more than two delivery points at one time.

Plan a schedule for the truck to collect products from all five delivery points and take them to the storage area while covering the least possible distance.

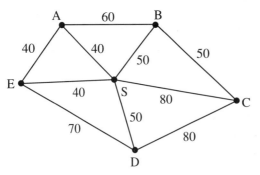

a What is the shortest distance it can travel to make all the collections?

b Beginning with S to A, list the route taken by the truck.

16.2 *Decision trees*

A decision tree diagram is a diagram which gives you information from which you are able to find an answer to a question or to sort items into different categories.

It works in a way which is similar to flow diagrams.

EXAMPLE 1

State what is being described by the following:

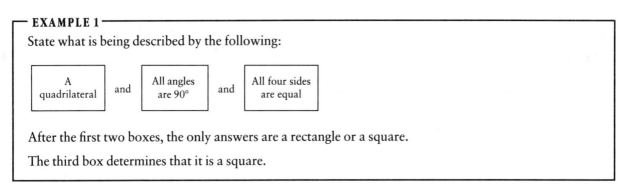

After the first two boxes, the only answers are a rectangle or a square.

The third box determines that it is a square.

EXAMPLE 2

Draw a diagram which will sort quadrilaterals into ordinary quadrilaterals, trapeziums, kites and parallelograms.

One such diagram is:

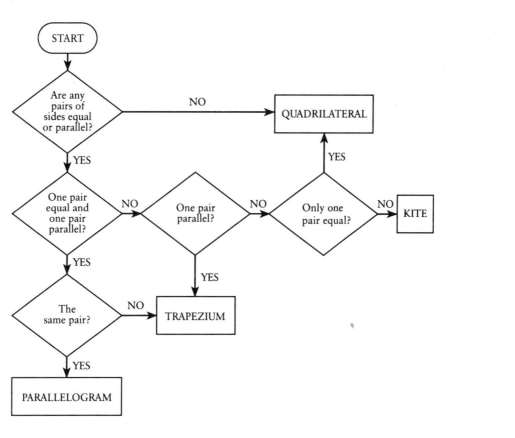

EXERCISE 16.2

You may wish to refer to pp. 1, 10, 211–12 and 241.

1 State what is being described by the following:

a

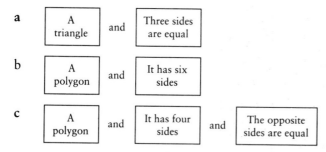

| A triangle | and | Three sides are equal |

b | A polygon | and | It has six sides |

c | A polygon | and | It has four sides | and | The opposite sides are equal |

2 Write down the possible answers after **a** the second box, **b** the third box, **c** the fourth box.

| A positive integer | and | Less than 5 | and | Even | and | A factor of 6 |

3 State what is being described by the following:

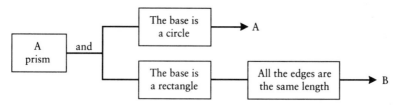

A prism — and — The base is a circle → A

The base is a rectangle — All the edges are the same length → B

4 Use the decision tree of Example 2 on p. 145 to determine in which category each of the following quadrilaterals should be placed.

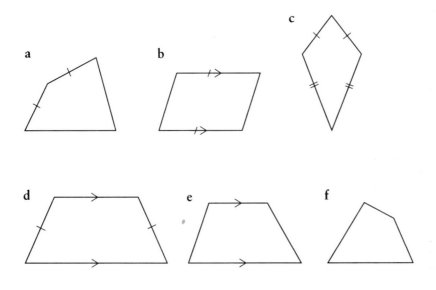

a   b   c   d   e   f

Arrows indicate that the pair of lines are parallel

and the marks, ⋀⋀ or ⋇⋇ , indicate that the lines are of equal length.

5   Maureen likes all the choices in the college vending machine and cannot
    make up her mind which item to choose.

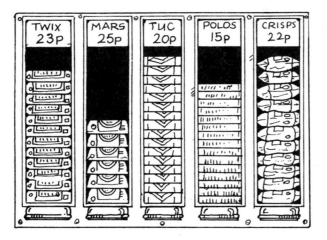

Complete the diagram below to help Maureen make up her mind. The
missing statements are in the following list:

At least 25p to spend?	Twix	yes	no	crisps
Chocolate covered?	savoury?	no	TUC	yes
Milk chocolate?	peanuts	yes	Mars	no

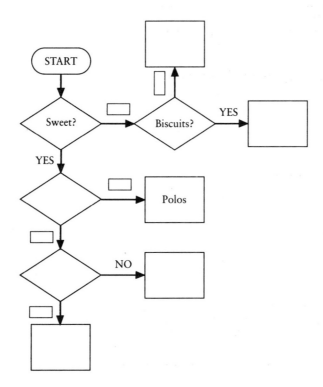

6 Copy the decision diagram for sorting clothes and write each of the
following statements in the correct box.

Yes   Keep it   Has it been worn in the last two years?   Oxfam
No   Jumble   Is it in good condition?

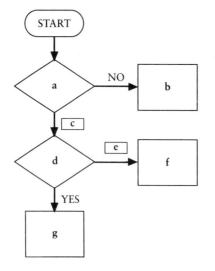

7 A craftsman is pricing one of his designs for sale.

a Complete the decision tree given below by replacing each letter with one
of the following statements:

- Damaged?
- Destroy
- Full price
- Half price
- Reduce by 20%
- Full price = £P
- Unsold for 6 months?
- Slightly damaged?

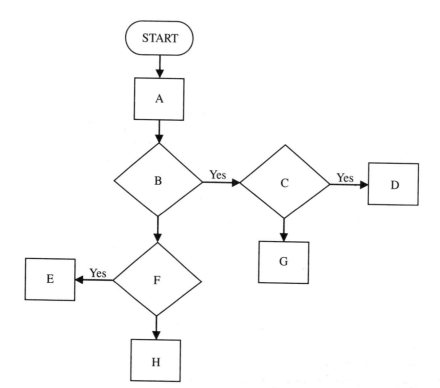

b What price is put on an ornament which has been unsold for 6 months, $P = £5$?

c What price is put on a brooch which is slightly damaged, $P = £7.50$?

d Design a decision tree diagram to sort:
(i) a mixed bundle of paint brushes
(ii) photographs or pictures for an exhibition.

8 The decision tree diagram given below is designed to sort the mail coming into the mail room of a small business.
Complete the diagram by replacing each letter with one of the following statements:

- Open letters
- Hand deliver
- Marked confidential
- Marked urgent
- Deliver goods
- Put into pigeon holes
- Return to sender
- Is it a letter?
- Do contents match delivery note?
- Does it contain cash or a cheque?
- Enter details of incoming mail in the log book

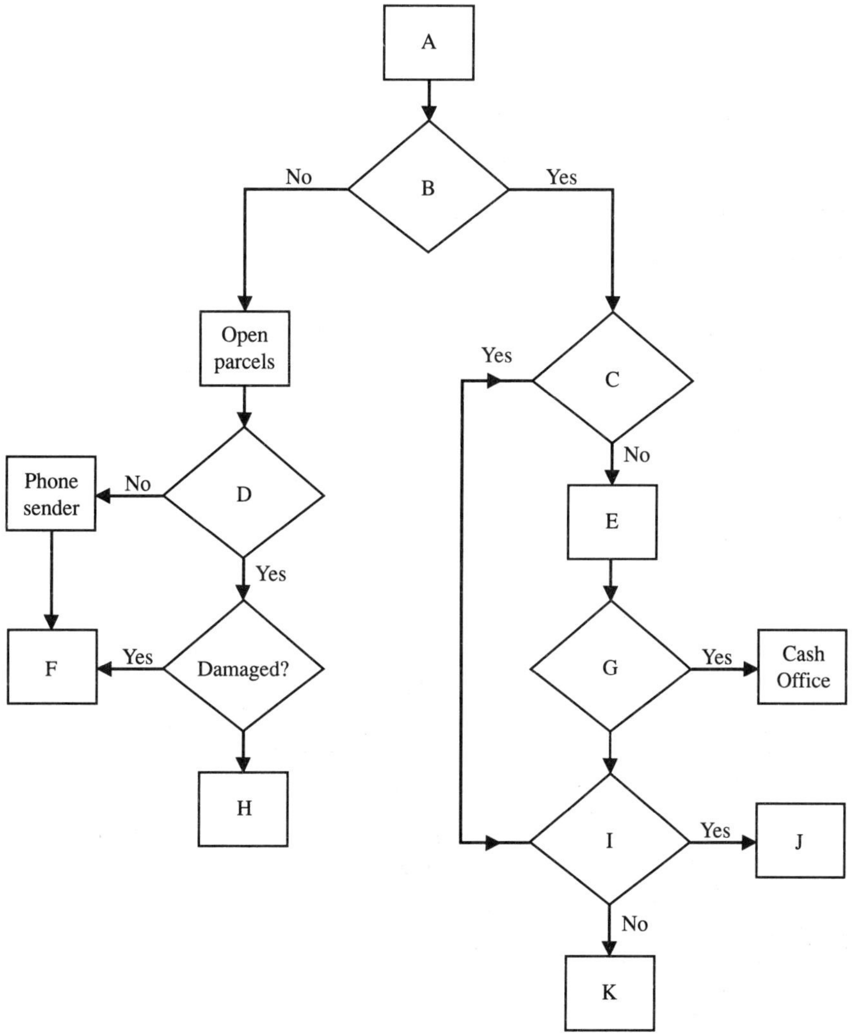

Design a decision tree diagram to:
(i) sort letters collected from a pigeon hole
(ii) sort a product on a supermarket shelf according to sell-by date.

9 When patients arrive at the casualty department of a hospital, they need to be assessed as to the seriousness of their injury or illness.
Some need to be attended to immediately while others, with relatively minor injuries, can afford to wait.

a Complete the decision tree diagram below to help casualty reception to deal with each arrival in the most appropriate way.

Each letter should be replaced with one of the following statements:

- Assess the patient's injury/ condition
- Is it an emergency?
- Send to casualty waiting room
- Is the patient conscious?

- Put into a cubicle for attention as soon as possible
- Is the patient's condition serious?
- Add to the waiting list

```
        ┌───────┐
        │   A   │
        └───┬───┘
            │
            ▼
          ◇ B ◇ ──Yes──▶ ┌──────────────┐
            │            │  Immediate   │
            │            │  attention   │
           No            └──────────────┘
            │
            ▼
          ◇ C ◇ ──No──▶ ┌──────────────┐
            │           │ Transfer to  │
            │           │  a trolley   │
          Yes           └──────┬───────┘
            │                  │
            ▼                  ▼
          ◇ D ◇ ──Yes──▶ ┌──────────────┐
            │            │      E       │
            │            └──────────────┘
           No
            │
            ▼
        ┌───────┐
        │   F   │
        └───┬───┘
            │
            ▼
        ┌───────┐
        │   G   │
        └───────┘
```

b Use the decision tree to decide the appropriate action for a patient suffering from:
   (i) a heart attack
   (ii) a broken arm.

c Design a decision tree to decide which benefits a family is entitled to (income support, child benefit, reduction of council tax, etc.).

10 The proprietor of a hotel, which has three storeys, receives a 'party booking'.
The decision tree diagram, when completed, gives a procedure for allocating rooms.

a Replace each letter in the diagram with one of the statements below:

- Ground-floor room available?
- First floor room available?
- Over 50 years of age?
- Second-floor room available?

- Difficulty climbing stairs?
- No room available
- Allocate room

- Allocate room
- Single room
- Twin bed room

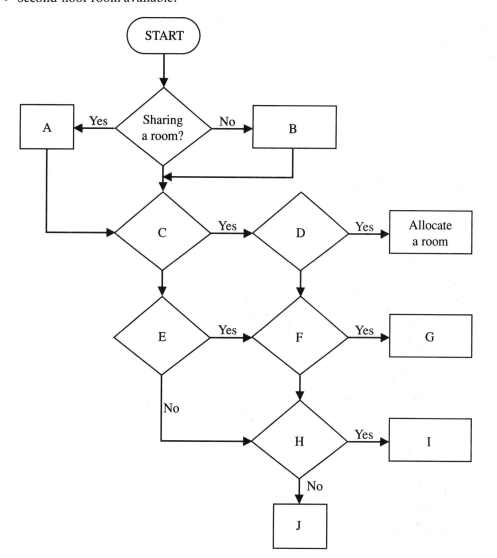

b Assuming that rooms are available, what type of room would be allocated to:
  (i) an elderly, but fit, couple
  (ii) a single, 26-year-old gentleman?

c Design a decision tree to:
  (i) sort stock in a leisure centre's sports shop
  (ii) load luggage onto a coach which will drop passengers off at different points.

11 The warehouse of a large electrical manufacturer receives goods from different factories and stores them in areas according to type.

   a Complete the decision tree diagram to show in which area each electrical item should be stored.
Replace each letter with one of the statements below:

- Laundry/washing?
- Leisure/entertainment?
- Goods larger than 0.5 cu ft?
- Goods received
- Beauty products?

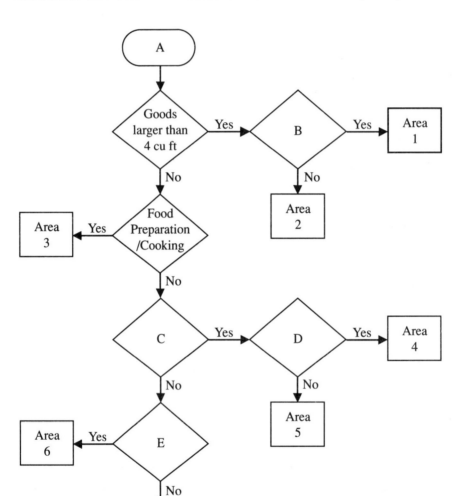

   b Use the decision tree to decide in which area the following goods should be stored:
- (i) a large freezer
- (ii) a hair dryer
- (iii) a video machine
- (iv) an iron.

   c Design a decision tree for the personnel department in a factory to follow when an employee has a grievance.

17 *Algebra*

17.1 *The basics of algebra*

From words to symbols

Every Saturday the milkman delivers the following to 16 Cromarty Street: 3 loaves of bread, 4 pints of milk and a dozen eggs.

He then presents his bill.

A sentence such as 'the cost of three loaves of bread, four pints of milk and a dozen eggs' is difficult to deal with mathematically.

Algebra is a mathematical language which enables us to deal with problems more easily.

Suppose we let:

b stand for 'the cost of a loaf of bread'
m stand for 'the cost of a pint of milk'
and e stand for 'the cost of a dozen eggs'.

The milkman's bill for 3 loaves of bread, 4 pints of milk and 1 dozen eggs becomes

$$3b + 4m + 1e \quad \text{or} \quad 3b + 4m + e$$

where $3b$ means 3 times b (or $3 \times b$).
We can miss out the 1 in front of the e
(e means $1 \times e$).

The foundation of algebra, as a science of equations, was laid down in the year 825 by an Islamic mathematician, Muhammad Ibn Musa al-Khwarizmi.

EXAMPLE 1

Don thinks of a number, multiplies it by 3, adds 4 and then divides this answer by the original number.
Write his final number in algebraic terms.

Let his first number be $\qquad n$

Multiply by 3: $\qquad 3n$

Add 4: $\qquad 3n + 4$

Divide by the original number: $\qquad \dfrac{3n + 4}{n}$

Final number $= \dfrac{3n + 4}{n}$

EXAMPLE 2

A holiday has two prices, one for adults and the other for children.
Write down an algebraic expression for the cost of a holiday for two adults and three children.

Let the cost for one adult be £A and the cost for one child be £C:

Cost for 2 adults $= £2A$

Cost for 3 children $= £3C$

Cost of the holiday $= £2A + £3C = £(2A + 3C)$

EXERCISE 17.1

Simplify the following phrases and sentences by translating them into algebraic expressions:

1 The sum of seven times x and five times y.

2 The difference between q and twice p.

3 Double the number a and divide by the number b.

4 A number is formed by multiplying a number x by five and then subtracting eight.

5 A number is formed by dividing a number y by four and then adding six.

6 The cost of admission to an art exhibition for 4 adults and 3 children.

7 To make purple paint, an artist mixes 4 cl of blue paint, 6 cl of red paint and 2 cl of white paint.

8 The cost of 4 reams of paper, 3 packs of pens and 2 bottles of Tipp-ex®.

9 The charge levied by a tax adviser who on your behalf writes 6 letters, makes 8 phone calls and has 2 interviews with you.

10 The number of beds in a hospital that has 22 NHS wards and 3 private wards.

11 The time spent by a social worker whose case-load is 4 teenagers, 5 retired couples and 3 single mothers.

12 The entrance fee to a leisure centre for 3 adults and 5 children.

13 The total paid in deposits to a travel agent who has taken 15 bookings in a day: 7 for a flight package, 5 for a ferry crossing to France, and the remainder for holidays in England.

14 The cost of fitting a door in a house for which a carpenter needs 2 handles, 3 hinges, and 22 screws.

15 Owen's commission if he sells 55 appliances of which 28 are fridges, 12 are microwaves, and the rest are washing machines.

Collecting like terms

Mrs Goodman empties her son's pockets on washing day and finds two sweets, one dirty hanky, two pencils, two more sweets and another pencil.

The contents of the pocket can be listed in algebraic terms as

$$2s + 1h + 2p + 2s + 1p$$

The list can be simplified if articles of the same kind are added together. This is called **collecting like terms**. If we collect the like terms from Master Goodman's pocket, the list becomes $b + 3p + 4s$ (which cannot be simplified further as each term is different).

Addition and subtraction

Only like terms may be added or subtracted.

Like terms are those which are multiples of the same algebraic variable.

For example, $3a$, $7a$ and $-8a$ are all like terms.

The expression $3a + 7a - 8a$ can be simplified to $2a$.

The terms $7a$, $3b$ and $4c$ are unlike terms and the expression $7a + 3b + 4c$ cannot be simplified any further.

EXAMPLE 1

Simplify the following expression:

$$2a + 3c + a + 4b + 2c + b$$

$$2a + 3c + a + 4b + 2c + b = (2a + a) + (4b + b) + (3c + 2c)$$
$$= 3a + 5b + 5c$$

EXAMPLE 2

Simplify the following by collecting like terms:

$$5x + 2y - 4z + 3x - y + z$$

$$5x + 2y - 4z + 3x - y + z = (5x + 3x) + (2y - y) + (z - 4z)$$
$$= 8x + y - 3z$$

EXERCISE 17.2

Simplify the following by collecting terms:

1 $2x + 3x$

2 $8n - n$

3 $3a - a + 6a$

4 $5y - 6y + 3y$

5 $3a + 2a + c + b + 2a + 3c + 5b$

6 $x + 2y + z + 3y + 8z$

7 $5p + 3q + 2r - q + 7p - 3p - r$

8 $2x - y + 3x - 2y + z$

9 $a + b - 2a + c - 2b + 3c$

10 $3x - y + \frac{1}{2}y - 2\frac{1}{2}y + 8y$

Substitution

The letters in an algebraic expression stand for numbers or amounts.

For example, in the expression $3b + 4m + e$, b stands for the cost of a loaf of bread, m for the cost of a pint of milk and e for the cost of a dozen eggs.

The advantage of the letters is that the amounts are not fixed, they can change or vary.

The letters are called **variables**. The numbers, which are constant, are called **coefficients**.

If a loaf of bread costs 54p, a pint of milk 29p and a box of eggs 63p (i.e. $b = 54$, $m = 29$, $e = 63$), then

Weekly bill $= 3b + 4m + e$

$$= (3 \times 54) + (4 \times 29) + 63$$

$$= 341 \text{ pence}$$

If, however, prices rise and $b = 56$, $m = 31$, $e = 66$, then

Weekly bill $= 3b + 4m + e$

$$= (3 \times 56) + (4 \times 31) + 66$$

$$= 358 \text{ pence}$$

┌─ **EXAMPLE 1** ─────────────────────────

Evaluate $\dfrac{3x - y}{x + y}$ when $x = 3$, $y = -1$

$$\frac{3x - y}{x + y} = \frac{(3 \times 3) - (-1)}{3 + (-1)} = \frac{9 + 1}{3 - 1} = \frac{10}{2} = 5$$

└───

EXERCISE 17.3

1 Evaluate the following expressions when $x = 3$, $y = 5$, $z = 2$.

   a $2x + y$ d $\dfrac{12}{z}$ g $3z - 12x$ j $xy + z$

   b $3x - 2y$ e $\dfrac{y}{10}$ h $2x - 5z$ k $y - xz$

   c $y + 4z$ f $4z - 6$ i $x + y - 4z$ l $yz - 4x$

2 Evaluate each of the expressions in question 1 when $x = -1$, $y = 3$, $z = -2$.

3 Evaluate the following expressions if $x = 4, y = 3, z = -2$:

a y^2

d $\dfrac{x}{y}$

g $2x^2 - yz$

j $\dfrac{2y}{x - z}$

b xyz

e $xz + y$

h $\dfrac{x + y}{x - y}$

k $\dfrac{x + 2z}{y}$

c $2z^2$

f $\dfrac{y}{2z}$

i $x(x + y)$

l $(x + y)(x + z)$

4 Evaluate each of the expressions in question 3 when $x = -2, y = \frac{1}{2}$, $z = -1$.

Multiplication and division

Multiplication of algebraic terms is usually easier than multiplication in arithmetic. For example:

$$a \text{ multiplied by } 4 \ = a \times 4 \ = 4a$$
$$p \text{ multiplied by } q \ = p \times q \ = pq$$
$$x \text{ divided by } y \quad = x \div y \ = \frac{x}{y}$$
$$a \text{ multiplied by } a \ = a \times a \ = a^2$$

Algebraic terms are usually listed in alphabetical order with the constant first.

The rules for directed numbers are the same as on pp. 7–8. For example:

$$(+x) \times (+y) \ = xy$$
$$(-x) \times (+y) \ = -xy$$
$$(+x) \div (-y) \ = -\frac{x}{y}$$
$$(-x) \div (-y) \ = \frac{x}{y}$$

EXAMPLE 1

Simplify $5 \times p \times 6 \times q \div 3 \div r$

Collect numbers and letters separately:

$$5 \times p \times 6 \times q \div 3 \div r = (5 \times 6 \div 3) \times (p \times q \div r)$$
$$= \frac{10pq}{r}$$

EXAMPLE 2

Simplify $(3x) \times (-2y) \times (-z)$

$(3x) \times (-2y) \times (-z) = (3 \times -2 \times -1) \times (x \times y \times z)$

$= 6xyz$

EXAMPLE 3

Simplify $3a \times (2b)^2 \times (-a^2)$

$3a \times (2b)^2 \times (-a^2) = (3 \times 2^2 \times -1) \times a \times b^2 \times a^2$

$= -12a^3b^2$

EXERCISE 17.4

Simplify:

1 $5 \times x$

2 $3 \times m \times n$

3 $2 \times y \div z$

4 $a \times c \times b$

5 $2 \times p \times 3 \times r \times q$

6 $c \div 2d \times 8b$

7 $(-2x) \times (-3y)$

8 $(4p) \div (-2q)$

9 $(6x) \times (-3y) \div (-2z)$

10 $a \times a \times a$

11 $a \times a \times b \times b$

12 $3a \times a^2$

13 $3a \times b^2 \times a^2$

14 $2a^2b \times -3bc$

15 $3ab^2 \times 2ab \times bc^2$

16 $(-3a)^2 \times b$

17 $(-2ab) \times (3b)^2$

18 $(-2a) \times (-b) \div (-b$

19 $x^2y \times xy^2$

20 $12ab \div (-4c^2) \times (3a$

17.2 *Indices*

$$a \times a \times a = a^3$$

The number 3 is called an **index**. It shows, or indicates, the number of as which have been multiplied together to give the third power of a.

$$a^1 \times a^2 = a \times a \times a \qquad = a^3 \text{ i.e. } a^{(1+2)}$$
$$a^3 \times a^2 = a \times a \times a \times a \times a = a^5 \text{ i.e. } a^{(3+2)}$$

*In general: $\mathbf{a^x \times a^y = a^{(x+y)}}$

$$a^3 \div a^2 = \frac{a \times a \times a}{a \times a} = a \text{ i.e. } a^{(3-2)}$$

$$a^5 \div a^3 = \frac{a \times a \times a \times a \times a}{a \times a \times a} = a \times a = a^2 \text{ i.e. } a^{(5-3)}$$

*In general: $a^x \div a^y = a^{x-y}$

$$a^3 \div a^5 = \frac{a \times a \times a}{a \times a \times a \times a \times a} \quad = \frac{1}{a \times a} \quad = \frac{1}{a^2}$$

but $\quad a^3 \div a^5 = a^{(3-5)} = a^{-2} \qquad$ i.e. $\frac{1}{a^2} \quad = a^{-2}$

*In general: $\qquad a^{-x} = \frac{1}{a^x}$

$$a^3 \div a^3 = \frac{a \times a \times a}{a \times a \times a} = 1$$

but $\quad a^3 \div a^3 = a^{(3-3)} = a^0$

*In general: $\qquad a^0 = 1$

*The rules for indices can be summarised as follows:

$$a^x \times a^y = a^{(x+y)}$$

$$a^x \div a^y = a^{(x-y)}$$

$$a^{-x} = \frac{1}{a^x}$$

$$a^0 = 1$$

EXAMPLE 1

Simplify $x^5 \div x^3 \times x^2$

$$x^5 \div x^3 \times x^2 \quad = \frac{x \times x \times x \times x \times x \times x \times x \times x \times x \times x}{x \times x \times x \times x} = x^4$$

or $\quad x^5 \div x^3 \times x^2 \quad = x^{(5-3+2)} = x^4$

---

*EXAMPLE 2

Simplify $\dfrac{5x^2y \times 3y^3}{6xy^2}$

$$\frac{5x^2y \times 3y^3}{6xy^2} = \frac{5 \times x \times x \times y \times 3 \times y \times y \times y}{6 \times x \times x \times y \times y} = \frac{5xy^2}{2}$$

or $\quad \dfrac{5x^2y \times 3y^3}{6xy^2} = \dfrac{5 \times 3}{6} \times x^{(2-1)} \times y^{(1+3-2)} \qquad = \dfrac{5xy^2}{2}$

EXERCISE 17.5

Simplify the following expressions:

1 $x^5 \times x^3$

2 $x^3 \times x \times x^2$

3 $x^7 \div x^4$

4 $x^4 \div x^5$

5 $x^4 \div x^4$

*6 x^{-2}

*7 x^0

*8 $3x^3 \times 2x \div 4x^2$

*9 $2x^3 \div 4x^5$

*10 $(-2x)^2$

*11 $(3x)^2 \times (-2x^2)$

*12 $\dfrac{7x^3 \times (-3x)}{6x^4}$

17.3 *Brackets*

The milkman's order for 16 Cromarty Street is three loaves of bread, four pints of milk and one dozen eggs per week. After five weeks the milkman will have delivered five times this amount.

Suppose the cost of a loaf of bread is b, the cost of a pint of milk is m, and that a dozen eggs costs e. Then suppose that we want to work out the total cost after five weeks.

The neatest way to write this cost in algebraic terms is to use a bracket:

Cost after 5 weeks = $5(3b + 4m + e)$

To 'remove' the bracket from the expression, each term must be multiplied by 5:

$$5(3b + 4m + e) = 15b + 20m + 5e$$

If the number outside the bracket is a negative number, take care: the rules for multiplication of directed numbers must be applied.

EXAMPLE 1

Remove the bracket from: **a** $4(3x - 2y)$ **b** $-2(x - 3y)$

a $4(3x - 2y) = 4 \times 3x - 4 \times 2y$

$\qquad\qquad\quad = 12x - 8y$

b $-2(x - 3y) = -2 \times x - (-2) \times 3y$

$\qquad\qquad\quad = -2x + 6y$

---

*EXAMPLE 2

Remove the brackets and simplify:

a $3(2x - y) - 2(x - 4y)$ **b** $a(a + b) - b(a + 2b)$

a $3(2x - y) - 2(x - 4y)$ $= 6x - 3y - 2x + 8y$
$= 4x + 5y$

b $a(a + b) - b(a + 2b)$ $= a^2 + ab - ba - 2b^2$
$= a^2 - 2b^2$ (since $ba = ab$)

EXERCISE 17.6

Remove the brackets and simplify:

1 $4(5x + 2y)$

2 $3(2a - 4b)$

3 $-2(3p - 6q)$

4 $5(x - 3y + 2z)$

5 $-(a - b - c)$

*6 $x(3x - y + 2z)$

*7 $-a(a + b - c)$

*8 $x(2x^2 + 3x + 2)$

*9 $4y(y^2 - 3y + 1)$

*10 $-5x(1 - 2x + x^2)$

*11 $2(x - 2y) + 3(x + 2y)$

*12 $y(y + 4) - 3(y + 4)$

*13 $5(2a + 3b) - (a - 2b)$

*14 $2(p - 6q) + 3(2p - q)$

*15 $5x(x - y) - 2x(2x + 3y)$

---

*17.4 *Common factors*

The process which is the reverse of multiplying out brackets is called **factorising**.

Factorising is a very important technique in algebra. It enables expressions to be simplified and hence makes the solving of problems easier.

Factors have already been met in Section 1.4 on p. 10 and a factor in algebra is the same as a factor in arithmetic. Remember: a factor is a number which will divide exactly into a given number.

Consider the number $2x + 6y$.

2 is a factor of each part (or term) of this number and therefore of the whole number.

$$\therefore 2x + 6y = 2 \times x + 2 \times 3 \times y$$
$$= 2 \times (x + 3 \times y)$$
$$= 2(x + 3y)$$

$(x + 3y)$ and 2 are both factors of $2x + 6y$.

EXAMPLE 1

Factorise $6p + 3q + 9r$.

The factor which is common to each term is 3.

$\therefore 6p + 3q + 9r = 3(2p + q + 3r)$

EXAMPLE 2

Factorise $x^2 + xy + 6x$.

The factor which is common to each term is x

$\therefore x^2 + xy + 6x = x(x + y + 6)$

EXAMPLE 3

Factorise $2x^2 - 4xy$.

This expression has more than one common factor.
Both 2 and x are common factors.

$\therefore 2x^2 - 4xy = 2x(x - 2y)$

$2x^2 - 4xy$ therefore has three factors: 2, x and $(x - 2y)$.

EXERCISE 17.7

Factorise the following expressions:

1 $\quad 4x + 12y$	6 $\quad 12s + 20t$	11 $\quad 6xy + 3x$	16 $\quad 7p - 14q + 7r$
2 $\quad 3p - 6q$	7 $\quad xy + xz$	12 $\quad 5x - 10x^2$	17 $\quad 2a^2 + 4ab - 8a$
3 $\quad 5a + 10$	8 $\quad xy + x^2$	13 $\quad 2a + 8b - 4c$	18 $\quad 3p^2 + 6pq - 9p$
4 $\quad 10b - 5$	9 $\quad y^2 - 2y$	14 $\quad 9x - 3y - 6z$	19 $\quad x^2y + xyz + xy^2$
5 $\quad 14m - 21n$	10 $\quad 2y^2 - 4y$	15 $\quad 15x - 5y + 10$	20 $\quad 4pqr - 12p^2q$

17.5 *Equations*

Forming equations

Many problems are solved more quickly if they are first written in algebraic terms.

An equation is, in algebra, the equivalent of a sentence. All equations must contain an equals sign.

The following problem is solved by first translating into algebra.

EXAMPLE 1

My brother is twice as old as I am and the sum of our ages is 42.
How old am I?

English	Algebra
My age	x (years)
My brother's age	$2x$
The sum of our ages	$x + 2x$
The sum of our ages is forty-two	$x + 2x = 42$

In algebra the problem becomes: $x + 2x = 42$

$3x = 42$ (collecting like terms)

$x = 14$ (dividing by 3)

This translates back into English as:
My age is 14 years.

EXAMPLE 2

I think of a number, treble it, add seven and the answer is 19. Form an equation using this information.

Let the number thought of be n.
Then

treble the number add seven is nineteen becomes
$$3n \quad + \quad 7 \quad = \quad 19$$

EXERCISE 17.8

For each of the following, rewrite the problem as an algebraic equation:

1 Five added to a number gives the answer twelve.

2 Seven subtracted from a number leaves thirteen.

3 If 4 is added to twice a number, the answer is equal to 10.

4 Seven times a number is twenty-one.

5 Six subtracted from five times a number gives the answer twenty-nine.

6 Ten added to half of a number gives the answer twenty-two.

7 Think of a number, double it, subtract three and the answer is three.

8 Think of a number, divide by four, subtract three and the answer is three.

9 A rectangular tile has a length which is double its width. The perimeter of the tile is 18 cm.

10 The earring shown is made of strands of silver wire. The middle strand is 2 cm longer than the smallest strand and the largest strand is 5 cm longer than the middle strand. The total length of the wire is 27 cm.
Let x be the length of the middle strand.

11 In an office, the number of phones is three times the number of faxes. The total number of phones and faxes is twenty.

12 An office stocks three sizes of envelopes: foolscap, A5, and A4. The business uses twice as many A5 envelopes as A4, and uses 20 more foolscap envelopes than A5. In one day the business uses 135 envelopes.

13 The length of a desk is double its width. The perimeter of the desk is 12.6 feet.

14 The number of pills prescribed by a paediatrician varies according to the child's weight. Those heavier than average receive 6 more than the norm, whereas those lighter than average receive 4 less than the norm. The paediatrician sees 30 children of whom 10 are overweight and 6 are underweight, and he prescribes 906 pills.

15 In a step aerobics class, teenagers achieve twice as many steps as senior citizens. The number of steps completed by two teenagers and three senior citizens is 77.

16 In a theme park, the number of rides which may be taken depends on the child's height. There are only two rides on which a child under 3 ft is *allowed*, but there are only three rides which a bigger child up to 4 ft 6 in is *prohibited* from taking. The total number of rides possible for a family of two adults, one child between 3 ft and 4 ft 6 in, and two children under 3 ft is 37.

17 A parts supplier to the motor industry provides wheel hubcaps, headlight housings and rear fog-light housings. The number of parts supplied to a car manufacturer, for one day's production of cars, is 1750. Each car has one rear fog-light. Let x be the number of cars produced on that day.

18 The parts supplier provides similar parts for two cars made by another manufacturer. For every car made with one rear fog light, two are made with two rear fog lights. The manufacturer uses 10 350 parts from the supplier in a day. Let x be the number of cars produced with one fog light.

Solving equations

Once a problem has been written as an algebraic equation, the problem can be solved by solving the equation.

To solve $3n + 7 = 19$ means finding the value of n which makes the equation true.

To do this, the 7 and 3 must be eliminated from the LHS (left-hand side) of the equation to leave n = the solution.

An equation must always be balanced, i.e. the LHS must always equal the RHS (right-hand side).

In the equation above

$3n + 7$ balances 19

If 7 is deducted from the LHS, the equation will no longer be balanced.

To maintain the balance, 7 must also be deducted from the RHS, giving $3n = 12$.

$3n$ must now be reduced to 1n by dividing both sides by 3, giving $n = 4$.

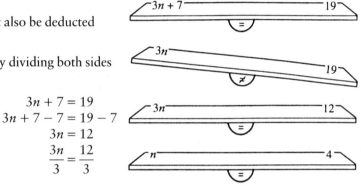

The stages are:

$$3n + 7 = 19$$

Subtract 7 from both sides:

$$3n + 7 - 7 = 19 - 7$$

giving

$$3n = 12$$

Divide both sides by 3:

$$\frac{3n}{3} = \frac{12}{3}$$

giving

$$n = 4$$

$$\therefore \text{ The number was 4.}$$

EXAMPLE 1

Solve the equation $\frac{1}{2}x - 1 = 6$.

$$\frac{1}{2}x - 1 = 6$$

Multiply through by 2 to remove fraction: $x - 2 = 12$

Add 2 to each side: $x - 2 + 2 = 12 + 2$

$$x = 14$$

EXAMPLE 2

Solve the equation $2(x - 3) = 5$.

$$2(x - 3) = 5$$

Multiply out the bracket: $2x - 6 = 5$

Add 6 to each side: $2x = 11$

Halve each side: $x = 5\frac{1}{2}$

EXERCISE 17.9

1 – 8 Solve the equations formed in questions 1 – 8 of Exercise 17.8 to find the number.

Similarly, for each of the questions 9–18, solve the equations formed in questions 9–18 of Exercise 17.8 to find:

9 the width of the tile.

10 the length of the longest strand of silver wire

11 the number of faxes

12 the number of foolscap envelopes

13 the length of the desk

14 the number of pills given to an overweight child

15 the number of steps taken by a teenager

16 the number of rides a child between 3 ft and 4 ft 6 in can take

17 the number of cars made in one day

18 the number of cars made in one day.

In the following questions, solve the equations to find the value of x:

19 $x + 7 = 11$

20 $5x = 15$

21 $4x - 5 = 19$

22 $\dfrac{3x}{4} = 6$

23 $12 - x = 9$

24 $17 - 2x = 5$

25 $2(x - 6) = 8$

26 $\dfrac{x}{2} + 3 = 7$

27 $\dfrac{x}{3} - 2 = 1$

28 $\dfrac{2x}{5} + 2 = 10$

17.6 *Harder equations*

The method used above can be very time-consuming and, when solving more difficult equations, a quicker method is used.

For the equation

$$3n + 7 = 19$$

when 7 is subtracted from both sides, we know it will disappear from the LHS; therefore it is only necessary to write it on the RHS:

$$3n = 19 - 7$$

i.e. the 7 has *changed sides* and has *changed sign* from + to −.

We now have:

$$3n = 12$$

Similarly, when both sides are divided by 3 we know that the LHS will be reduced to n.

Showing the division on the RHS only we have:

$$n = \frac{12}{3} = 4$$

i.e. the 3 has *changed sides* and *changed sign* from $\times$ to $\div$.

The rule for eliminating a quantity from one side of an equation is

change to the opposite side and change to the opposite sign.

This process is called **transposing**.

EXAMPLE 1

Solve the equation $5x - 4 = 3x + 12$

In this type of equation, the x terms should be collected on one side of the equation and the numerical terms on the other, i.e. $3x$ must be eliminated from the RHS and -4 from the LHS.

$$5x - 4 = 3x + 12$$

Transposing $3x$ and -4 gives: $\quad 5x - 3x = 12 + 4$

$$2x = 16$$
$$x = 8$$

Answers to algebraic equations should *always* be checked by substituting back into the LHS and RHS of the original equation, as shown below:

$$\text{LHS} = 5x - 4 \ = 5 \times 8 - 4 \ = 36$$
$$\text{RHS} = 3x + 12 = 3 \times 8 + 12 = 36$$
$$\text{LHS} = \text{RHS, so the solution is correct.}$$

EXAMPLE 2

Solve $2(2x - 5) = 3(x - 4)$

$$2(2x - 5) = 3(x - 4)$$

Multiply out the brackets: $\qquad 4x - 10 = 3x - 12$

Transpose $3x$ and -10: $\qquad 4x - 3x = 10 - 12$

$$x = -2$$

---

*EXAMPLE 3

Solve $4(x + 3) - 2(x - 5) = 46$

$$4(x + 3) - 2(x - 5) = 46$$

Multiply out the brackets: $\quad 4x + 12 - 2x + 10 = 46$

Collect terms: $\qquad\qquad\qquad 2x + 22 = 46$

Transpose 22: $\qquad\qquad\qquad\qquad 2x = 24$

Divide by 2: $\qquad\qquad\qquad\qquad\quad x = 12$

EXERCISE 17.10

Solve the following equations to find the value of x:

1 $7x + 3 = 5x + 11$	5 $3(x - 5) = 12$	9 $3(2x - 1) = 7(x - 1)$
2 $5x - 2 = 2x + 7$	6 $5 + 2(x + 1) = 11$	*10 $(x + 5) + 2(3x - 2) = 8$
3 $6x - 4 = 10 - x$	7 $2(x + 7) + 4 = 18$	*11 $4(x + 2) + 2(x + 3) = 32$
4 $3 - 2x = 4 - 5x$	8 $2(x - 4) = (x + 2)$	*12 $2(2x + 1) - 3(3x - 4) = 40$

Further problems

EXAMPLE 1

I buy a pizza and cut it into three pieces. When I weigh the pieces, I find that one piece is 8 g lighter than the largest piece and 5 g heavier than the smallest piece.
If the whole pizza weighs 360 g, how much does the smallest piece weigh?

Let the weight of the smallest piece be x grams
The weights of the other two pieces are $(x + 5)$ grams
                            and $(x + 5 + 8)$ grams

Total weight of the three pieces $= x + (x + 5) + (x + 13)$

$$\therefore x + (x + 5) + (x + 13) = 360$$
$$3x + 18 = 360$$
$$3x = 342$$
$$x = 114$$

The weight of the smallest piece is 114 grams.

EXAMPLE 2

This year, Dawn is three times as old as her brother Marcus, but in four years' time she will be twice as old. How old are Dawn and Marcus now?

Let Marcus' age now be x years
Then Dawn's age now is $3x$ years
In four years' time:
      Marcus will be $(x + 4)$ years
      Dawn will be $(3x + 4)$ years

Dawn will then be twice as old as Marcus

$$\therefore (3x + 4) = 2(x + 4)$$
$$3x + 4 = 2x + 8$$
$$3x - 2x = 8 - 4$$
$$x = 4$$

Marcus is 4 years old and Dawn is 12 years old.

EXERCISE 17.11

1 A rubber costs 25p more than a pencil. Twelve pencils and ten rubbers are bought for a bran tub. The cost of a pencil is x pence.

   a Write down, in terms of x:
     (i) the cost of a rubber
     (ii) the cost of 12 pencils
     (iii) the cost of 10 rubbers.

   b The total cost of the 12 pencils and 10 rubbers is £6.90. Using this information:
     (i) write down an equation in terms of x
     (ii) solve the equation to find x
     (iii) find the cost of one rubber.

2 A shop assistant accepts a £5 note from a customer and, in return, hands the customer two boxes of paper hankies and £2.50 change.

   a If x is the cost of one box of hankies, write down an expression for what the customer receives.

   b Write down an equation and solve it to find the cost of one box of hankies.

3 A pound of apples costs 5p more than a pound of pears. The cost of 5 pounds of apples and 3 pounds of pears is £4.65.
   What is the cost of one pound of pears?

4 An unframed picture costs £x. The cost of framing a picture is £2.20. Ian buys three pictures and frames two of them. He is given £7.50 change from a £50 note.

   a Write down an equation in terms of x.

   b Find the cost of an unframed picture.

5 The cost of a 'Monchique' tile is £x. The cost of a 'Penina' tile is 30p more.

   a Write down the cost in pounds of a 'Penina' tile.

   Janice buys 4 'Monchique' tiles and 7 'Penina' tiles for £19.70.

   b Write down an equation in x.

   c Find the cost of a 'Monchique' tile.

6 Postage on a sale leaflet is x pence and postage for a brochure is 26 pence greater. An estate agent posts 8 leaflets and 5 brochures for £6.63.

   a Write down an equation in x.

   b Find the cost of posting a leaflet.

7 An office operates a fax and photocopying service. The cost of a fax is 6 times the price of a photocopy. Marcus sends 4 faxes and makes 12 photocopies. He is charged £7.20.
   Find the cost of a fax.

8 Alan weighs 3 kg less than Barry who weighs 4 kg less than Colin.

   Barry weighs x kilograms and the total weight of the three boys is 193 kg.
   How much does Colin weigh?

9 Walking to college takes me twice as long as cycling. Taking a bus takes me 25 minutes longer than cycling. One week I walked five times, and next week I cycled twice and took the bus three times. The total times for travelling to college were the same for the two weeks.

   How long does it take me to cycle to college?

10 Mr Wilson regularly attends football matches when his team plays at home.

   a For x number of games he buys a seat in the stands. Each seat costs £9.
   Write down an expression for the cost of these x games.

   b For the remaining matches he buys a ticket for the terraces. Each ticket costs £5.
   If he attends 20 games in a season, write down an expression in x for the cost of tickets for the terraces.

   c Using your answers to **a** and **b**, write down and simplify an expression for the total cost for the season.

   d The cost for the season was £148. Write down an equation in terms of x.

   e Solve the equation to find the number of matches he watched from the stands.

11 At Gatwick airport 80 families were asked their destination by an interviewer. Five more were flying to Spain than Turkey. Twice as many were flying to Spain as were flying to the USA. Six were flying to Portugal, and nine gave a different country from these. Let x be the number flying to the USA.

   a In terms of x, write down:
     (i) how many were flying to Spain
     (ii) how many were flying to Turkey.

b Write down an equation in x. Hence find the number flying to Turkey.

12 There are x people at a double-glazing firm making phone sales. This is 4 more than the number of secretaries but 6 less than the number of travelling sales people. The total number of these employees is 35.

    a Write down an equation in x.

    b Find the number of secretaries.

13 A manufacturer sells a particular model of car with three different engine sizes: 1.3 litres, 1.6 litres and 1.9 litres. One garage finds that the 1.3 litre car sells least well. Twice as many 1.9 litre engine cars are sold as 1.3 litre and, in a three month period, the garage sells 20 more 1.6 litre cars than 1.9 litre. Let x be the number of 1.3 litre cars sold.

    a In terms of x, write down:
      (i) the number of 1.9 litre engine cars sold
      (ii) the number of 1.6 litre engine cars sold.

    b The garage sells 110 cars in the three month period.
    Form an equation in x and solve it to find the number of 1.6 litre cars sold.

17.7 *Trial and improvement*

Unless the equation is simple, it is rare to be able to solve it exactly.
The solution of the equation can be found by trial and improvement methods, or by graphical methods.
The trial and improvement method is shown in the worked examples below.

> ┌─ **EXAMPLE** ─
>
> By trial and improvement, solve the equation $x^3 = 30$ to two decimal places.
>
> If $x = 1$ then $x^3 = 1$
> $x = 2$ then $x^3 = 8$
> $x = 3$ then $x^3 = 27$
> $x = 4$ then $x^3 = 64$.
>
> $\therefore$ We have found two consecutive integers, 3 and 4, one giving x^3 below 30, and one giving x^3 above 30.
>
> $\therefore$ There is a solution of $x^3 = 30$ between $x = 3$ and $x = 4$.
>
> To find a closer approximation to its value, repeat this trial and improvement method for values between 3 and 4.
>
> If $x = 3.1$, then $x^3 = 29.791$
> $x = 3.2$, then $x^3 = 32.768$
>
> $\therefore$ There is a solution between $x = 3.1$ and $x = 3.2$.
>
> Repeating this produces:
>
> If $x = 3.10$ then $x^3 = 29.791$
> $x = 3.11$ then $x^3 = 30.080$
>
> $\therefore$ The solution is between $x = 3.10$ and $x = 3.11$.
>
> If $x = 3.105$ then $x^3 = 29.935$.
>
> $\therefore$ The solution is above 3.105.
>
> Hence the solution of $x^3 = 30$ is 3.11 (to 2 decimal places).

EXERCISE 17.12

By trial and improvement, solve the equations below to the relevant number of decimal places:

1 $x^2 = 15$ to 1 decimal place

2 $x^2 = 28$ to 2 decimal places

3 $x^3 = 14$ to 1 decimal place

4 $x^3 = 21$ to 2 decimal places

5 $x^3 + x^2 = 11$ to 1 decimal place

6 $x^3 - 2x^2 = 15$ to 2 decimal places

17.8 *Flow diagrams*

Frequently in Mathematics, the hardest part of solving a problem is deciding how to do it. For example:

$y = 3x + 11$. Find y when $x = 4$.

The calculation is simple, once you realise that you multiply 3 by 4 then add 11 to the answer.
This method can be shown in a diagram:

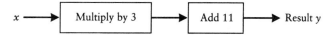

This diagram is called a **flow diagram** or **flow chart**.

A flow diagram does not have to refer to a numerical problem:

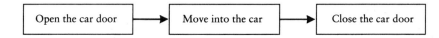

This is the normal way of getting into a car.

EXAMPLE

Find the relationship between x and y shown in the flow diagram below:

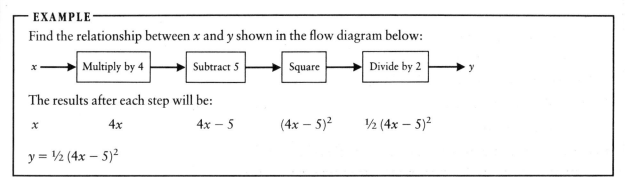

The results after each step will be:

x $4x$ $4x - 5$ $(4x - 5)^2$ $\frac{1}{2}(4x - 5)^2$

$y = \frac{1}{2}(4x - 5)^2$

EXERCISE 17.13

1 Draw a flow chart to represent each of these equations:

   a $y = 7x + 5$

   b $y = 3x - 11$

   c $y = 3x^2 + 5$

   d $y = (2x + 1)^2$.

2 Find the relationship between x and y shown in the flow chart:

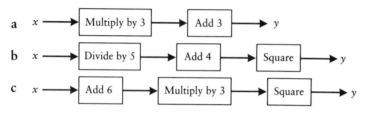

   a $x \longrightarrow$ Multiply by 3 $\longrightarrow$ Add 3 $\longrightarrow y$

   b $x \longrightarrow$ Divide by 5 $\longrightarrow$ Add 4 $\longrightarrow$ Square $\longrightarrow y$

   c $x \longrightarrow$ Add 6 $\longrightarrow$ Multiply by 3 $\longrightarrow$ Square $\longrightarrow y$

3 Draw a flow chart for each of these operations:

   a boiling a kettle

   b opening a door with a key

   c making a telephone call with a card

   d taking a photograph

   e making a plaster of Paris model with a mould

   f sending a fax

   g accepting payment from a customer by credit card

   h cleaning your teeth

   i putting someone in the recovery position after an accident

   j checking into an airport

   k going for a swim

   l fitting a new hinge to a door

   m changing a fuse in a plug.

Loops and decision boxes

A flow diagram can be extended so that the operation done depends on previous data.

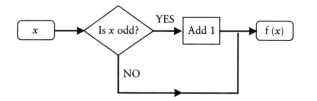

This converts all integer values of x into even numbers.

You will notice that the question 'Is x odd?' is in a diamond-shaped box with two arrows going from it, one marked 'No', and one marked 'Yes'.

If $x = 7$, the decision box (diamond-shaped) would have the answer 'Yes', which leads to the 'add 1' box and an answer of 8.

If $x = 10$, the decision box would produce the answer 'No' which leads to the result of 10.

All decisions are in diamond-shaped boxes.

EXAMPLE

Interpret the flow diagram:

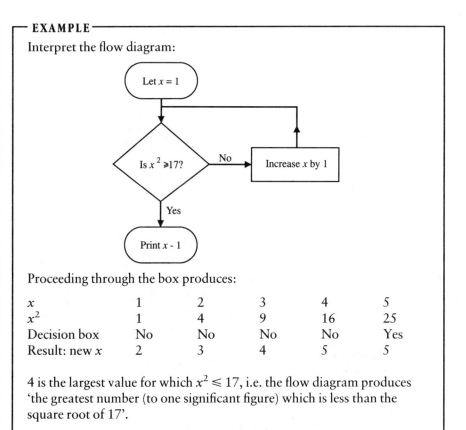

Proceeding through the box produces:

x	1	2	3	4	5
x^2	1	4	9	16	25
Decision box	No	No	No	No	Yes
Result: new x	2	3	4	5	5

4 is the largest value for which $x^2 \leqslant 17$, i.e. the flow diagram produces 'the greatest number (to one significant figure) which is less than the square root of 17'.

Just as in Exercise 17.13, flow charts with decision boxes are frequently used in non-algebraic situations.

To decide on a holiday, you might work through a flow chart, often in your head, similar to the one shown.

You would then be in a position to go into a travel agent and ask for a specific
holiday, possibly:

    I want to go on a package holiday to a hotel flying from my local airport.

or I want to go by car on a self-catering holiday not to a packaged complex.

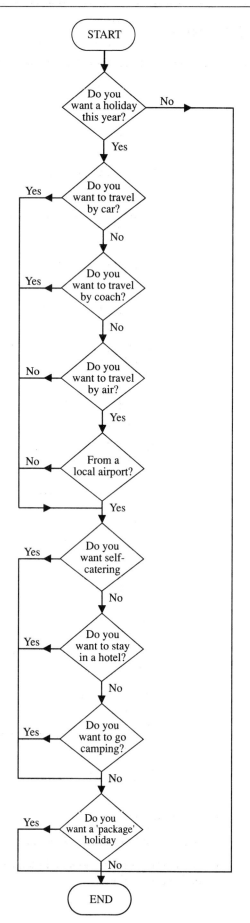

EXERCISE 17.14

1 The cost of a bouquet is calculated from the flow chart below.

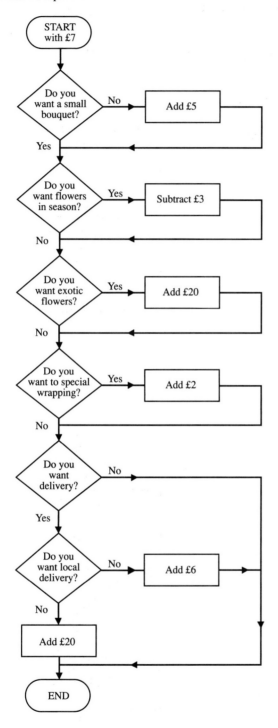

Find the cost of:

a the cheapest bouquet delivered locally

b a large bouquet with flowers in season in special wrapping delivered outside the local area.

2   The flow-chart below shows how to calculate car insurance premiums.

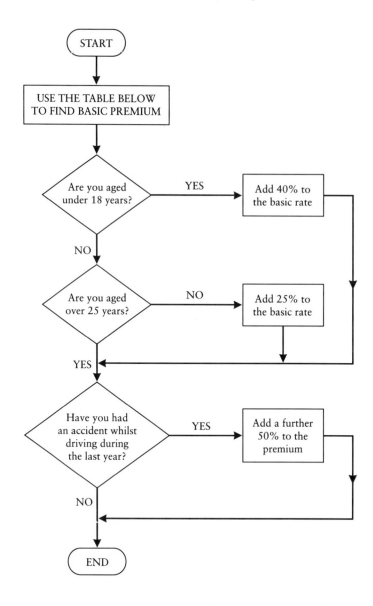

The table gives the Basic Rates of Car Insurance for Groups and Areas.

	GROUP 1	GROUP 2	GROUP 3	GROUP 4	GROUP 5
Area A	£360	£375	£405	£435	£480
Area B	£450	£495	£540	£600	£690
Area C	£675	£750	£825	£900	£1050

Calculate the insurance premium to be paid by each of the following:

a   Kerry, who is a 17-year-old student, has not had an accident, lives in Area B and drives a Group 2 car

b   David, who is 27 years old and lives in Area A, drives a Group 3 car, and had a driving accident 6 months ago.

3   To calculate the Council Tax, use the flow chart below.

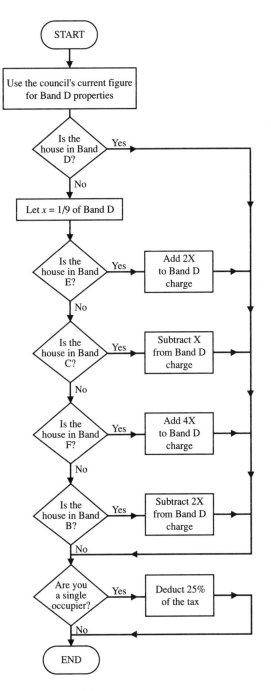

This flow chart can be extended to include Bands A, G and H.
Calculate the Council Tax payable by:

a Mr and Mrs Jackson living in a Band E property, with the Band D rate
set at £610

b Mrs Jenkins who lives alone in her Band B property, with the Band D
rate set at £310

c Mr and Mrs Stephens whose Band F house is in a town where the Band
D rate is set at £510.

4 The cost of placing a child in a nursery is calculated as follows:

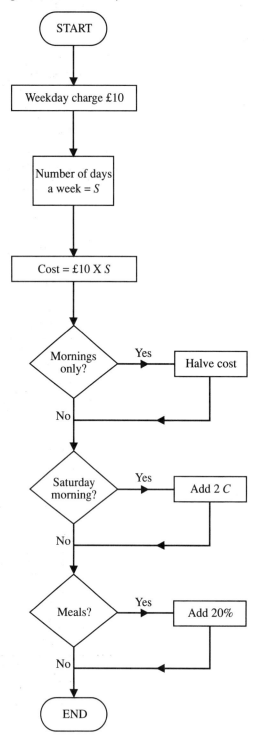

How much is the cost for:

a Anna who wants her son to be looked after for five whole days a week, including meals

b Rebecca who wants her daughter to attend the nursery for two mornings a week, with no meals?

5 The cost of delivering and installing a television is calculated from the flow chart shown.

Find the cost of delivery and installation for:

a Jane who lives 3 miles away from the shop and who has no video or satellite

b Carl who lives 9 miles away from the shop and who has a video and satellite.

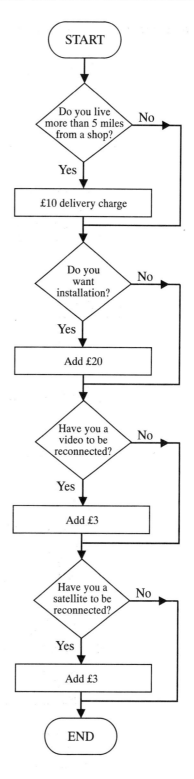

6 Draw a flow chart with decision boxes for:

a taking a photograph

b dealing with an incoming call on a switchboard

c dealing with an accident at work

d dealing with a holidaymaker's complaint

e fitting a door.

17.9 *Sequences*

A number of terms can form a pattern – for example, 1, 3, 5, 7, ...
Such numbers are said to form a **sequence**.

Each term of a sequence can be expressed in terms of the previous term.
In the series 1, 3, 5, 7, . . ., each term is 2 more than the previous term.
(The general term, or the nth term, can be written algebraically so that the nth
term, u_n equals the previous term, u_{n-1}, plus 2, i.e. $u_n = u_{n-1} + 2$.)

Alternatively the general term can be given in terms of its position. In the same
sequence, $u_n = 2n - 1$, where n takes the values 1, 2, 3, 4 . . . .
The method of obtaining the general term is similar to that used in the previous
section on flow diagrams.
In the above sequence, each term is 2 more than the previous term.
Therefore compare values of u_n with the values of $2n$.

When n is 1, 2, 3, 4, . . .
 terms of u_n are 1, 3, 5, 7, . . .
 terms of $2n$ are 2, 4, 6, 8, . . .

Clearly the u_n sequence is 1 less than the $2n$ sequence. Thus $u_n = 2n - 1$.

Both $u_n = 2n - 1$ and $u_n = u_{n-1} + 2$ express the sequence in symbolic notation.

EXAMPLE

Express in symbolic notation the general term of the sequence

$$7, 10, 13, 16, 19, \ldots$$

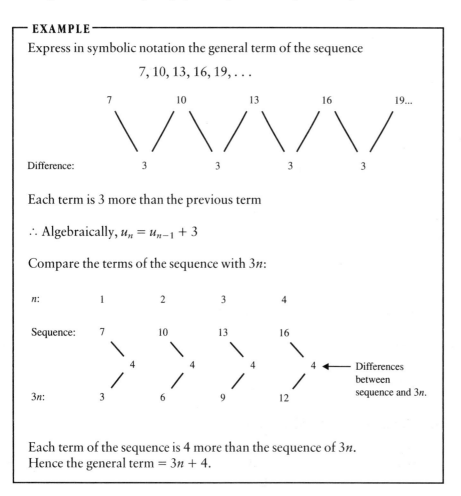

Each term is 3 more than the previous term

∴ Algebraically, $u_n = u_{n-1} + 3$

Compare the terms of the sequence with $3n$:

Each term of the sequence is 4 more than the sequence of $3n$.
Hence the general term $= 3n + 4$.

EXERCISE 17.15

In questions 1–3 express the sequences given in symbolic notation:

1 $2, 4, 6, 8, 10, \ldots$

2 $6, 4, 2, 0, -2, \ldots$

3 $1, 5, 9, 13, 17, \ldots$

4 Any term in the sequence of numbers such as

$$3, 7, 11, 15 \ldots$$

can be calculated using the formula

$$N = a + (n - 1)d$$

where:
a is the first term,
d is the difference between successive terms, and
n is the number of the term to be calculated

(i.e. $n = 3$ gives the third term).

a By taking $n = 4$, show that the formula is correct for the sequence given above.

b Find the eleventh term in this sequence.

c Rearrange the formula to make d the subject.

d The first term of another sequence is 2 and the eighth term is 23:
   (i) What is the difference between successive terms?
   (ii) Write down the first five terms in the sequence.

5 Count the number of shaded tiles in each of the mosaics shown below.
Give this number in symbolic notation.

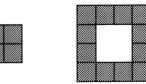
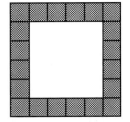

6 State the total number of tiles (both shaded and unshaded) in each of the patterns below.
Express this number in symbolic notation.

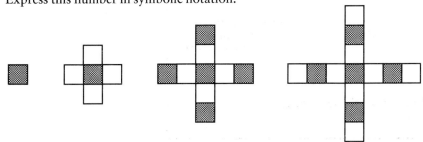

7 State the total number of discs in each of the patterns below.
Express this number in symbolic notation.

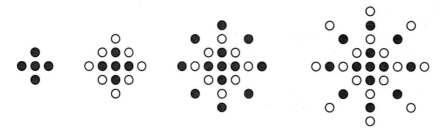

8 Prints of Constable's painting 'The Haywain' are in various sizes. These
are $3'' \times 5''$, $4'' \times 6''$, $5'' \times 7''$, $6'' \times 8''$, . . .

Express the perimeter in symbolic notation.

9 The time taken to photocopy a document is:
 • 20 seconds for 1 copy,
 • 30 seconds for two copies
 • 40 seconds for three copies, etc.

Express the time taken in terms of n, where n is the number of copies
required.

10 The amount of alcohol in Clive's bloodstream is measured every hour. At
midnight when he stops drinking, the amount is 130 mg.
At 1 am it is 120, and at 2 am it is 110. Assuming a steady decrease,
express the level in terms of t, the number of hours after midnight.

Hence, find the time Clive reaches 50 mg which is the maximum *safe* level
to be able to drive.

11 The cost of running a leisure centre varies according to the number of
visitors. The cost is:

 • £270 if 100 attend
 • £320 if 200 attend
 • £370 if 300 attend.

Express the cost in terms of n, the number of hundreds of visitors.

12 'WonderWhite Windows' is a company which makes and fits replacement
double-glazed windows. To price the installation, 'WonderWhite
Windows' uses the following scale for the time needed to travel to the
house and to fit different numbers of windows.
The time in hours is:

 • 11 for one window
 • 14 for 2 windows
 • 17 for 3 windows.

How long will it take 'WonderWhite Windows' to fit:

a 4 windows

b 5 windows?

Express the number of hours in terms of w, the number of windows fitted.

17.10 *Formulae*

Substitution in formulae

A second important use of algebra is to enable a relationship between two or more quantities to be expressed in a short but easily understood form. This is called a **formula**.

The volume of a cylinder is found by multiplying the area of the circular cross-section of the cylinder by its height. This is more neatly expressed by the formula

$$V = \pi r^2 h$$

In order to calculate the volume, the given values of r (radius) and h (height) are substituted into the formula.

EXAMPLE

The distance travelled by a vehicle in a given time can be found by using the formula:

$$s = ut + \tfrac{1}{2}at^2$$

where s is the distance travelled in metres, u is the starting velocity in metres per second, a is the acceleration in metres per second, and t is the time in seconds.

Find the distance travelled by a sports car:

a in 4 s if $u = 20$ m/s and $a = 2.5$ m/s^2

b in 10 s starting from rest with an acceleration of 3 m/s^2.

a $t = 4$, $u = 20$, $a = 2.5$

Substituting in $s = ut + \tfrac{1}{2}at^2$

gives $s = (20 \times 4) + (\tfrac{1}{2} \times 2.5 \times 4^2)$
$= 80 + 20$
$= 100$

The distance travelled was 100 m.

b $t = 10$, $u = 0$, $a = 3$

Substituting in $s = ut + \tfrac{1}{2}at^2$

gives $s = 0 + \tfrac{1}{2} \times 3 \times 10^2$
$= 150$

The distance travelled was 150 m.

EXERCISE 17.16

1 a The speed, or velocity, at which the sports car in the example above is travelling after a certain time, is given by the formula

$$v = u + at$$

Calculate the speed, in m/s, when
(i) $t = 4$, $u = 20$, $a = 2.5$
(ii) $t = 10$, $u = 0$, $a = 3.6$.

b The formula $V = 2.25v$ converts v m/s to V mph.
Calculate the sports car's speed in miles per hour for each of parts (i) and (ii) in **a**.

2 The formula for a straight line graph is

$$y = mx + c$$

Find the value of y if $m = 2$, $c = -3$ and $x = 4$.

3 To convert degrees Fahrenheit F to degrees Celsius C, the following formula is used:

$$C = \frac{5}{9}(F - 32)$$

Convert to degrees Celsius:

a 50°F,   b 77°F,   c 14°F.

4 The focal length of a lens is given by

$$\frac{1}{f} = \frac{1}{v} + \frac{1}{u}$$

Find f when: a $u = 12$, $v = 18$
                              b $u = 10.5$, $v = 7$.

5

A wedding dress is to be finished with an embroidered front bodice, decorated with pearls. The cost £C of the embroidered section is given by $C = h(2b + 3a)/20$, where h cm is the depth of the embroidered panel, a cm is the minimum width and b cm is the maximum width, as shown in the diagram.

Find the cost of the embroidery when

a $h = 25$, $a = 20$ and $b = 25$

b $h = 18$, $a = 18$ and $b = 19$.

6 When an amount of money, £P, is invested at a compound interest rate of $r\%$ per annum, the amount in the account after 2 years is given by

$$A = P\left(1 + \frac{r}{100}\right)^2$$

Find the amount in an account after 2 years if £1600 was invested at 9.5% per annum.

7 The cost, £C, of printing n posters for a concert is given by $C = 5.2 + 0.11n$.

a Find the cost of printing:
   (i) 100 posters   (ii) 1000 posters.

b Find the cost per poster when 400 are printed.

8 The number of bacteria, n, in a piece of meat t hours after it is taken out of a fridge is given by $n = 800 \times 2^{20t}$.
Find the number of bacteria after:

a 1 hour   b 3 hours   c 30 minutes.

9 The volume of medicine, $V\,cm^3$, in a bottle of height h cm is given by: $V = 8(h - 0.7)^2$.

Find the volume in a bottle of height:

a 8 cm   b 9 cm.

10 300 lockers are being painted at a leisure centre. The surface area (S sq in) of each locker is given by $S = 2h(18 + w) + 36w$, where h inches is the height and w inches is the width.
Find the surface area of a locker 6 feet high and 18 inches wide.

11 The volume of water, V cubic metres, in a swimming pool is given by $V = 30w(a + b)$, where a metres and b metres are the depths at the two ends and w metres is its width.

Find the volume of water when

a $a = 3$, $b = 2$ and $w = 20$

b $a = 4$, $b = 1.5$ and $w = 15$.

12 The combined resistance when three resistors are joined together in parallel is given by:

$1/r = 1/r_1 + 1/r_2 + 1/r_3$.
Find r, when $r_1 = 7$ ohms, $r_2 = 8$ ohms and $r_3 = 11$ ohms.

13 The cost, £C, of transporting a yacht from a manufacturer to a purchaser is estimated to be given by $C = 80 + 0.76m + 0.2s$, where m miles is the distance to be travelled by road and s miles is the distance to be travelled by sea. The purchaser wants the yacht delivered to Cherbourg. Delivery will involve a road distance of 50 miles and a sea distance of 120 miles.

Find the cost.

Speed or velocity equations

Speed is the rate of travel.

Common measures of speed are miles per hour (mph); kilometres per hour (km/h); metres per second (m/s).

To calculate speed you need to know the distance travelled and the time taken:

$$\text{Speed} = \frac{\textbf{Distance travelled}}{\textbf{Time taken}}$$

Unless the speed is constant over the whole distance, this will be an **average speed** for the journey.

Rearranging this formula will give:

$$\text{Distance travelled} = \text{Speed} \times \text{Time taken}$$

and

$$\text{Time taken} = \frac{\text{Distance travelled}}{\text{Speed}}$$

EXAMPLE 1

A car travelling at a speed of 65 miles per hour takes $2\frac{1}{2}$ hours for a journey.

What distance has the car covered in this time?

> In 1 hour the car travels 65 miles
> In $2\frac{1}{2}$ hours the car travels $65 \times 2\frac{1}{2}$ miles
> $\qquad\qquad\qquad = 162.5$ miles

or Distance $= \text{Speed} \times \text{Time} = 65 \times 2\frac{1}{2}$ miles
$\qquad\qquad\qquad\qquad\qquad = 162.5$ miles

EXAMPLE 2

A family travelling with a car and caravan in France cover a journey of 238 kilometres travelling at an average speed of 70 kilometres per hour.

How long does the journey take?

To travel 70 km takes 1 hour

To travel 1 km takes $\dfrac{1}{70}$ hour

To travel 238 km takes $\dfrac{1}{70} \times 238$ hours

$\qquad\qquad\qquad = 3.4$ hours

$\qquad\qquad\qquad = 3$ hour 24 minutes

or Time $= \dfrac{\text{Distance}}{\text{Speed}} = \dfrac{238\,\text{km}}{70\,\text{km/h}}$

$\qquad\qquad\qquad = 3$ hours 24 minutes

EXERCISE 17.17

1 Find the average speed, in the most appropriate units, for each of the following:

    a a journey of 162 miles which took 3 hours

    b a 1500 m race which was won in a time of 2 minutes 54.4 seconds.

    c a journey of 286 km which took $3\frac{1}{4}$ hours.

2 Find the distance covered:

    a by a car travelling at 85 km/h for 2.4 hours

    b by an aircraft travelling at 600 mph for 4 hours 36 minutes

3 Find the time taken

    a to travel 186 km at an average speed of 62 km/h

    b to travel 306 miles at an average speed of 40 mph

4 Andy goes running every evening for 45 minutes. If he runs at a speed of 10 mph, how far does he run?

5 **a** A race for small yachts has three 'legs' of distances 8 km, 6 km and 10 km. The average speed for the winning yacht was 6.2 kilometres per hour.
How long did it take the winning yacht to complete the course?

    b The second yacht finished 8 minutes after the winner.
What was its average speed?

18 *Graphs*

18.1 *Graphs and curves*

This unit deals with line graphs. The lines may be straight or curved, but they illustrate a relationship between two quantities. This relationship must be clear to anyone looking at the graph.

Graphs are used by many bodies to convey information quickly and with impact!

For example, these graphs were used by:

a holiday company

a Government department

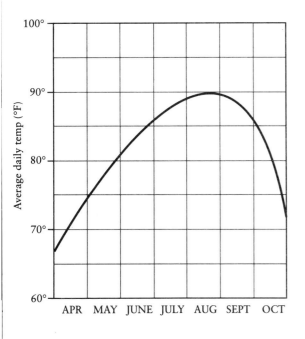

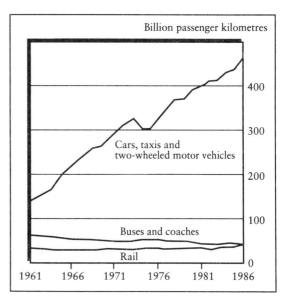

(Source: Department of Transport)

Many graphs involve time, which is always measured along the horizontal axis. The vertical axis then provides a measure of something that changes with time.
Whenever one measurable quantity changes as a result of another quantity changing it will be possible to draw a graph.

18.2 *The interpretation of graphs*

Once a graph has been drawn, information can be found from it very quickly.

EXAMPLE 1

The graph shows a cross-section through a river bed. The distance from point A on one bank of the river to point B, directly opposite on the other bank is 20 m.

Soundings were taken of the depth of the water at various points and plotted against the distance from A.

Find, from the graph:

a the depth of the river at a distance of 12 m from A

b the distances from A at which the depth of the river is 2.8 m.

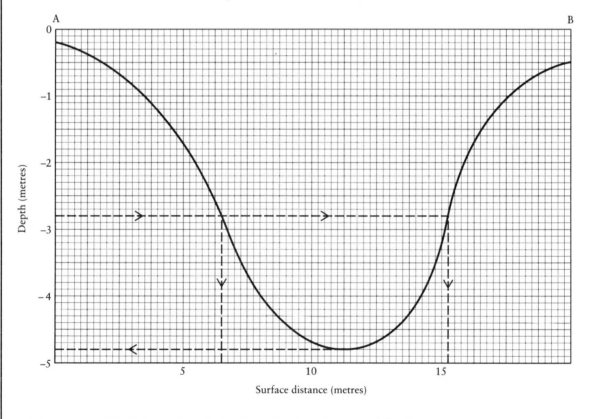

a The distance 12 m is located on the horizontal axis and a vertical line is drawn from this point to meet the graph. A horizontal line is then drawn across to the vertical axis and the distance is read off.

The distance is −4.8 m, i.e. the depth of the water is 4.8 m.

b The depth of 2.8 metres is located on the vertical axis at the point −2.8 and a horizontal line is drawn from this point which meets the curve at two points.
Vertical lines are drawn down to the horizontal axis and the two distances are read off.

The distances from A are 6.50 m and 15.25 m.

If a connection between two variables can be expressed algebraically, i.e. by an equation, then every point lies on the line or curve. If one value is known, the other can be found exactly, or as accurately as the scale of the graph allows.

For example, using the graph which shows the depth of a river (Example 1 above) the depth of the river can be given correct to the nearest 10 cm.

Often, however, the connection is not exact (as in Example 2 below) and, given one variable, only a rough estimate of the other variable can be found.

EXAMPLE 2

Each year thousands of tourists visit Britain, and the money which they spend here is a very welcome addition to the British economy.
The larger the number of tourists staying in Britain, the larger the amount of money spent will be. However, the relationship between the number of tourists and the amount of money spent is not an exact linear relationship. For example, double the number of tourists will not necessarily spend double the amount of money.

The line drawn in the graph below is the one which best represents the relationship between the number of tourists and the money they spend.

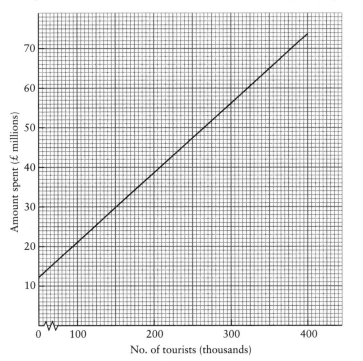

Values read from the graph are likely to be approximate, but the graph could be used to make predictions.

a Approximately how much money is spent by 250 thousand tourists?

b Predict the number of tourists needed to produce an income of £60 million.

From the graph:

a The amount of money spent is £47.5 million.

b The number of tourists required is 320 000.

EXERCISE 18.1

In the following questions state whether the answer found from the graph is
exact, within the limits of the graph's accuracy, or whether it is a rough estimate.

1   The graph shows the relationship between the percentage of rejected mugs
    found by different potteries and the selling price of the mug.

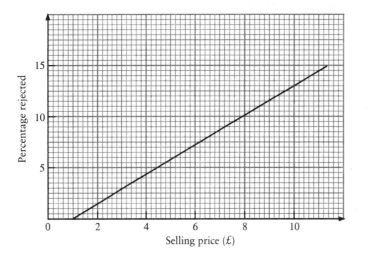

a   If the mugs sell at £5 each, what percentage is rejected?

b   If 13% of the mugs are rejected, what is the selling price?

2   The graph shows the number of complete patterns in a roll of dress
    material against the length of material bought.

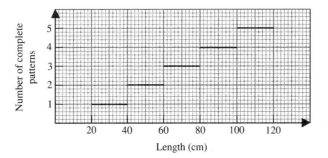

a   If 1.2 m of material is bought, how many complete patterns will there
    be?

b   A skirt is to be made with 3 complete patterns plus an allowance of
    12 cm for hem and waist band.
    What is the shortest length of material which could be bought?

3   The time a company allows its employees for lunch depends on their
    position in the company. The graph shows the amount of time allowed
    according to monthly salary.

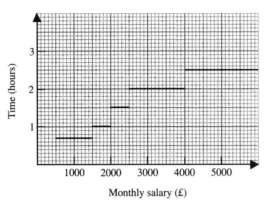

Monthly salary (£)

a   How long would the company allow an employee earning £2400 per
    month?

b   An employee is allowed a lunch break of 2 hours. What is the minimum
    salary earned?

4   The cost of sending an international fax, according to the time taken, is
    shown on the graph below.

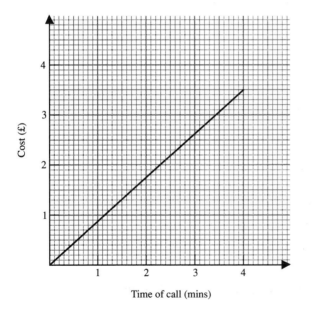

Time of call (mins)

a   What is the cost of sending a fax which takes $2\frac{1}{2}$ minutes?

b   If a fax cost £1.10 to send, how long did it take?

5   The length of time for which a chicken should be cooked depends on the
    weight of the chicken, as shown on the graph below.

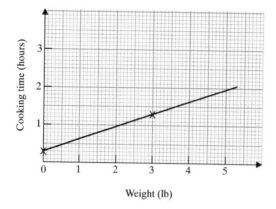

Weight (lb)

   a For how long should a chicken weighing 4 lb be cooked?

   b A chicken weighing $2\frac{3}{4}$ lb was cooked for 50 minutes.
       Was this long enough?

   c Why is it important to cook chickens for the correct length of time?

6   A pharmaceutical company delivers medicines to chemists. The distance
    travelled by the delivery vans against the time taken was recorded and the
    results plotted on a graph.

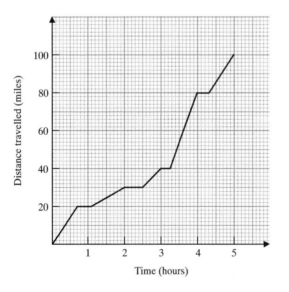

Time (hours)

   a If the time taken was 2 hours, how far had the van travelled?

   b One driver had to travel a distance of 70 miles. How long did the
       journey take?

7   A leisure centre's income depends on the number of visitors, as shown on
    the graph below.

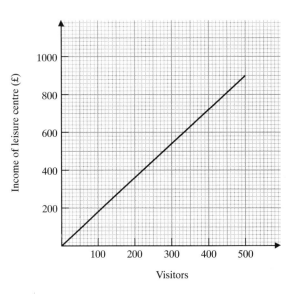

a How much is the income if the number of visitors is 300?

b If the income was £810, how many people visited the centre?

8   In a ladies hairdressers, the more skilled the stylist is, the more customers
    she tends to have and the more she is paid.
    The number of customers against weekly pay is shown on the graph below.

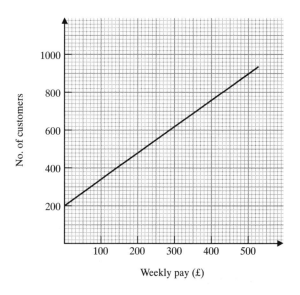

a One week one of the hairdressers was paid £260. How many customers
   did she have?

b If a stylist attended to 70 customers, what was her weekly pay, to the
   nearest £10?

9   Generally, the more a customer pays a building firm for the flat roof on an
    extension, the longer the roof lasts.
    The graph shows the expected life of a roof according to the price paid.

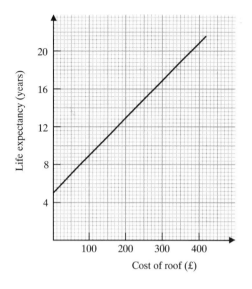

a   For how long might a roof costing £250 be expected to last?

b   For how long might a roof costing £350 be expected to last?

10 The depth of tread on a vehicle's tyres depends on the mileage covered. A
    firm regularly checks the tyres of its vehicles and notes the mileage. The
    results are shown on the following graph.

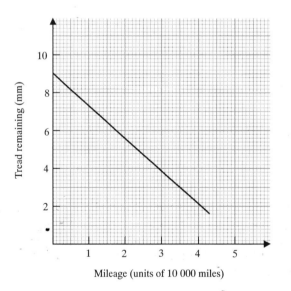

a   If the mileage was 36 000 miles, what was the depth of tread on the
    tyres?

b   If the depth of tread was 5 mm, what was the mileage covered, to the
    nearest 1000 miles?

18.3 *Graph plotting*

When plotting graphs a certain procedure should be followed.

1   Choose the scales.   4   Plot the points.

2   Draw the axes.   5   Join the points.

3   Scale the axes.

The information from which the graph is to be drawn is usually given in a table.

EXAMPLE

£1000 is invested in a savings account for 5 years. The amount in the account at the end of each year is shown on the table:

Number of years (x)	0	1	2	3	4	5
Amount in £ (y)	1000	1100	1210	1331	1464	1610

Plot the graph and find

a the amount in the account after $2\frac{1}{2}$ years

b the length of time for which the money must be invested to amount to £1500.

1   Choose the scales:

  (i) Find the range of values for each axis.
      On the horizontal axis the range is 5.
      On the vertical axis the values range from 1000 to 1610, i.e. the range is 610.

 (ii) Count the number of large squares in each direction on the graph paper.

      The graph paper provided here has 18 large squares in both directions and a grid with five small divisions in each large division.

      The aim is to draw as large a graph as possible, but the scale must be easy to read.

      Taking the 18 large division width for the horizontal axis, the range of 5 does not divide exactly into 18.

      A convenient scale would be 2 large divisions representing 1 year. On the vertical axis, a range of 610 does not divide into 18 large divisions, but 14 cm is divisible by 700. There will be little wastage of space if a scale of 2 large divisions representing £100 is chosen. The axis is scaled from £1000 to £1650.

2   Draw the axes.

Once the scales have been chosen, there is no problem in placing the axes.

The origin can be placed 2 large divisions from the left and 2 large divisions from the bottom edges of the graph paper.

This allows space for labelling the axes. Label the origin O.

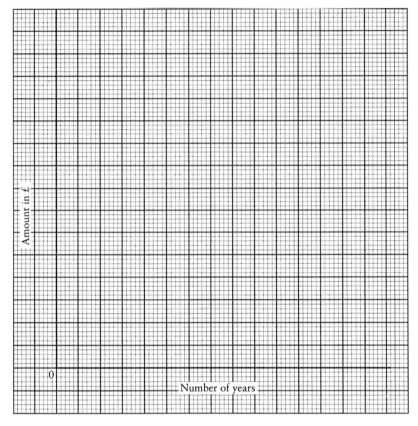

3   Scale the axes:

Mark the position of each year along the horizontal axis as shown on the following graph.

Mark the position of each £100 along the vertical axis as shown.

4   Plot the points.

Plot the six points given as explained on p. 201.

5   Join the points.

The points are joined with a **smooth** curve.

Trace through the points with a pencil, but without touching the paper, to find the shape of the curve. When you are satisfied that the path of the curve is smooth, draw the curve through the points in one movement.

If the values of the coordinates have been rounded, the line may not pass exactly through each point.

6   To find the required information draw appropriate lines on the graph
    (see p. 188) and read off the values:

    a £1270   **b** 4.3 years

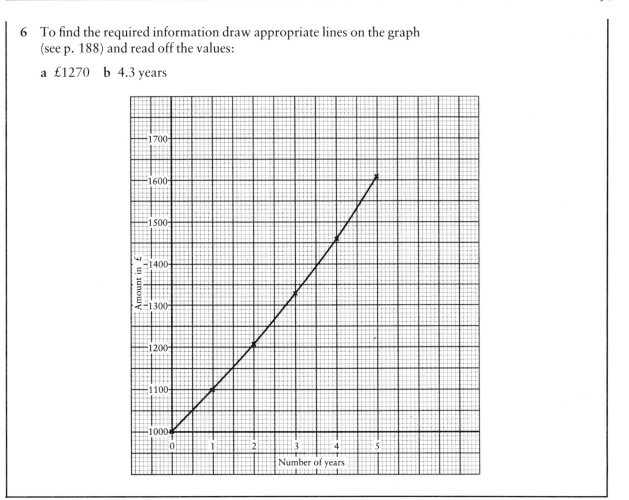

EXERCISE 18.2

In the following questions, you are given the information connecting the two
variables in a table. In each case plot the points and join them with a smooth curve.

1   Mrs Lister weighed herself now and again through the year. After one
    Christmas she found her weight was over $10\frac{1}{2}$ stone.

    She joined Weightwatchers and was determined to reach her target weight
    of $8\frac{1}{2}$ stone before the next Christmas.

    The table shows her weight in stones and pounds at the beginning of each
    given month. (1 stone = 14 lb.)

Month/year	Jan/90	May/90	Sep/90	Jan/91	May/91	Sep/91
Weight in st–lb	9–2	9–12$\frac{1}{2}$	10–6	10–8	10–4	9–6

    a What weight was Mrs Lister in August 1990?

    b What was the heaviest weight she reached?

    c During which months did she weigh 9 stone 7 lb?

    d Do you think she would have reached her target weight before Christmas 1991?

2 While at a party, William spills a glass of red wine over the table cloth.

The stain spreads rapidly in a circular shape and the table shows how the area increases as the diameter of the stain increases.

Diameter (cm)	0	2	4	6	8	10
Area (cm²)	0	3	12	27	48	75

a What area does the stain cover when the diameter is 9 cm?

b What is the radius of the stain when its area is 50 sq cm?

c The stain stops spreading when its diameter is 10.9 cm. What area does the stain eventually cover?

3 The table shows the average number of hours the sun shone during a day in the middle of each month, recorded at a Spanish resort.

	Jun	Jul	Aug	Sep	Oct	Nov	Dec	Jan	Feb	Mar	Apr	May	Jun
Hours of sunshine	16	15.5	14	12	10	8.5	8	8.5	10	12	14	15.5	16

a During which months might you expect an average of about $10\frac{1}{2}$ hours of sunshine in a day?

b What were the average hours of sunshine at the beginning and end of May?

c Which monthly periods had the smallest increase in hours of sunshine?

4 One day when Heather is having a bath, she notices that the water level is gradually decreasing and realises that the plug is leaking. When she started her bath the depth of water was 300 mm. Plot the points given in the table below to show the depth of water remaining at a given time.

Time (in minutes)	0	1	2	3	4	5
Depth of water (in mm)	300	110	41	15	5.5	2.0

a What was the depth of the water after $2\frac{1}{2}$ min?

b After how long was the bath half empty?

c What was the drop in water level after $1\frac{1}{2}$ min?

5 Two young children have a swing in the garden. On one particular day it is Lucy's turn on the swing and Tony pulls the swing back through an arc of 100 cm and then releases it.

The table shows the position of the swing (distances are measured along the arc of the swing) at different times during its motion.

Time (in seconds)	0	0.2	0.4	0.6	0.8	1.0	1.2	1.4
Distance (in cm)	100	89	57	13	−34	−74	−97	−98
Time (in seconds)	1.6	1.8	2.0	2.2	2.4	2.6	2.8	3.0
Distance (in cm)	−77	−38	9	54	87	100	91	61

a How long does it take for one complete swing?

b In what position is the swing after 0.7 seconds?

c How long does it take to travel through 50 cm?

d How long does it take to travel through 250 cm?

18.4 *Conversion graphs*

A graph is a very useful means of converting quickly from one quantity to another.

Ranjit is planning a summer holiday in France. He sees in the newspaper that the exchange rate is 10.2 FF = £1, but he wants to be able to compare French prices with prices at home quickly and easily. Before he goes he draws a pocket-size conversion graph which he can keep handy while on holiday.

He knows that:

- A conversion graph is a straight line, so he only needs to plot two points (though a third point is useful as a check).
- Most conversion graphs go through the point (0,0).
- Either variable can be measured along the vertical or horizontal axis.

As Ranjit will mainly be changing from francs to pounds he measures francs along the horizontal axis.

He knows that £1 = 10.2 FF and that the graph goes through the origin. He plots these two points. They are very close together so he finds another point further from the origin.

£10 = 102 FF is an easy one to calculate.

He then draws a straight line through the three points.
(If the line does not pass through all the points there is a mistake and the calculations must be checked.)

This is what his graph looks like:

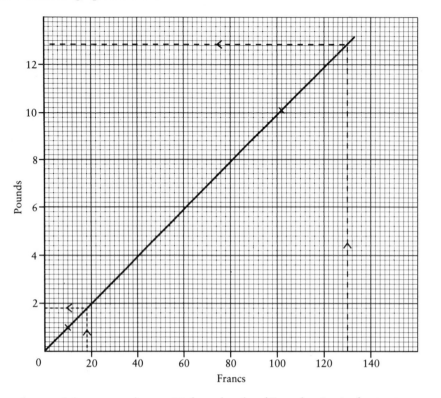

From the graph he can see that an 18-franc bottle of French wine is cheap at less than £1.80 and a meal for two costing 130 francs is about £12.80.

EXERCISE 18.3

1   The equation $F = 1.8C + 32$ converts degrees Celsius to degrees Fahrenheit.
Draw a graph of F against C for values of C up to $40°$.

Use your graph to answer the following:

a   The temperature of the solution for processing black and white film should be 20°C.
What is this in degrees Fahrenheit?

b   The temperature of an office should be between 19.4°C and 22.8°C.
Does a temperature of 64°F comply with the regulations?

c   People begin to suffer from hypothermia when the body temperature drops below 95°F.
What is this temperature in °C?

d   The temperature on a very hot day in August reached 32°C.
What was the temperature in °F?

e   The factory act requires the temperature of a working area where heavy work is done to be between 12.8°C and 15.6°C.

Would the employees be comfortable if the temperature was 58°F?

2   An artist draws a design for a poster on A4 paper and then enlarges it to A3 size.

Length on A3 = 1.41 × Length on A4

Draw a graph of A3 sizes against A4 for values up to 30 cm.

a   The A4 size poster measures 20.7 cm × 29.7 cm.
What is the size of the A3 poster?

b   The caption is to be in letters 2.5 cm high.
What height should the letters be in A4 format?

3   An international business which trades with Japan needs to convert from pounds to yen and vice versa.
Draw a conversion graph given that the exchange rate is £1 = 154 yen.

Use your graph to convert:

a   3500 yen to pounds   b   £11 to yen.

4 Since 1977, hospitals have recorded weights of babies in kilograms. However, many parents prefer the imperial units of pounds and ounces.

Draw a graph to convert kilograms to pounds and ounces and use your graph to find the weight, in pounds and ounces, of a baby weighing:

a 4 kg   **b** 2.75 kg.

5 Five miles is approximately equal to eight kilometres.
Draw a graph to give a rough conversion between miles and kilometres.

a A family on holiday in France sees a sign board on the A10.
Convert the distances given on the sign board to miles.

A10	
ORLEANS	106
TOURS	245
POITIERS	350
BORDEAUX	560

b A French family on holiday in Britain travels 64 miles.
How far have they travelled in kilometres?

6 Goods are sent from a factory in Britain to the Gulf. During the journey, the driver discovers that the vehicle's fuel gauge is faulty. He knows how many miles he can travel on a litre of fuel, but in Saudi Arabia the fuel is sold in US gallons. Draw a graph to convert US gallons to litres. (1 US gallon = 3.79 litres.)

a If he puts 25 gallons into the tank, how many litres is this?

b His petrol consumption is 3 miles per litre. How many miles can he expect to travel before he needs more fuel?

18.5 *Cartesian coordinates*

In the early seventeenth century, the French mathematician René Descartes introduced the idea of a grid for locating and plotting points.

Onto this grid, called a **cartesian** graph, are drawn two straight lines at right angles to one another, called the **rectangular axes**.

Usually the axes cross at the **origin**, O, or starting point. The axes are scaled as number lines with positive numbers to the right and above the origin and negative numbers to the left and below the origin.

The position of any point (A, say) can then be described by two numbers: one referring to the horizontal axis x and one to the vertical axis y.

The two numbers are called the **cartesian coordinates**, after Descartes.

In general, the coordinates are called x- and y-coordinates, written as (x, y), and are plotted by first counting along the horizontal or x-axis and then along the vertical or y-axis.

In the diagram opposite A is at the point $(3, -2)$.

It is usual to plot a point on a graph using a cross (+ or ×) or a dot (·).

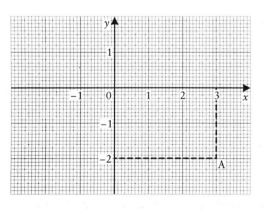

18.6 *Straight-line graphs*

Drawing straight-line graphs

An equation of the form $y = mx + c$ can be represented graphically by a straight line.

To draw a straight line requires **two** points, but it is better to find **three** points as a check.

EXAMPLE

Draw a graph to represent the line $y = 3x - 2$ for values of x from -3 to 3.

1   Choose the scales.

Choose three values for x between -3 and 3, e.g. $-3, 0, 3$. Calculate the corresponding y-values and write the three pairs of coordinates in a table:

x	-3	0	3
y	-11	-2	7

The range for y is 18 and for x is 6.
Suitable scales are 1 large division to 1 unit on the x-axis
and 1 large division to 2 units on the y-axis.

2, 3   Draw and scale the axes.

As the negative values of x equal the positive values, set the y-axis near the centre of the graph paper.

The x-axis must be drawn above the halfway mark to allow for more negative values of y.

The axes are scaled in both positive and negative directions.

4, 5   Plot and join the points.

If several graphs are drawn using the same set of axes, each graph should be labelled with its equation.

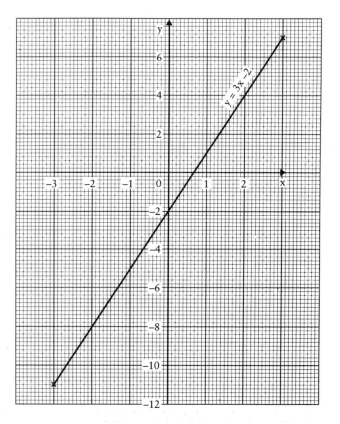

EXERCISE 18.4

Calculate and plot three points for each of the following lines.

Draw the graphs of each set of equations using the same axes.

1 $y = x$
$y = x + 3$
$y = x - 1$
$y = x - 2$

2 $y = 2x$
$y = 2x + 3$
$y = 2x - 1$
$y = 2x - 2$

3 $y = -x$
$y = -x + 3$
$y = -x - 1$
$y = -x - 2$

4 $y = -3x$
$y = -3x + 2$
$y = -3x - 1$
$y = -3x - 3$

5 $y = \frac{1}{2}x$
$y = \frac{1}{2}x + 2$
$y = \frac{1}{2}x - 1$
$y = \frac{1}{2}x - 3$

6 $y = -\frac{1}{2}x$
$y = -\frac{1}{2}x + 2$
$y = -\frac{1}{2}x - 1$
$y = -\frac{1}{2}x - 3$

7 a What do the equations in each set have in common:
   (i) in their algebraic form,
   (ii) in their graphical form?

b What conclusion can you draw from this?

8 a What do the equations $y = x$, $y = 2x$, $y = -x$, $y = -3x$, $y = \frac{1}{2}x$, and $y = -\frac{1}{2}x$ have in common?

b What conclusion can you draw from this?

9 What does the constant term on the RHS of an equation tell you about the graph of that line?

10 Compare the graphs in questions 3, 4 and 6. What does a negative coefficient of x tell you about the graph of that line?
(See p. 156 if you need a reminder about what a 'coefficient' is.)

EXERCISE 18.5

1 An art student needs to frame a series of pictures and photographs for an exhibition.
He calculates that, if the framing costs £1.50 per foot, the cost of framing (£C) is given by:

$$8C = P + 8$$

where P is the perimeter of a picture in inches.
Draw a graph of C against P and use it to find:

a the cost of framing three pictures with perimeters 28″, 50″ and 42″

b the size of picture which could be framed for £5.25.

2 The 'golden section' is used in architecture and painting where perfect proportions are required. It is the division of a line so that the ratio of one part of the whole is the same as the ratio of the parts:

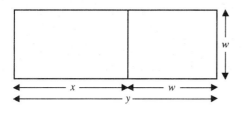

i.e. $y : x$ is the same as $x : w$.
An approximate relationship between x and y is given by $y = 1.618x$.

Draw a graph of this relationship for values of x from 0 to 10, and use it to find approximate values of y, x and w when:

a $x = 6.2\,\text{cm}$ **b** $y = 6.5\,\text{cm}$.

3 A firm measures the effectiveness of its advertising campaign by calculating the return on money invested as:

$$\text{Return} = \frac{\text{Increase in profit} - \text{Investment}}{\text{Investment}} \times 100$$

If the money invested was £5000, then

$$R = \frac{P}{50} - 100$$

Draw a graph of R against P for values of P up to 5000.

a What is the return if the profits increased by:
(i) £7500   (ii) £3000?

b If a return of 25% is required, what increase in profit must be made?

4 For incomes between £3445 and £5945, the amount of income tax paid per year at single person's rate, is given by:

$$T = \tfrac{1}{5}I - 689$$

where T is the tax and I is the annual income. Draw a graph of T against I and find:

a the amount of tax paid by a clerk whose annual income was £5695

b the amount earned if the tax paid was £150.

5 Estimates of a person's height as an adult can be made from their height at 3 years of age.

If H = adult height, h = height at age 3,

for women $H = 1.73 \times h$
for men $H = 1.87 \times h$

Draw graphs of both lines on the same axes and use your graphs to find:

a an estimated full height for a woman and a man who were both 95 cm tall at 3 years of age

b the possible height at 3 years of a man who is 168 cm tall.

6 If I take vigorous exercise, the number of calories I will 'burn up' is given by:

$$C = 59 \times T$$

where C is the number of calories and T(min) is the time.

Draw a graph of C against T and find for how long I will need to exercise if I wish to use up:

a 500 calories   b 250 calories.

7 Delays in aircraft take off times cost travel firms money. A company estimates that an average cost per head for delays is given by:

$$C = 2T - 2$$

where C is the cost per head (£) and T is the time delay (hours).
Draw a graph and estimate:

a the cost per head for a delay of $7\tfrac{1}{2}$ hours

b the cost for a party of 250 if the delay is $5\tfrac{1}{4}$ hours

c the delay if the cost per head has reached £10.

8 An estimate of the taxi fare from an Australian airport into town can be calculated by:

$$C = 2D - 6$$

where C is the cost in $A and D is the distance in miles.

Draw a graph of C against D for values of D from 0 to 20.

a Find an estimate of the fare if the distance into town is 14 miles.

b If the taxi fare was $A9, find an estimate for the distance to town from the airport.

9 In a factory, iron is smelted and made into nuts, bolts, hinges, etc. The weight of iron produced is related to the volume by:

$$W = 7.9 \times V$$

where W is the weight in kg and V is the volume in litres.

Draw a graph connecting weight and volume and find:

a the weight of iron products made from a volume of 2500 cc

b the volume required to produce 10 kg of iron products.

10 In a quality control experiment increasingly heavy weights were hung on springs to test their elasticity.

For springs of the correct elasticity

$$L = 2.5W + 300$$

where L(mm) is the stretched length of a spring and W(kg) is the weight hung on the spring.
Draw a graph of L against W and find:

a the length when the weight is 55 kg

b the weight which should stretch a spring to a length of 45 cm

c the unstretched length of a spring.

*18.7 *Gradients and intercepts*

All linear (straight-line) equations are of the general form:

$$y = mx + c$$

where m is the gradient of the line and c is the intercept along the y-axis, providing the origin O is at the intersection of the axes.

The **gradient** of a line is the increase in the vertical value for every unit (i.e. 1) increase in the horizontal value.

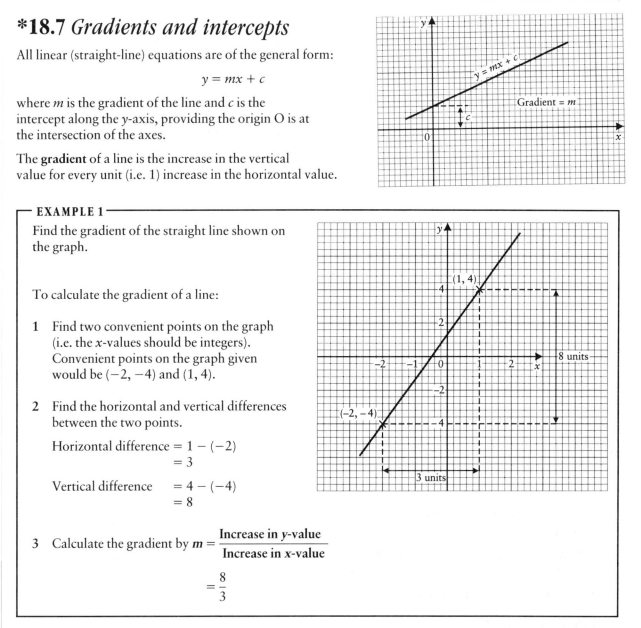

— **EXAMPLE 1** —

Find the gradient of the straight line shown on the graph.

To calculate the gradient of a line:

1   Find two convenient points on the graph (i.e. the x-values should be integers). Convenient points on the graph given would be $(-2, -4)$ and $(1, 4)$.

2   Find the horizontal and vertical differences between the two points.

Horizontal difference $= 1 - (-2)$
$\qquad\qquad\qquad = 3$

Vertical difference $\;= 4 - (-4)$
$\qquad\qquad\qquad = 8$

3   Calculate the gradient by $\boldsymbol{m} = \dfrac{\textbf{Increase in }\boldsymbol{y}\textbf{-value}}{\textbf{Increase in }\boldsymbol{x}\textbf{-value}}$

$\qquad\qquad = \dfrac{8}{3}$

— **EXAMPLE 2** —

Find the equation of the line shown.

1   Gradient of line $= m \;= \dfrac{\text{Increase in }y\text{-value}}{\text{Increase in }x\text{-value}}$

$\qquad\qquad = \dfrac{1 - 3}{2 - (-2)}$

$\qquad\qquad = -\dfrac{2}{4} = -\dfrac{1}{2}$

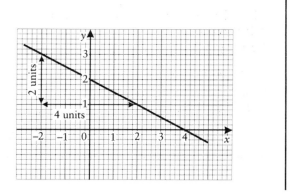

Alternatively,

/ is a positive gradient and \ is a negative gradient

From the graph:

$$\text{Gradient of line} = m = -\frac{2}{4} = -\frac{1}{2} \text{ or } -0.5$$

2 The line crosses the *y*-axis at the point $(0, 2)$, i.e. the intercept along the *y*-axis is $c = 2$

3 The equation of the line is $y = mx + c$

$$\therefore y = -\frac{1}{2}x + 2$$

$$2y = -x + 4 \text{ or } x + 2y = 4$$

EXERCISE 18.6

1 What are the gradients of the following lines?

a $y = 3x + 2$ c $y = 4 - 2x$ e $3y = 2x + 6$ g $x + y = -2$ i $x + 3y = 6$

b $y = 2x - 5$ d $2y = x - 2$ f $4y = 2 - 8x$ h $2x + y + 4 = 0$

2 For each of the equations in question 1, state the intercept along the *y*-axis.

3 Find the equation of each of the following straight line graphs:

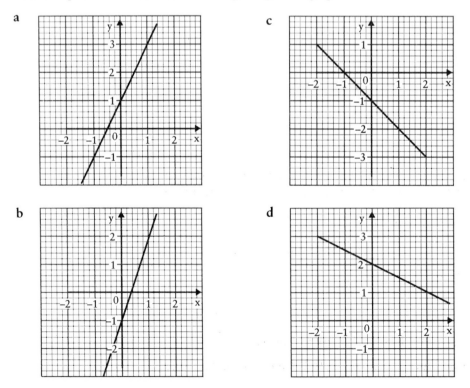

4 Each of the following sketch graphs represents one of the equations:

a $y = 2x + 1$ **c** $y = 3 - x$ **e** $x = -1$

b $2y = x$ **d** $y = 2$ **f** $x + y = -1$

Which is which?

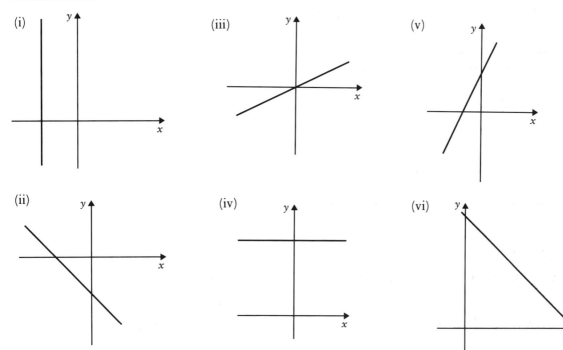

(i)   (iii)   (v)

(ii)   (iv)   (vi)

5 The amount of light entering a camera is controlled by the shutter speed and the aperture.

The table below shows shutter speeds and aperture settings which allow equal amounts of light to the film.

Aperture (A)	f22	f11	f5.6	f2.8
Shutter speed (S)	1/66	1/125	1/250	1/500

Plot the points (A, S) and draw a line to fit the points.

a What is the equation of your line?

b What should the shutter speed be for an aperture setting of f8?

6 When a retailer tries to sell large amounts of a particular item, the price per item will generally affect the demand, i.e. a lower unit price will often result in an increased demand.
Plot the points (x, y) given in the table below:

Price per unit (x)	20	15	10
Demand per week (y) (in thousands)	6	10	15

Draw a line to fit the points.

a Find an equation for your line.

b Use your line to predict the demand if the price dropped to 5p.

c At 5p per item the demand was actually 23 000. Comment on this result.

7   Patients who cannot take food by mouth are fed by intravenous drips
    which the nurse sets to deliver the required number of drips per minute.
    The doctor's prescription states the quantity
    (Q ml) to be given per hour.

    The setting for the drip feed (D) is 15 drops per minute when the
    prescription requires 60 ml per hour.

    The drip is set at 20 drops per minute when the quantity prescribed is 80 ml
    per hour.

    Draw axes of D against Q and plot two points to represent the information
    given.

    Draw a line through the points.

    What is the equation of your line?

8   The table below shows the pulse rates for healthy people of different ages
    taking exercise.

Age	20	25	30	35	40	45	50
Pulse rate	120	117	115	110	108	105	100

    a   Plot the points and fit a straight line to the points.

    b   Find the equation of your line.

    c   What are the appropriate pulse rates for:
        (i)   someone 55 years of age
        (ii) someone 18 years of age?

9   If you screw through thin sheet metal, a pilot hole is required. (A pilot hole
    is an initial hole which is smaller than the diameter of the screw.) The drill
    size required for the pilot hole is given on the table below for different
    screw sizes.

Screw gauge	4	6	8	10
Pilot drill size (mm)	2.0	2.5	3.0	3.5

    Draw a graph of drill size against screw size.

    a   Find the equation of your line.

    b   Use your equation to find the drill size for a
        pilot hole for a screw of size 12.

19 *Geometrical Shapes*

Geometry is one of the oldest branches of mathematics. The name is derived from the Greek words 'ge', meaning earth, and 'metrein', the verb to measure. The Ancient Babylonians, Egyptians and Greeks all contributed to the development of geometry.

19.1 *Lines and angles*

Lines

Lines can be curved or straight.

There are very few straight lines in nature, but much of geometry is concerned with straight lines.

On a flat surface – and most ancient civilisations believed the earth to be flat – a straight line is the shortest distance between two points.

A **point** marks a position and has no size.

The line below joins the two points A and B:

A   B

To indicate a point in a line, it is usual to mark the point with a small 'dash':

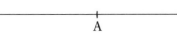

A

Straight lines are drawn using a ruler, a rule or a straight edge.

Angles

When two straight lines meet they form an angle. The angle between AO and OB is called the angle AOB (or it could be called BOA).

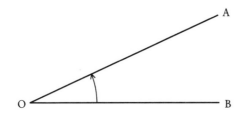

The size of the angle AOB is a measure of how far the line OA has been rotated from a starting position along OB. If we continue to rotate OA in a clockwise direction until it once again lies along OB, it will have been rotated through a full circle or **360 degrees** (also written as **360°**).

The reason there are 360 degrees in a full circle is because the Babylonians believed there were 360 days in the year. An angular measure was derived in order to chart the movements of the stars, which took one year for a full rotation about the earth.

A rotation through half of a circle, or half-turn, is a turn through 180°.

A rotation through a quarter of a circle, or a quarter-turn, is a turn through 90°.

An angle of 90° is usually called a **right angle**.

Right angles occur a great deal in the man-made world. If you look around any room, you will see many examples of right angles.

Draughtsmen use a set square for drawing and checking right angles.

Two lines which intersect at right angles are called **perpendicular lines**. The diagram on the right shows two perpendicular lines.

The special symbol for a right angle has been used in the diagram.

Other types of angle are:

acute angles, of size between 0° and 90°

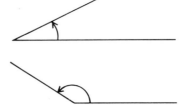

obtuse angles, of size between 90° and 180°

Parallel lines

Lines which do not intersect, no matter how far they are extended, are called **parallel lines**.

There are many examples of parallel lines around us.

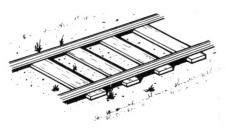

Railway lines

Bars on a gate

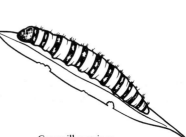

Caterpillar stripes

19.2 *Polygons*

Plane figures which are bounded by straight lines are called polygons.

Triangles

A **triangle** is a three-sided polygon.

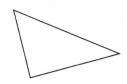

Isosceles triangles

An isosceles triangle has two sides equal in length and the angles opposite these sides equal in size.
In the diagram below, the equal sides are marked with dashes and the equal angles with arcs.

$$AB = AC$$

$$\text{Angle B} = \text{Angle C}$$

which we can also write as

$$\text{Angle ABC} = \text{Angle ACB}$$

$$\text{or} < ABC = < ACB$$

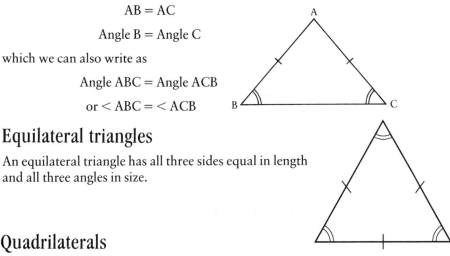

Equilateral triangles

An equilateral triangle has all three sides equal in length and all three angles in size.

Quadrilaterals

As the name suggests, **quadrilaterals** are four-sided polygons.

A line joining two vertices of a polygons is called a **diagonal**.

Some special quadrilaterals are described below:

A **parallelogram** is a quadrilateral which has both pairs of opposite sides parallel.

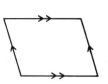

A **rectangle** is a parallelogram which has all its angles of 90°.

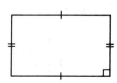

A **square** is a rectangle which has four sides of equal length (or a rhombus with angles of 90°).

Pentagons

A pentagon is a polygon with five sides.

Pentagon

A **hexagon** is a polygon with six sides.

Regular hexagon

A **trapezium** is a quadrilateral which has one pair of opposite sides parallel.

A **regular polygon** has all its sides equal in length and all its angles equal in size.

19.3 *Circles and angles*

Definitions

A circle is a set of points which are a fixed distance from a given point.
The given point is the **centre** of the circle and the fixed distance is the **radius**.

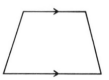

Radius

O

The **circumference** is the perimeter of the circle.

An **arc** is a section of the circumference.

A **chord** is a line joining two points on the circumference.

A **diameter** is a chord which passes through the centre.

A **tangent** is a line which touches the circle at one point only.

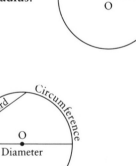

Circumference

Chord

O

Diameter

Arc

Tangent

EXERCISE 19.1

In the child's sorting tray below, identify each lettered shape.

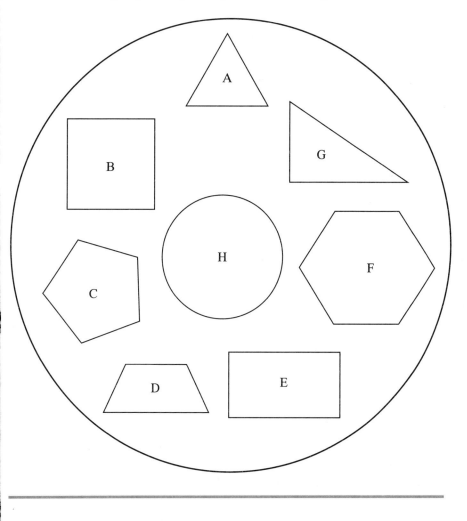

19.4 *Tessellations*

A tessellation is a pattern which when repeated will completely cover a plane without leaving any gaps. The pattern can either be one shape, or a combination of shapes.

Simple shapes which tessellate are:

Squares

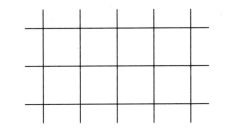

Equilateral triangles

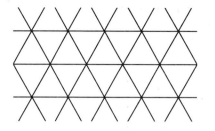

Regular hexagons

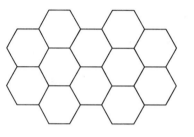

Parallelograms

Most shapes, for example regular pentagons,
cannot tessellate.

In 1891, a Russian crystallographer named Fedorov showed that there are only
17 different ways in which a basic pattern can be repeated. These repeating
patterns are found frequently on dress materials, wallpaper, etc.

Any triangle can be placed with an identical triangle to form a parallelogram.
Since parallelograms tessellate, any triangle can be the basis of a tessellation.
Here is an example:

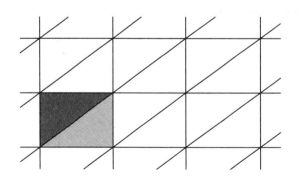

A shape which tessellates need not be regular. Here is an example:

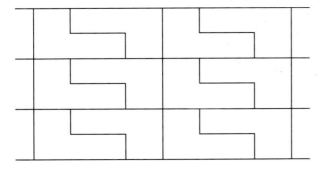

A tessellation can be formed by using two (or more) basic shapes. For example, regular octagons, (polygons with eight sides) and squares form a tessellation. One such pattern is:

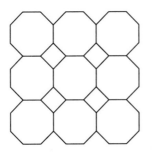

EXAMPLE

Combine equilateral triangles and squares to form a tessellation.

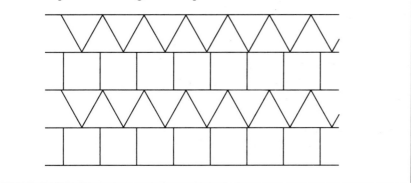

EXERCISE 19.2

1 Draw a tessellation based on each of the following shapes:

   a   **b**   **c**

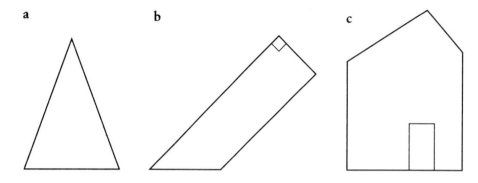

2 Square tiles of side 15 cm and rectangular tiles 5 cm by 15 cm are used to
tile a bathroom wall, part of which is shown.

The wall measures 3.3 m by 2.4 m. How many of each type are needed to
tile the wall?

3 Which additional shape is needed for this shape to tessellate?

4 Draw a tessellation based on each of the following shapes:

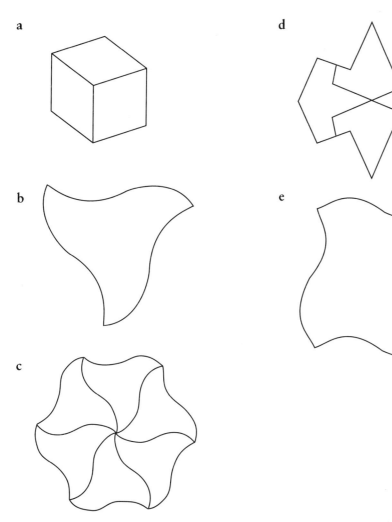

a

b

c

d

e

19.5 *2D representation of 3D objects*

It is common to see in newspapers pictures of three-dimensional objects, e.g. boxes, houses, people. These pictures are printed on paper and hence are in two dimensions.

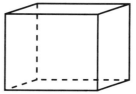

The diagram on the right
represents a cuboid.
The edges you can see are shown as solid lines
and the edges of the cuboid which you cannot see are shown as dotted lines.
These diagrams are usually drawn with one of the horizontal directions in the
x direction (as if it were a graph) with the vertical direction of the body being
in the y direction. The second horizontal direction is shown at an angle.

This diagram represents a **cube**.

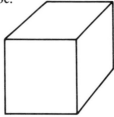

A **cube** is a solid with six square faces (or sides), hence the length, breadth and height of a cube are all equal.

A sphere is drawn as a circle:

Circles are drawn as ovals, and a cylinder is drawn to have two oval ends.   or

Similar representations can be shown using isometric paper. This paper uses a tessellation of equilateral triangles. The lines on the paper go in three directions, each of which represents a dimension.
The lines up and down represent the vertical dimension.
The other two directions on the isometric paper represent the two horizontal dimensions.
Thus on the cuboid shown AB and AD represent the two horizontal dimensions (length and width) and AE is the vertical dimensions (height).
The cuboid has a base 6 units by 3 units with a height of 4 units.

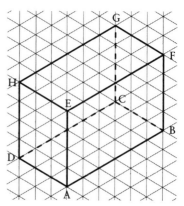

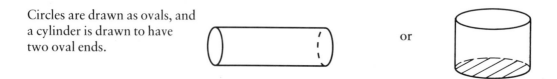

EXAMPLE

Draw a triangular prism of length 8 units. The isosceles triangular face has a base of 4 units and a perpendicular height of 4 units.
Note: The base AB is 4 units in length,
the length AD is 8 units and the height PQ
of the triangular face is 4 units.

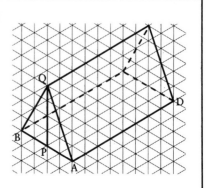

20 *Mensuration*

20.1 *Perimeters of polygons*

As we saw in the last unit, a **plane figure** is a two-dimensional shape which is bounded by lines called **sides**.

Here are some examples:

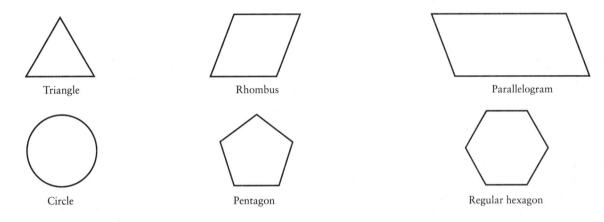

Triangle   Rhombus   Parallelogram

Circle   Pentagon   Regular hexagon

The **perimeter** of a plane figure is the total length of the sides.

EXAMPLE 1

A photograph frame has a metallic surround. The outer and inner perimeters of the surround are edged with gold.

Find the total length of the outer and inner perimeter and hence the length of the gold edging.

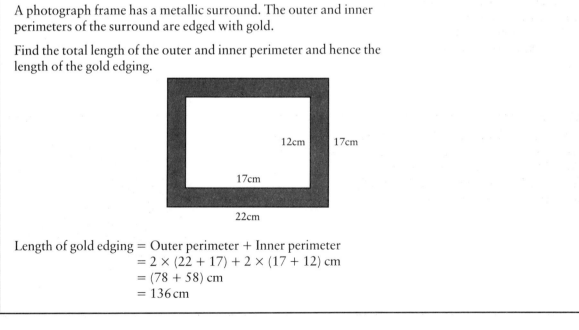

Length of gold edging = Outer perimeter + Inner perimeter
$$= 2 \times (22 + 17) + 2 \times (17 + 12) \text{ cm}$$
$$= (78 + 58) \text{ cm}$$
$$= 136 \text{ cm}$$

EXAMPLE 2

Find the perimeter of the shape given:

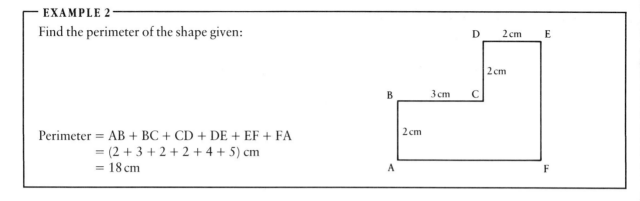

Perimeter = AB + BC + CD + DE + EF + FA
= (2 + 3 + 2 + 2 + 4 + 5) cm
= 18 cm

EXERCISE 20.1

1 Find the perimeter of each of the following:

  a a rectangle of length 8 cm and width 3 cm

  b a square of side 7 m

  c a rhombus of side 6 inches.

2 Find the perimeter of each of the following shapes:

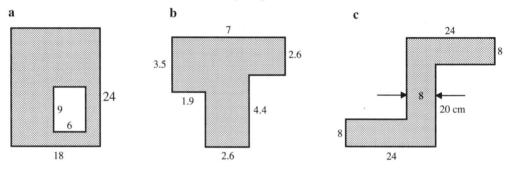

3 A canvas for an oil painting is stretched on a canvas frame 75 cm by 35 cm.

  What is the perimeter of the frame?

4 A craft stall sells earrings which are made from gold wire bent into a rectangle. Each rectangle is 12 mm by 6 mm.

  a How much gold wire is needed for a pair of earrings?

  b How many pairs of earrings can be made from wire which is 1 metre in length?

5 What is the perimeter of a sheet of paper which is:

  a size A4 **b** size A3?

6 A photographic firm supplies cardboard frames for college photographs. The outer measurements of the frame are 25.5 cm wide and 20 cm high and the border is 2.5 cm wide.

  a What are the inside measurements of the frame?

  b What is the total (outer plus inner) perimeter?

7   A child's playpen has sides of length 230 cm by 160 cm.

What is the perimeter of the playpen?

8   The WC in a toilet for the disabled takes up an area of floor space 50 cm wide by 90 cm long. Allowances of 100 cm, in total, on the width and 110 cm on the length are made for wheelchair access.

a   What are the dimensions of the toilet?

b   What is the perimeter of the toilet?

9   A leisure centre marks out its indoor tennis courts with white plastic strip, as shown in the diagram.

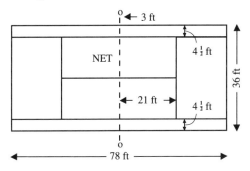

What length of white plastic strip is needed for each tennis court?

10 Shown on the right is the plan of a hotel bedroom. When redecorating, an attractive frieze is pasted, at ceiling height, all round the walls.
What length of frieze is needed for this room?

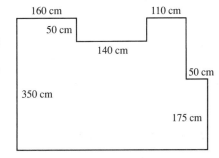

11 A manufacturer of fitted kitchens makes cupboard doors which are 60 cm by 35 cm. The doors are edged with a thin strip of wood.

What length of wood is needed for a pair of doors?

12 a   A firm makes 1000 piece jigsaw puzzles which are 19 inches by 27 inches.
What is the perimeter of a completed jigsaw?

b   The firm decides to produce a portable board for its jigsaw puzzles which will be 8 inches wider than the completed puzzle on each side.
(i) What are the dimensions of the board?
(ii) What is the perimeter of the board?

20.2 *Area*

Area is a measure of the surface covered by a given shape.

EXAMPLE 1

Consider the shapes below and place them in ascending order according
to their area.

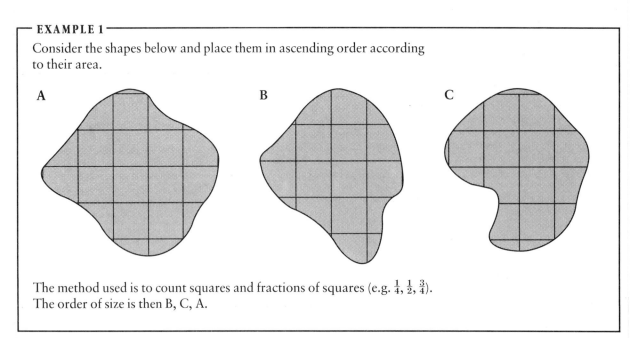

The method used is to count squares and fractions of squares (e.g. $\frac{1}{4}, \frac{1}{2}, \frac{3}{4}$).
The order of size is then B, C, A.

Figures which have straight sides (polygons) are much easier to compare.

EXAMPLE 2

Consider the following polygons:

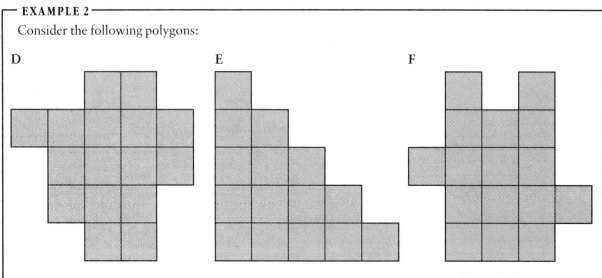

a Which shape has the smallest area?

b Which shapes have the same area?

c What is the area of shape F?

The number of squares which a shape covers is the most convenient way
of describing its area, but the squares must be of a standard size to enable
comparisons to be made.

The square used in the diagrams above is a 1 centimetre square.

The area of a 1 cm square = 1 square centimetre or $1\,cm^2$.

The area ▢ = $1\,cm^2$.

The answers are: **a** E   **b** D and F   **c** 16 square centimetres

The most common measures of an area are based on:

square of side 1 cm: area = 1 square centimetre = $1\,cm^2$

square of side 1 m: area = 1 square metre   = $1\,m^2$

square of side 1 mm: area = 1 square millimetre = $1\,mm^2$

The imperial units for area are, 1 square inch = $1\,in^2$

1 square foot = $1\,ft^2$

1 square yard = $1\,yd^2$

Area of rectangle

EXAMPLE 1

What is the area of the rectangle shown?
(Each square represents $1\,cm^2$.)

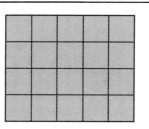

The rectangle covers 20 squares, each of area $1\,cm^2$.

∴ Area of rectangle = $20\,cm^2$

EXAMPLE 2

What is the area of this rectangle?

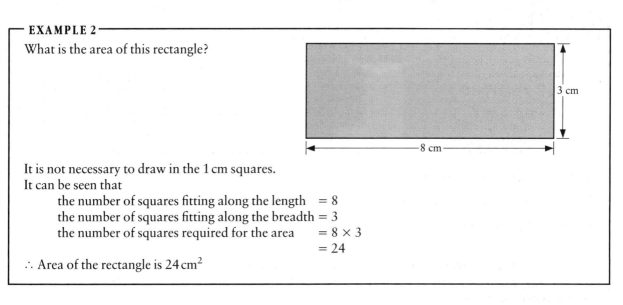

It is not necessary to draw in the 1 cm squares.
It can be seen that

the number of squares fitting along the length   = 8
the number of squares fitting along the breadth = 3
the number of squares required for the area   = 8 × 3
                                                = 24

∴ Area of the rectangle is $24\,cm^2$

For a rectangle: **Area = Length × Breadth**   For a square: **Area = Length × Breadth**

$$A = L \times B$$ $$A = L^2$$

Some shapes, which are more complicated, can be split up into rectangles in order
to find the area.

EXAMPLE 3

Find the area of this shape.

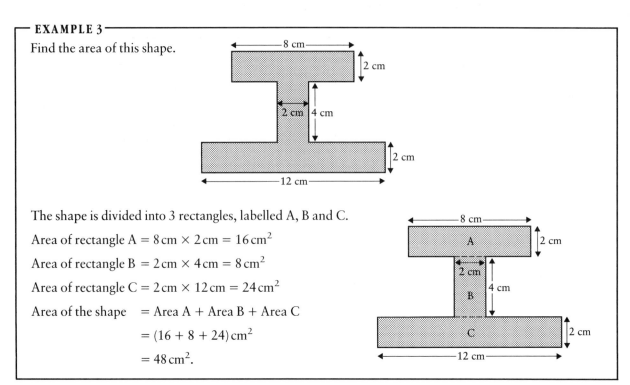

The shape is divided into 3 rectangles, labelled A, B and C.

Area of rectangle A = $8\,\text{cm} \times 2\,\text{cm} = 16\,\text{cm}^2$

Area of rectangle B = $2\,\text{cm} \times 4\,\text{cm} = 8\,\text{cm}^2$

Area of rectangle C = $2\,\text{cm} \times 12\,\text{cm} = 24\,\text{cm}^2$

Area of the shape $= \text{Area A} + \text{Area B} + \text{Area C}$

$\qquad\qquad\quad = (16 + 8 + 24)\,\text{cm}^2$

$\qquad\qquad\quad = 48\,\text{cm}^2.$

In some cases it is quicker to subtract areas than to add.

EXAMPLE 4

Find the area of this shape.

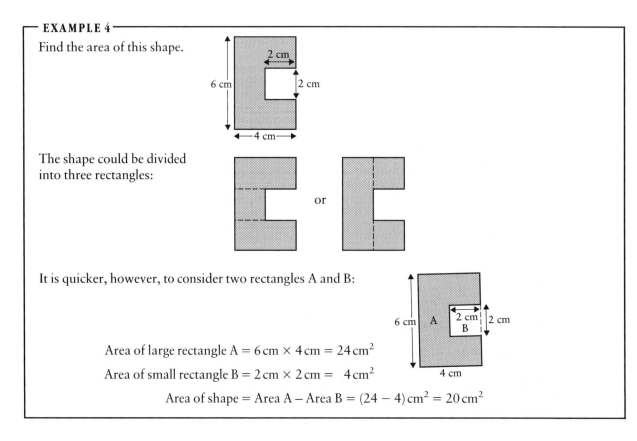

The shape could be divided
into three rectangles:

It is quicker, however, to consider two rectangles A and B:

Area of large rectangle A = $6\,\text{cm} \times 4\,\text{cm} = 24\,\text{cm}^2$

Area of small rectangle B = $2\,\text{cm} \times 2\,\text{cm} = 4\,\text{cm}^2$

Area of shape = Area A − Area B = $(24 - 4)\,\text{cm}^2 = 20\,\text{cm}^2$

EXERCISE 20.2

1   Write down the areas of the following rectangles. (Each square represents 1 cm².)

a 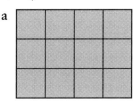 b 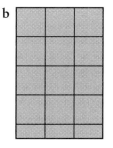 c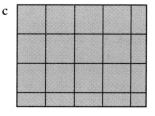

2   Calculate the area of a rectangle with dimensions:

   a 12 cm × 5 cm   c 10 cm × 7.5 cm   e 22.8 cm × 11.6 cm

   b 15 cm × 20 cm   d 17.5 cm × 2.5 cm   f 15.5 cm × 15.5 cm.

3   A rectangular piece of land covers an area of 156 cm².

   a If its length is 13 m, what is its width?

   b What is its perimeter?

4   A square has its perimeter which is 22 cm long.
    What is the area of the square?

5   A rectangular design is made from 24 panes of coloured glass, each measuring 11.5 cm by 6.5 cm.

   a If the rectangle is at least two panes wide, how many different rectangles can be made?
      State the dimensions of each rectangle.

   b Find: (i) the perimeter   (ii) the area of each of your rectangles.

6   A piece of card, 20 cm square, is used to make a surround for a picture.

   a What size square is cut out if the frame is 4 cm wide?

   b What is the area of the card surround?

7   What is the area of: a an A4 sheet of paper   b an A5 sheet of paper?

8   What area of card is used in making the photograph frame in question 6 of Exercise 20.1?.

9   What area is enclosed by the playpen in question 7 of Exercise 20.1?

10 A doctor's surgery is to have a new sink fitted. A rectangular hole, 40 cm by 30 cm. is cut out of a bench top measuring 160 cm by 60 cm.

    What area of bench top remains?

11 The hotel bedroom shown in question 10, Exercise 20.1, is to have a new fitted carpet.
    What area is to be carpeted?

12 Tarquin enjoys doing jigsaw puzzles. He buys the 1000 piece jigsaw and board mentioned in question 12, Exercise 20.1.

When he has completed the puzzle, what is the area of uncovered board surrounding the puzzle?

13 A window manufactured by a double-glazing firm requires 24 panes of glass, each measuring 26.5 cm by 21.5 cm.

What is the total area of glass in the window?

14 A factory produces rectangular steel plates which are 128 cm by 92 cm. The plates are marked with a line along each side, 2 cm in from the edge. Rivet holes are then drilled 4 cm apart along this line.

a What is the perimeter of the plate?

b What is the length of the line marked out for the rivets?

c How many rivets are needed for each plate?

d What is the area of the plate in square metres?

Area of triangle

Draw a rectangle ABCD and mark a point E anywhere along AB.
Join ED and EC.

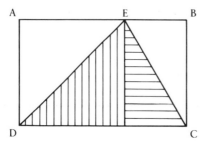

If triangles ADE and BCE are cut out, they can be placed on top of triangle DEC so that they exactly cover triangle DEC.

Area of triangle DEC = Half the area of rectangle ABCD
Area of rectangle ABCD = Length DC × Width BC
DC is the base of triangle DEC and BC equals its height.

Therefore: **Area of triangle DEC $= \frac{1}{2}$ Base $\times$ Height**

$$A = \tfrac{1}{2}\, b\, h$$

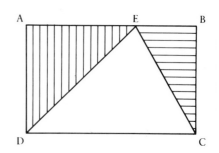

EXAMPLE 1

Show that the area of the triangle below is $\frac{1}{2}$ Base × Height.

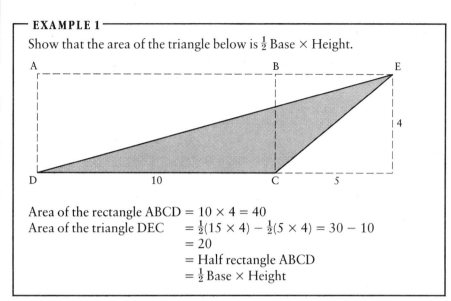

Area of the rectangle ABCD = $10 \times 4 = 40$
Area of the triangle DEC $= \frac{1}{2}(15 \times 4) - \frac{1}{2}(5 \times 4) = 30 - 10$
$= 20$
$=$ Half rectangle ABCD
$= \frac{1}{2}$ Base × Height

EXAMPLE 2

Find the area of the following:

a   **b**

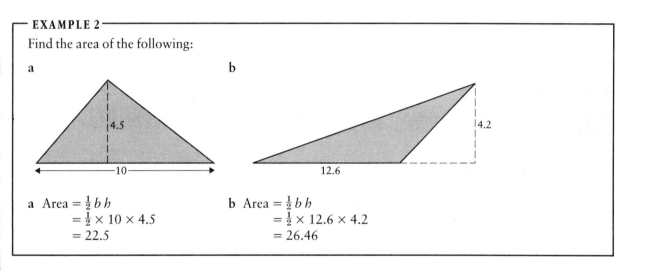

a   Area $= \frac{1}{2} b h$ **b**   Area $= \frac{1}{2} b h$
        $= \frac{1}{2} \times 10 \times 4.5$ $= \frac{1}{2} \times 12.6 \times 4.2$
        $= 22.5$ $= 26.46$

EXAMPLE 3

A triangle has an area of 35 cm^2 and a height of 4 cm.
What is the length of its base?

$$A = \tfrac{1}{2} b h \qquad or \qquad A = \tfrac{1}{2} b h$$

$$35 = \tfrac{1}{2} \times b \times 4 \qquad\qquad b = \frac{2A}{h}$$

$$= 2b \qquad\qquad\qquad = \frac{2 \times 35}{4} = 17.5$$

$$b = \frac{35}{2} = 17.5$$

Base $= 17.5$ cm   Base $= 17.5$ cm

EXERCISE 20.3

1 Find the areas of the following triangles:

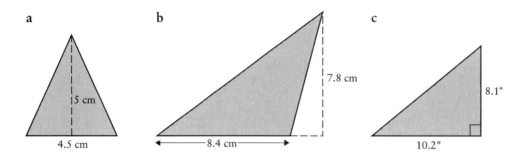

a

b

c

5 cm

4.5 cm

7.8 cm

8.4 cm

8.1″

10.2″

2 Find the area of a triangle with:

a Base = 16 cm, Height = 11 cm   **c** Base = 10.5 in, Height = 1 ft

b Base = 28 mm, Height = 17.5 mm   **d** Base = 4.6 m, Height = 8.4 m

3 **a** A triangle has an area of 40 m^2 and a height of 8 m.
       What is the length of its base?
     b A triangle has a base of length 12 cm and an area of 96 cm^2.
       What is its height?

4 Calculate the missing dimension in the following triangles:

a Area = 144 cm^2 Base = 18 cm   Height = ? cm

b Area = 52 cm^2 Base = ? cm   Height = 13 cm

c Area = 45 mm^2 Base = 7.5 mm   Height = ? mm

d Area = ? m^2 Base = 7.2 m   Height = 3.4 m

e Area = ? in^2 Base = 5.5 in   Height = 8.6 in

Area of a parallelogram

A parallelogram is a quadrilateral (four-sided figure) which has both pairs of opposite sides parallel.

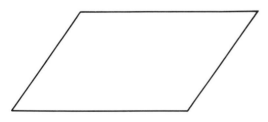

Any parallelogram can be divided into two identical triangles by drawing in a diagonal.

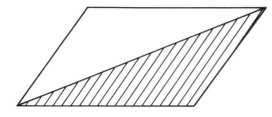

Area of the parallelogram = 2 × Area of one triangle

$$A = b \times h$$

EXAMPLE 1

Find the area of a parallelogram with base 12.5 cm and height 8.2 cm.

$$A = b \times h$$
$$= 12.5 \times 8.2 \, \text{cm}^2$$
$$\text{Area} = 102.5 \, \text{cm}^2$$

EXAMPLE 2

A parallelogram has a base of 14 cm and an area of 168 cm².
What is the height of the parallelogram?

$$A = b \times h \qquad or \qquad A = b\,h$$

$$168 = 14 \times h \qquad\qquad h = \frac{A}{b}$$

$$h = \frac{168}{14} = 12 \qquad\qquad h = \frac{168}{14} = 12$$

Height = 12 cm Height = 12 cm

EXERCISE 20.4

1 Find the areas of the following parallelograms:

  a Base = 10 cm   Height = 12 cm

  b Base = 12.6 cm   Height = 6 cm

  c Base = 34.7 in   Height = 13 in

  d Base = 1.3 m   Height = 26 cm

  e Base = 19.2 mm   Height = 10.3 cm.

2   Find the missing dimension for the following
    parallelograms:

   a Area = $24\,\text{cm}^2$ Base = ?   Height = $10\,\text{cm}$

   b Area = $1.3\,\text{m}^2$ Base = $3.9\,\text{m}$ Height = ?

   c Area = ?   Base = $8.4\,\text{cm}$ Height = $16\,\text{mm}$

   d Area = $0.68\,\text{m}^2$ Base = $17\,\text{cm}$ Height = ?

   e Area = $2.4\,\text{yd}^2$ Base = ?   Height = $3\,\text{ft.}$

3   Find the height of a parallelogram which has:

   a area $32\,\text{cm}^3$, base $4\,\text{cm}$ **c** area $42\,\text{in}^2$, base $8\,\text{in.}$

   b area $36\,\text{cm}^2$, base $9\,\text{cm}$

4   Find the base of a parallelogram which has:

   a area $70\,\text{cm}^2$, height $10\,\text{cm}$ **b** area $20\,\text{cm}^2$, height $11.1\,\text{cm.}$

Area of a trapezium

The area of a trapezium is:

$\dfrac{1}{2} \times$ **Sum of parallel sides $\times$ Perpendicular height**

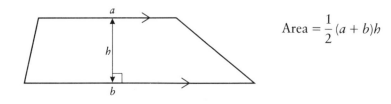

$$\text{Area} = \frac{1}{2}(a + b)h$$

EXAMPLE

Trapezium PQRS has PQ parallel to SR. PQ = $8\,\text{cm}$, SR = $13\,\text{cm}$, and the
perpendicular distance from S to PQ is $9\,\text{cm}$.

Find area PQRS.

$\text{Area} = \dfrac{1}{2}(13 + 8) \times 9$

$\qquad = \dfrac{1}{2} \times 21 \times 9$ (evaluate inside of
$\qquad\qquad\qquad$ bracket first)

$\qquad = 94.5\,\text{cm}^2$

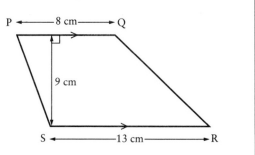

EXERCISE 20.5

1 Find the areas of the following trapeziums.

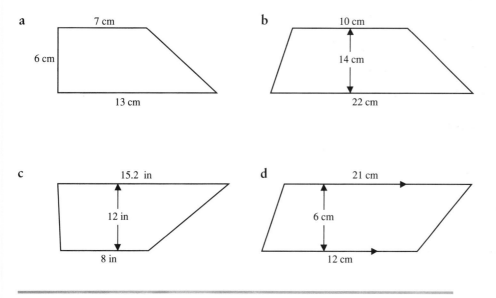

a 7 cm 6 cm 13 cm

b 10 cm 14 cm 22 cm

c 15.2 in 12 in 8 in

d 21 cm 6 cm 12 cm

EXERCISE 20.6

1 An architect designs a marble pediment to go above the door of a mansion house. The pediment is triangular in shape with a base length of 2.8 m. The height is a quarter of the length of the base.

What is the area of the pediment?

2 The design opposite is part of a mosaic floor, similar to one in the Grand Master's Palace in Rhodes.

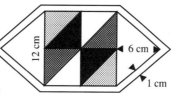

Calculate the area, excluding the surround, covered by each of the four different colours of tiles (shown by the different shading).

3 A building society's new branch has a floor plan as shown in the diagram on the left. The floor of the public area is to be carpeted.

What area of carpet is required?

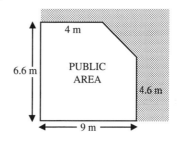

4 m

6.6 m PUBLIC AREA

4.6 m

9 m

4 A stationery business sells envelopes. The net of one of their envelopes is shown in the diagram. The shape is cut out of paper and is then folded along the dotted lines.

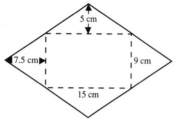

What area of paper is used for each envelope?

5 The tables at a day nursery have tops which are trapeziums, as shown in the diagram.

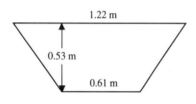

Two tables fit together to form a hexagon.

a What is the area of a single table top?

b What is the area of a hexagonal table top?

6 The same nursery, as in question 5, has a child's sand pit in the garden. The sand pit is 3 m long and 2.5 m wide and is surrounded by a path 0.5 m wide.

What is the area of the path?

7 A hotel lounge has a small stage built at one end for the dance band.

a The shape of the stage is a trapezium, as shown in the diagram. What is the area of the stage?

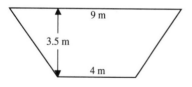

b In front of the stage is a dance floor which is 4 m square. Coffee tables and arm chairs are placed on the remaining floor area.

If the hotel lounge is 14 m by 10 m, what area is left on which the hotel can place tables and chairs?

8 The diagram below shows a design for flower beds to be planted out along the promenade of a seaside resort.

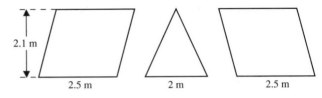

What is the total planting area?

9 Warning triangles are manufactured for a garage to the specifications shown.

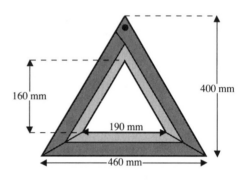

Calculate the surface area of the plastic in the triangle.

10 A carpenter makes a drop-leaf table in walnut. The centre of the table is a 1 m square and the two leaves are trapeziums, as shown in the diagram.

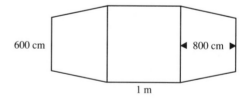

What is the total area of the table top?

20.3 *The circumference and area of a circle*

Circumference of a circle

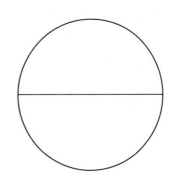

The **perimeter** of a circle is called the **circumference**.

Take a long piece of thread or thin string and cut off a piece equal to the length of the diameter of the circle on the right.

Cut off a second length equal to the length of the circumference. (You will need to take care when measuring the circumference.)

Compare the two lengths of thread and you should find that the longer piece is just over three times the length of the shorter piece. That is:

$$\text{Circumference} \approx 3 \times \text{Diameter}$$

This formula was good enough for the mathematicians of ancient times, but we now have an accurate value for this multiple of the diameter.

The multiple is given the symbol π, the Greek letter for 'p', pronounced 'pi'.

If you have a π button on your calculator, press it and you will see that $\pi = 3.141592654$.

In fact, the number goes on for ever, but 9 decimal places are adequate for most purposes!
For all circles:

$$\textbf{Circumference} = \pi \times \textbf{Diameter}$$

$$C = \pi d$$

or $$\textbf{Circumference} = 2 \times \pi \times \textbf{Radius}$$

$$C = 2\pi r$$

In calculations, you may use the 'pi' button or an appropriate approximation,

e.g. $\pi = 3$ for a rough estimate,
$\pi = 3.14$ for a more accurate answer.

You will usually be told in an examination which value of π to use.

EXAMPLE 1

Find the circumference of a circle with radius 6 cm. (Take $\pi = 3.14$.)

$$\text{Circumference} = 2 \times \pi \times r$$
$$= 2 \times 3.14 \times 6\,\text{cm}$$
$$= 37.68\,\text{cm}$$

EXAMPLE 2

A circle has a circumference of length 30 m. Find:

a a rough estimate of the diameter

b an estimate of the diameter, correct to 2 d.p.

a For a rough estimate take

$$C \approx 3 \times d$$

$$\therefore d \approx \frac{C}{3} = \frac{30}{3} = 10$$

The diameter is 10 m:

b $$C = \pi \times d$$

$$\therefore d = \frac{C}{\pi} = \frac{30}{3.14} \text{ or } \frac{30}{\pi}$$

and use the π button on your calculator.

The diameter = 9.55 m (to 2 d.p.).

Exercise 20.7

1 Use the π button on your calculator (or take $\pi = 3.14$) to calculate the missing lengths below. Give your answers correct to 1 d.p.

   a Diameter = 10 cm Radius = ? Circumference = ?

   b Diameter = ? Radius = ? Circumference = 27″

   c Diameter = ? Radius = 3.5 mm Circumference = ?

   d Diameter = ? Radius = ? Circumference = 51 cm

   e Diameter = ? Radius = ? Circumference = 6.12 m

2 The diameter of a £1 coin is 23 cm.
   What is the length of its circumference, correct to 2 d.p.?

3 The radius of a 1p coin is 5.5 mm.
   What is the length of its circumference in centimetres, correct to 2 d.p.?

4 The Doric columns of the Parthenon in Athens have a height of 35 ft, which is $5\frac{1}{2}$ times the diameter of the base.
   What is the circumference of the base of the column?

5 A circular clock face is designed so that the minute hand travels 48 cm in 1 hour and the hour hand travels 27 cm in 12 hours.
   What length should the designer make:

   a the minute hand

   b the hour hand?

6 An art shop sells posters which are rolled and packed into cardboard cylinders. The diameter of each cylinder is 7.2 cm.
What is the circumference of the cylinder?

7 A confectioner's decides to tie bows of ribbon around its speciality chocolates for Mother's Day. The chocolates are packed in round boxes which are sold in two sizes.

    a If an allowance of 40 cm is made for tying the bow, what length of ribbon is needed for the 16 cm diameter box? (Give your answer to the nearest cm.)

    b A 70 cm long ribbon (including 38 cm for the bow) is needed for the smaller box of chocolates. What is the diameter of the smaller box, to the nearest centimetre?

8 Amy cycles to keep fit. The wheel of her bicycle has a diameter of 672 mm.

    a What is the circumference of the wheel in centimetres?

    b How many metres has she travelled when the wheels have turned 50 times?

9 An exercise class uses hula hoops made from 290 cm of plastic tubing bent into a circle.

What is the diameter of a hoop, to the nearest centimetre?

10 Ecuador and Sumatra are on opposite sides of the world.
The radius of the Earth is 6370 km.

How far is it from Ecuador to Sumatra, travelling along the Equator?

11 A theme park has an aerial railway track around the perimeter of the park. Tourists can travel in carriages to various stations on the track. Sonia and Iain board a carriage at one station and get off at a station which is halfway round the perimeter. They have travelled a distance of 2.5 km.

How far would they have to walk between the stations, if they could walk straight across the theme park?

12 A rope works produces rope for ship-yards. One of their ropes is 8 cm thick. String is wrapped exactly 9 times around the end of the rope to prevent fraying.

    a What is the circumference of the rope?

    b What length of the string is required for the two ends of a rope?

13 The outer frame of a wrought iron gate requires 548.8 cm of wrought iron. The gate is 82 cm wide.

What is its overall height?

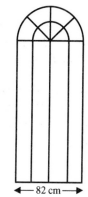

←— 82 cm —→

Area of a circle

A circle with radius l has an area $= \pi$

A circle with radius r has an area $= \pi \times r^2$.

For all circles:

$$A = \pi r^2$$

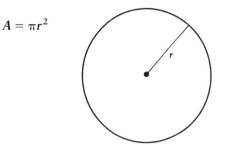

EXAMPLE 1

A circle is drawn which has a diameter of 6 cm.
What is the area of the circle?

$$\text{Diameter} = 6 \, \text{cm}$$
$$\text{Radius} = 3 \, \text{cm}$$
$$\text{Area} = \pi \times r^2$$
$$= \pi \times 3 \times 3 \, \text{cm}^2$$
$$= 28.3 \, \text{cm}^2 \text{ (to 3 s.f.)}$$

EXAMPLE 2

A circle has an area of 10 m².
What is the radius of the circle?

$$\text{Area} = \pi r^2$$
$$\pi \times r^2 = 10$$
$$r^2 = \frac{10}{\pi}$$
$$r = \sqrt{\frac{10}{\pi}} \qquad = 1.78 \, \text{m (to 3 s.f.)}$$

EXERCISE 20.8

1   Use the π button on your calculator, or take
    $\pi = 3.14$, to calculate the area of:

    a a circle of radius 7.1 cm

    b a circle of radius 29.5 in

    c a circle of diameter 13.6 mm

    d a semicircle of radius 4.9 cm

    e a semicircle of diameter 9.28 m

2   By taking an approximate value for π of 3,
    estimate the length of the radius of a circle with
    area:

    a 27 cm²   b 150 in²   c 108 cm²   d 48 m²
    e 300 ft²

3   Calculate the length of the radius, correct to 3 s.f.,
    for each of the circles in question 2 above.

4   A potter's wheel has a dimater of 30 cm or 12
    inches.
    What is the area of the top surface of the wheel:

    a in square centimetres

    b in square inches?

5 The pattern shown in the diagram was given to students in Babylonian times to calculate areas. Find the areas of each of the sections labelled **a**, **b** and **c**.

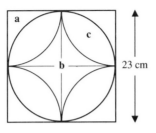

6 Mrs Conway runs a craft stall in the market. One of her lines is lavender bags, which she makes from circles of linen of radius 8 cm.

   a What is the area of each circle?

   b How many circles can Mrs Conway mark out across the width of a piece of linen if it is 122 cm wide?

7 A Young Enterprise Group at an FE college sets up a business making and selling circular drinks coasters which picture local scenes. Each coaster is made from a square of wood of area 56.25 cm^2.

   a What is the largest possible diameter of a coaster?

   b What is the largest possible area of a coaster?

8 A flower bed in a rest-home has a radius of 6 m.

   a What is its area?

   b If a rose needs an area of 3 m^2, approximately how many roses could be planted in the flower bed?

9 A circular table in a geriatric ward is to be recovered with green baize to make a card table. The diameter of the table is 1.5 m and the baize covering costs £6.20 per m^2.

   What is the cost of the baize covering, to the nearest pound?

10 What is the area of the theme park in question 11, Exercise 20.7, which is enclosed by the railway track?

11 A discotheque has a circular dance floor which covers 50 m^2.
   What is the diameter of the dance floor, correct to 1 d.p.?

12 A glass factory makes circular mirrors.
   What surface area has to be 'silvered' if a mirror has a diameter of 48 cm?

13 Mr Swain's firm makes fibre glass fish ponds. Each fish requires a surface area of 1000 cm^2.
   If a circular pond is intended to contain 10 fish, what is the smallest radius (correct to the nearest centimetre) that must be used for this pond?

20.4 *Volume*

Volume is a measure of the amount of space which is taken up by a solid shape.

Solids are three-dimensional shapes, i.e. they have length, breadth and height.

A **cube** is a solid with six square faces (or sides), hence the length, breadth and height of a cube are all equal.

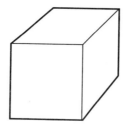

A cube which is 1 cm long, 1 cm wide and 1 cm high has a volume of 1 cubic centimetre (= $1\,cm^3$).

Similarly, the volume of a cube of side 1 metre is 1 cubic metre (= $1\,m^3$).

In imperial units the measures of volume are cubic feet, cubic inches, etc.

A **cuboid** is a solid with six rectangular faces.

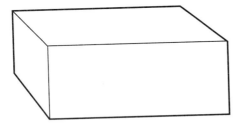

To find the volume of a cuboid we need to find out how many unit cubes it contains.

EXAMPLE

A cuboid which is 6 cm × 4 cm × 3 cm can be divided as shown:

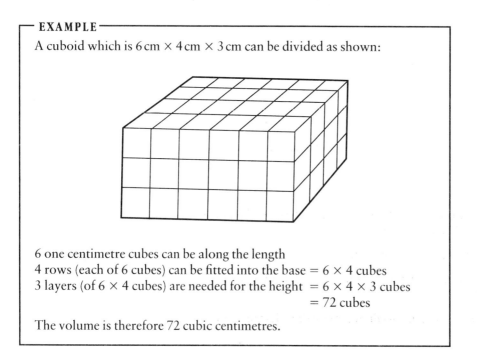

6 one centimetre cubes can be along the length
4 rows (each of 6 cubes) can be fitted into the base = 6 × 4 cubes
3 layers (of 6 × 4 cubes) are needed for the height = 6 × 4 × 3 cubes
                                                                              = 72 cubes

The volume is therefore 72 cubic centimetres.

Volume of a cuboid = Length × Breadth × Height

$$V = L \times B \times H$$

For a cube, *Length = Breadth = Height*, and

$$V = L^3$$

EXERCISE 20.9

1   Calculate the volume of the following cuboids:

   a Length = 6 cm   Breadth = 5 cm   Height = 3 cm

   b Length = 3.4 m   Breadth = 2.6 m   Height = 5.8 m

   c Length = 0.7 m   Breadth = 0.6 m   Height = 0.8 m

   d Length = 30 cm   Breadth = 22 cm   Height = 22 mm

   e Length = 2 m   Breadth = 60 cm   Height = 1 m

2   The base of a cuboid has an area of 12 cm². The volume of the cuboid is 40 cm³.
   What is the height of the cuboid?

3   Calculate the volume of a cube of side:

   a 8 cm   **b** 11 cm   **c** 4.1 cm

4   Enrico designs and makes statutary and garden ornaments. A plinth for a statue of Hermes is to be cuboid in shape and measure 56 cm × 60 cm × 66 cm.
   What volume of artificial stone mixture will be required for the plinth?

5   A stage set requires a collapsible wall to be made out of polystyrene blocks. Each block measures 42 cm × 28 cm × 10.5 cm and there are 80 blocks in the wall.
   What volume of polystyrene is needed to make the wall?

6   What volume of paper is contained in a full box made from the net shown?

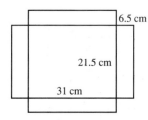

7   **a** Janine makes and decorates cakes for special occasions. Her largest tin is 40 cm square with a height of 9 cm.

     What volume of fruit cake would fill the tin?

   b The next two sizes of cake tin are 32 cm square by 7 cm high and 24 cm square by 6 cm high.

     What volume of cake is there in a wedding cake using all three cake tins?

8   A child at a day nursery has 27 wooden blocks, each a cube of edge 1 inch. She builds one large cube using all the blocks.

   a What is the volume of the large cube?

   b What is the length of an edge of the large cube?

9   Boxes of toilet rolls are ordered in bulk by the Sundowners Rest Home. Each box measures 46 cm by 23 cm by 24 cm.

   How much storage space would be taken up by one dozen boxes?

10 A hotel in the tropics regularly sprays its rooms to kill mosquitos. Half a fluid ounce of anti-mosquito liquid, when diluted, sprays a volume of $15 \, \text{m}^3$.

   How many fluid ounces of liquid are required to spray a room $7 \, \text{m} \times 5.5 \, \text{m} \times 3 \, \text{m}$?

11 A dining room in an hotel in Spain is air-conditioned. The dining room is 32 m by 18 m by 3.8 m high. The air needs to be changed every 20 minutes.

   What volume of air per minute does the air conditioning unit supply?

12 Delicate dental equipment is packed into boxes full of polystyrene beads for protection. The boxes are 40 cm by 15 cm by 12 cm, and the dental equipment occupies a volume of $3500 \, \text{cm}^3$.

   What volume of polystyrene is needed for each box?

13 A microwave is manufactured with an oven capacity of 0.8 cubic feet. The oven is 16 inches wide and 8 inches high.

   What is the depth of the oven?

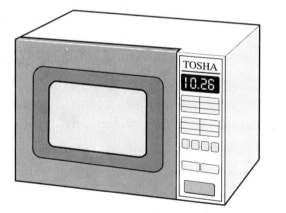

Volume of a prism

A **prism** is a solid which has a constant cross-section (i.e. the cross-section of the top is exactly the same as the cross-section of the base).

Some common prisms are:

(i) a **cylinder** (with a cross-section which is a circle)

(ii) a **triangular prism**

(iii) a **rectangular prism** or cuboid

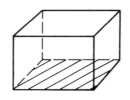

For a prism:

Volume = Area of cross-section × Height

For a cylinder:

Volume = Area of circle × Height

$$V = \pi r^2 h$$

EXAMPLE 1

A Toblerone packet is a triangular prism.
The triangular cross-section has an area of 2.25 cm^2 and the length of the packet is 16.8 cm.
What is the volume of the Toblerone packet?

Volume = Area of cross-section × Length

$= 2.25 \, \text{cm}^2 \times 16.8 \, \text{cm}$

$= 37.8 \, \text{cm}^3$

EXAMPLE 2

Find the volume of a cylinder with a base radius of 3.5 cm and a height of 8 cm.

Volume of cylinder = Area of base × Height

$= \pi r^2 h$

$= \pi \times 3.5 \times 3.5 \times 8 \, \text{cm}^3$

$= 307.9 \, \text{cm}^3$

EXAMPLE 3

Find the volume of a block of wood of length 12 cm which has a constant cross-section as shown in the diagram.

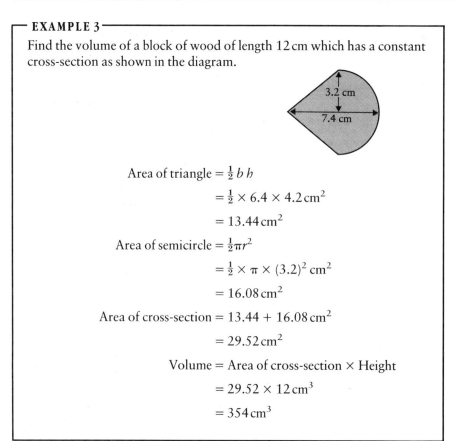

$$\text{Area of triangle} = \tfrac{1}{2}\,b\,h$$
$$= \tfrac{1}{2} \times 6.4 \times 4.2 \,\text{cm}^2$$
$$= 13.44 \,\text{cm}^2$$
$$\text{Area of semicircle} = \tfrac{1}{2}\pi r^2$$
$$= \tfrac{1}{2} \times \pi \times (3.2)^2 \,\text{cm}^2$$
$$= 16.08 \,\text{cm}^2$$
$$\text{Area of cross-section} = 13.44 + 16.08 \,\text{cm}^2$$
$$= 29.52 \,\text{cm}^2$$
$$\text{Volume} = \text{Area of cross-section} \times \text{Height}$$
$$= 29.52 \times 12 \,\text{cm}^3$$
$$= 354 \,\text{cm}^3$$

EXERCISE 20.10

1 Calculate the volume of a cylinder with:

    a Radius = 4 cm   Height = 12 cm
    b Radius = 9 cm   Height = 12 cm
    c Diameter = 14 in   Height = 11 in
    d Diameter = 8.4 cm   Length = 7 cm.

2 Find the volume of the following solids which have a length as given and a uniform cross-section as shown in the diagram.

    a Length = 15 cm   **b** Length = 5 cm   **c** Length = 10.5 cm

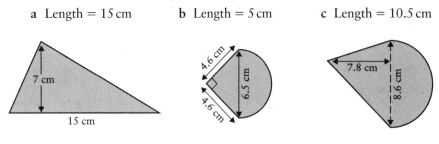

3 A greenhouse is 10 m long and has a cross-section which is a square of side 5 m on top of which is a triangle, as shown in the diagram.

The overall height of the greenhouse is 7.5 m.
Calculate the volume of air inside the greenhouse.

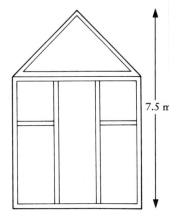

4 A tunnel is excavated from a hillside. The length of the tunnel is 300 m and its cross-section is as shown:

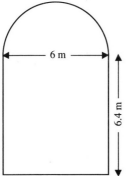

Calculate the volume of earth which is removed to make the tunnel.

5 A glassblower makes triangular prisms of crystal for chandeliers.
Each prism has a cross-section as shown in the diagram and a length of 9 cm.

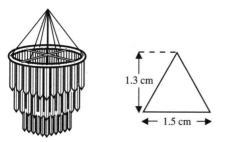

a Calculate the volume of glass in one crystal.

b Calculate the total volume of glass required for a chandelier with 54 crystals.

6 Clay pots for the garden have an internal diameter of 30 cm and an internal height of 28 cm.

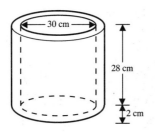

a What volume of soil will a pot hold?

The thickness of the clay is 2 cm.

b What is the external diameter of a pot?

c What is the external height of a pot?

d Find the external volume and hence the volume of clay used in making the pot.

7 Mrs Andrews has a small business making and selling home-made food. The home-made soup is sold in $\frac{1}{2}$ litre (500 cc) tins.

Mrs Andrews decides to change the shape of the tin while keeping the capacity the same.

a She decides on a height of 12 cm.
What diameter should she order for the new tins?

b She decides to have another tin which is broader than its height and orders a diameter of 12 cm.
What height should the new tin be?

8 A firm makes wedge-shaped foam cushions, as shown in the diagram. These are designed to relieve back pain and are particularly useful for people who have to sit for long periods of time, such as office workers or people travelling.

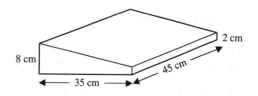

What volume of foam is used in each cushion?

9 A house needs to be adapted for wheelchair access.
Concrete ramps are to be built outside the front and back door, as shown.

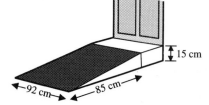

a What is the volume of one ramp?

b What volume of concrete is required for the ramps?

10 A pharmacist stocks oxygen cylinders for customers who have breathing problems. The shape of the container is a cylinder on top of which is a hemisphere. The overall height of a container is 120 cm and the diameter is 20 cm.
The volume of a hemisphere is given by $V = \frac{2}{3}\pi r^3$, where r is the radius of the hemisphere.

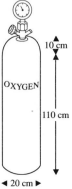

a Calculate the volume of the hemisphere.

b Calculate the volume of the cylindrical section.

c What is the total volume of the container?

d What is the capacity of an oxygen cylinder? ($1000 \text{ cm}^3 = 1$ litre.)

11 A small mountain tent has the dimensions shown in the diagram.

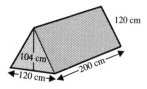

a Calculate the volume of the space inside the tent.

b Calculate the area of canvas used in making the tent, including the base.

12 A charter air company gives canvas flight bags to its business-class customers.

The bags are cylindrical in shape, as shown in the diagram. They have a length of 60 cm and a diameter of 30 cm.

a Calculate the capacity of a bag to the nearest 100 cm^3.

b What is the bag's capacity to the nearest 0.01 m^3?

13 A firm manufacturers two sizes of cocoa tin. The height of the larger tin is 10 cm and its diameter is 4.46 cm.

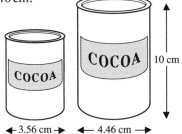

a What is the volume of the tin?

The smaller tin has a diameter of 3.56 cm and a volume of 79.6 cm^3.

b What is the height of the smaller tin to the nearest cm?

14 A section of metal pipe has an outer diameter of 5 cm and the metal is 3 mm thick. The section of pipe is 18 cm long.

a What is the internal diameter of the pipe, in cm?

b What is the area of metal in the cross-section of the pipe?

c What volume of metal was used in making this section of pipe?

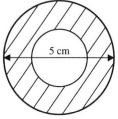

21 *Time and Travel Graphs*

21.1 *Distance –time graphs with straight lines*

Graphs which connect distance and time are called distance–time graphs.

Graphs which connect velocity and time are called velocity–time graphs.

EXAMPLE

One Sunday at 12 o'clock, a family set out for a picnic at a well-known beauty spot, 25 miles from their home.

They travelled at a steady speed and arrived at their destination at 12.45 pm.

After $3\frac{1}{4}$ hours at the picnic spot they set off for home.

Unfortunately the traffic was very heavy and they only managed to average 20 mph.

The family's day can be represented by a 'travel graph' which measures distance from home along the vertical axis and time along the horizontal axis.

The vertical axis is scaled from 0 to 25 miles and the horizontal axis from 12 noon to 6.00 pm.

At 12 noon they were at 0 miles (home) and at 12.45 pm they were at 25 miles (the picnic spot). These two points are plotted and the line joining them represents the family's outward journey.

For $3\frac{1}{4}$ hours they are not travelling and this is represented by a horizontal line from 12.45 pm to 4.00 pm, 25 miles from home.

If their average speed on the return journey was 20 mph then after 1 hour they were 5 miles from home.

The point (5.00, 5) is plotted and a line is drawn through it to meet the horizontal axis.

The graph is shown in the column opposite.

They arrived home in time for their favourite programme.

Find:

a the time at which they arrived home

b at what times they were 10 miles from home

c their average speed on the outward journey.

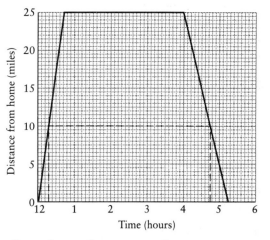

From the graph we can see that:

a they arrived home at 5.15 pm.

b on the outward journey they were 10 miles from home after 0.3 hours, i.e. at 12.18 pm; on the homeward journey they were 10 miles from home after 4.75 hours, i.e. at 4.45 pm.

c Their average speed on the outward journey is given by

$$\text{Average speed} = \frac{\text{Total distance}}{\text{Total time}} = \frac{25 \text{ miles}}{45 \text{ mins}}$$

$$= \frac{25 \text{ miles}}{0.75 \text{ hours}}$$

$$= 33.3 \text{ mph}$$

EXERCISE 21.1

1   Nessa is invited to stay with her French agent in Nice. Below is Nessa's
    itinerary for travelling from Calais to Nice along the A6 and a map
    showing the distances involved.

Distance in kilometres

Arrive Calais	1400	Continental time
Arrive Paris	1700	Dinner stop
Depart Paris	1800	
Arrive Valance	0400	Refreshment stop
Depart Valance	0430	
Arrive Nice	0800	

Draw a travel graph of Nessa's journey and use
it to calculate the average speeds, to the nearest km/h,
for the three sections of the journey:

a   Calais to Paris,   b   Paris to Valance,
c   Valance to Nice.

2   The graph below represents Mr Phillip's journey to work one morning. The
    first 10 miles of his journey is through a built-up area and then he joins the
    motorway. Unfortunately, there has been an accident and he is held up for
    some time. He leaves the motorway at the next exit and completes his
    journey on the ordinary roads.

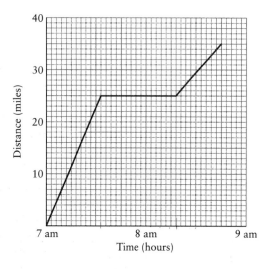

a   How long did the journey through the built-up area take him?

b   What was his average speed on the motorway section of the journey,
    until he had to stop?

c   For how long was he held up?

d   At what time did he arrive at work?

e   How far did he travel from home to work?

f   What was his average speed for the whole journey?

3 Barry and Ali have been told to cycle to keep fit.

a They live 5 miles apart and decide to meet at a barn 2 miles from Barry's house. His friend, Ali, leaves home at 9.00 am and cycles at a steady speed of 12 mph. Barry does not leave until 10 minutes later. He arrives at the barn 10 minutes after Ali.

Draw a graph to represent their journeys.
 (i) When did each man arrive at the barn?
 (ii) At what speed did Barry cycle?

b On another occasion they decide that they will keep cycling towards each other until they meet.
Ali leaves home at 9.30 am and Barry leaves at 9.35 am, both cycling at 12 mph.

Draw a graph to find:
 (i) at what time they meet,
 (ii) how far each man will have travelled.

4 Draw a graph to represent the following journey:

Susan left home at 10.00 am and drove to her friend Valerie's house, 15 minutes away, for coffee. Her average speed was 32 mph. The two friends chatted for 45 minutes and then Susan drove her friend to the local leisure centre, 2 miles away, arriving at 11.12 am. They spent 1 hour 24 minutes swimming. Then Susan drove home, dropping Valerie off on the way. Her average speed for the return journey was 25 mph.

a How far did she drive to her friend's house?

b At what time did they leave Valerie's house?

c At what time did Susan arrive home?

5 Roy delivers spare parts to garages in his area.

a Roy made three deliveries.
 (i) How long did his longest delivery take?
 (ii) How long did his shortest delivery take?

b Give a possible explanation for his third stop.

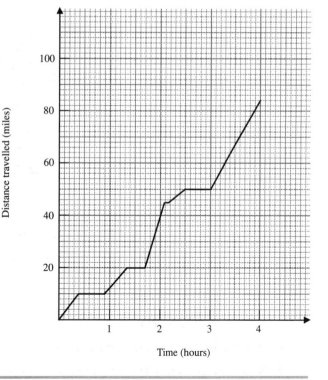

*21.2 Distance–time graphs with curves

A straight-line graph has a constant gradient, but if the graph is a curve, the gradient is continually changing.

For the function

$$s = 25t + 3t^2$$

which connects distance s with time t,

the distance s is changing at different rates at different times.

The gradient, which is $\dfrac{\text{Distance travelled}}{\text{Time taken}}$, gives the **average** rate of change of

distance over the given time interval, i.e. the average speed or average velocity.

At a particular instant, the rate of change of distance, i.e. the **speed or velocity**, is given by the gradient of the curve at that point in time.

The **gradient of a curve** at a given point is the **gradient of the tangent** drawn to the curve at that point.

EXAMPLE

A car is braking for traffic lights. The lights change to green when the car's speed is 4 m/s. The driver accelerates and, during the next 6 seconds, the distance travelled, s metres, after a time t seconds, is given by the formula:

$$s = 4t + t^2$$

a Draw up a table of values to show the distance travelled by the car in the first 6 seconds.

b Draw the graph of s against t.

c Find the average speed of the car during the third and fourth seconds.

d By drawing a tangent to the graph, find the speed of the car after 2 seconds.

a

t	0	1	2	3	4	5	6
s	0	5	12	21	32	45	60

b See opposite.

c Average speed $= \dfrac{\text{Distance travelled}}{\text{Time taken}}$

$\phantom{\text{Average speed}} = \dfrac{32 - 12}{2}$ from the graph

$\phantom{\text{Average speed}} = 10\,\text{m/s}$

d Speed after 2 s = Gradient of the tangent at $t = 2$

$\phantom{\text{Speed after 2 s}} = \dfrac{36 - 12}{5 - 2} = \dfrac{24}{3}$

$\phantom{\text{Speed after 2 s}} = 8\,\text{m/s}$

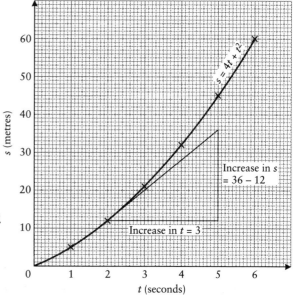

EXERCISE 21.2

1 A cyclist rounds a corner and sees a tree across the road. He brakes and the distance travelled, *s* metres, in the next *t* seconds is given by

$$s = 6t - t^2$$

  a Draw the distance–time graph for values of *t* from 0 to 3 seconds.

  b What is the gradient of the curve at $t = 3$?

  c How far does the cyclist travel after he starts braking?

  d By drawing a tangent to the curve, find the speed of the cyclist immediately before he started to brake.

2 **a** Draw the graph of $y = 2x^2 + 3x - 1$ for $-3 \leqslant x \leqslant 2$.

  b By drawing appropriate lines to the graph, find the gradient of the curve at:
  (i) $x = -2.5$, (ii) $x = 1.25$.

3 A train entering a station reduces its speed so that the distance, *s* metres, covered in time *t* seconds, is given by

$$s = 36t - \tfrac{1}{4}t^2$$

  a Draw the graph of *s* against *t* for $0 \leqslant t \leqslant 40$.

  b By drawing an appropriate line on the graph, find the speed after 30 seconds.

4 **a** Draw the graph of *y* against *x* for the function

$$y = 3x^2 + 5x + 2$$

  taking values of *x* from -4 to $+4$.

  b Find the gradient of the curve at the points where:
  (i) $x = -3$, (ii) $x = 2\tfrac{1}{2}$.

5 A stain is spreading in such a way that the area, $A\,\mathrm{cm}^2$, of the stain after *t* seconds is given by

$$A = \tfrac{1}{2}t^2 + 3t + 12$$

  a Draw up a table of values for *A* against *t* when $t = 0, 2, 4, 6, 8, 10$.

  b Draw the graph of *A* against *t*.

  c Find the amount by which the area increased during the third second.

  d By drawing a suitable line on the graph, find the rate of increase of *A* when $t = 5$.

6 A stone is catapulted vertically upwards and its height, *h* metres, after time *t* seconds, is given by

$$h = 20t - 5t^2$$

  a Plot the graph of *h* against *t* for values of *t* from 0 to 4 seconds.

  b Use the graph to find:
  (i) the maximum height to which the stone rises
  (ii) the times when the stone is at a height of 12 m.

  c By drawing an appropriate line on the graph, find the speed of the stone after:
  (i) 1 second, (ii) 2.5 seconds.

*21.3 *Velocity–time graphs*

For the function $v = 25 + 6t$,
the velocity (*v* metres per second) changes for various times (*t* seconds).
The gradient, which is

$$\frac{\text{Change in velocity}}{\text{Time taken}},$$

gives the average rate of change of velocity over a given time interval, i.e. the acceleration.

Note. Velocity, v metres per second, may be written as v m/s (or v m s^{-1}).
Acceleration is the change in velocity per second and has units of metres per
second per second, which may be written as m/s^2 or m s^{-2}.
At a particular instant, the rate of change of velocity, i.e. the acceleration, is
given by the gradient of the curve at that point in time.

The **area** under the curve shows the product of the velocity and time. Since

Velocity × Time = Distance

the distance travelled is the area under the graph.

EXAMPLE 1

The velocity–time graph shows a cyclist travelling at 6m/s for 10 seconds.
The distance travelled is found by use of the formula:

Distance = Velocity × Time

∴ Distance = 6×10 m
$\qquad\qquad = 60$ m

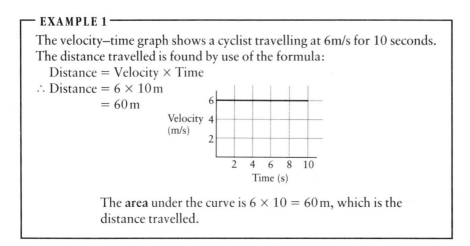

The **area** under the curve is $6 \times 10 = 60$ m, which is the
distance travelled.

EXAMPLE 2

The velocity of a lorry (v m/s) is given by:

$v = 10 + 0.9t$

between times $t = 0$ and $t = 10$ seconds.
Find:

a the acceleration after 3 seconds

b the distance travelled in the first 5 seconds

c the distance travelled in the fourth second.

It is often helpful to draw a velocity–time graph before you start on the
question. This graph is shown below:

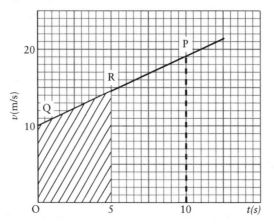

a The graph shows that the velocity is changing during the ten seconds. There is no time when the velocity is constant. Since the line is straight the gradient of the graph is a constant, i.e. the acceleration is constant. Hence the acceleration is the same of all points between P and Q.

$$\text{Acceleration} = \frac{\text{Change in velocity (between P and Q)}}{\text{Change in time (between P and Q)}}$$

$$= \frac{19 - 10}{10}$$

$$= 9/10$$

$$= 0.9 \text{ m/s}^2$$

b Distance travelled in the first 5 seconds is area OQRS
$$= \frac{1}{2} \times 5 \times (10 + 14.5) \text{ (i.e. the area of a trapezium, see}$$
p. 230)

$$= 61.25 \text{ m}$$

c Distance travelled in the fourth second

$$= \text{Distance travelled between } t = 3 \text{ and } t = 4$$

$$= \tfrac{1}{2} \times 1 \times (12.7 + 13.6)$$

$$= 13.15 \text{ m}$$

EXERCISE 21.3

1 The velocity v m/s of a car is given by $v = 15 + 1.3t$ for values of t from 0 to 20, where t is the time in seconds.
Find:

a the acceleration when $t = 3$

b the distance travelled in the first 5 seconds

c the distance travelled in the third second i.e. from $t = 2$ to $t = 3$.

2 The velocity of a parachutist before she pulls the ripcord is v m/s, where v is given by $v = 0.1 + 7t$. She pulls the ripcord when her velocity is 28 m/s.
Find:

a the time t when she pulls the ripcord

b the distance she falls before she pulls the ripcord

c the acceleration before she pulls the ripcord.

3 **a** The velocity of a waterskier, v m/s, is given by $v = 8 + 0.6t$ for time from $t = 0$ to $t = 15$ seconds.

Find:
  (i) his acceleration
  (ii) the distance travelled between $t = 5$ and $t = 15$.

b He lets go of the rope after 15 seconds, and his velocity changes to $v = 17 - 4T$ until he stops (T is the time, in seconds, from when he lets go of the rope).
Find the distance until he stops.

4 The velocity of a Tour de France cyclist in kilometres per hour descending an Alpine pass is given by:
$$v = 30 + 180t$$

where t is the time in hours.
The cyclist reaches 48 kph before he brakes for a corner.
Find:

a the time taken until he starts braking

b the distance travelled before he starts braking.

EXAMPLE

The velocity of a car is given by $v = 7 + 0.2t^2$ between the time $t = 0$ and $t = 10$.

Draw the velocity–time graph and use it to find:

a the acceleration after 5 seconds.

b the distance travelled between $t = 2$ seconds and $t = 6$ seconds.

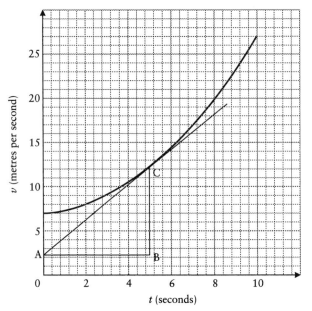

Because the graph is a curve, it is not possible, without using A-level Mathematics, to find the exact values of the acceleration or the distance. To find the acceleration, a tangent must be drawn where $t = 5$, to obtain the gradient of the curve at that point.

Using triangle ABC, gradient is $10/5 = 2$.

To find the distance travelled, it is necessary to estimate the area under the curve between $t = 2$ and $t = 6$.
Carefully counting the squares, noting how part of two small squares can give a whole square:
this area is   3 large squares and 119 small squares.
i.e.   4.19 large squares.
One large square is 2 units horizontally and 5 units vertically, and hence is $2 \times 5 = 10$ metres.
∴ The distance travelled in this time interval is 41.9 metres.

EXERCISE 21.4

1 The velocity of a motor bike v m/s is given by $v = 12 + 0.6t^2$.
Draw a graph of v against t for values of t from 0 to 6 where t is the time in seconds.
Find:

a the acceleration when $t = 4$

b the distance travelled in the first 2 seconds

c the distance travelled in the fourth second (i.e. from $t = 3$ to $t = 4$).

2 A car driver sees a sign 'Warning: Stop Sign Ahead'. He starts braking and his speed in m/s is given by $v = 39 - 6t$ until he stops.
Draw a graph of v against t for $0 \leqslant t \leqslant 3$.
Find:

a his retardation

b the distance travelled until he stops

c the speed when he is halfway to the stop sign.

(*Note*. When the acceleration is negative it is called 'retardation'.)

3 The velocity of a car v m/s is given by $v = 15 + 0.4t^2$.
Draw a graph for values of t from 0 to 10.
Find:

a the acceleration when $t = 6$

b the distance travelled in the first 3 seconds

c the distance travelled in the fifth second (i.e. from $t = 4$ to $t = 5$).

4 The velocity of a lorry v m/s starting from rest is given by $v = 0.7t + 0.6t^2$
Draw a graph for values of t from 0 to 10.
Find:

a the acceleration when $t = 5$

b the distance travelled in the first 10 seconds.

*21.4 *Growth and decay*

Another type of function which is connected with time is a growth (or decay) function. Examples of growing functions are bacteria and rabbit populations, the value of an antique car or work of art, compound interests.

A decaying, or shrinking, function becomes smaller as time passes. Examples are: the value of a car that is not antique, the radioactivity of some substances, the value of factory machinery, and the population of an endangered species.

Functions that are getting smaller are said to **depreciate**; functions that are getting larger **appreciate**.

EXAMPLE

The number of bacteria in a piece of cheese doubles every hour.
Assuming there are 100 bacteria present at the beginning, draw a graph to show the number present over the next 6 hours and find:

a the number of bacteria after $2\frac{1}{4}$ hours

b the rate of growth after $4\frac{1}{4}$ hours.

The table of values for time t and number of bacteria n is:

t	0	1	2	3	4	5
n	100	200	400	800	1600	3200

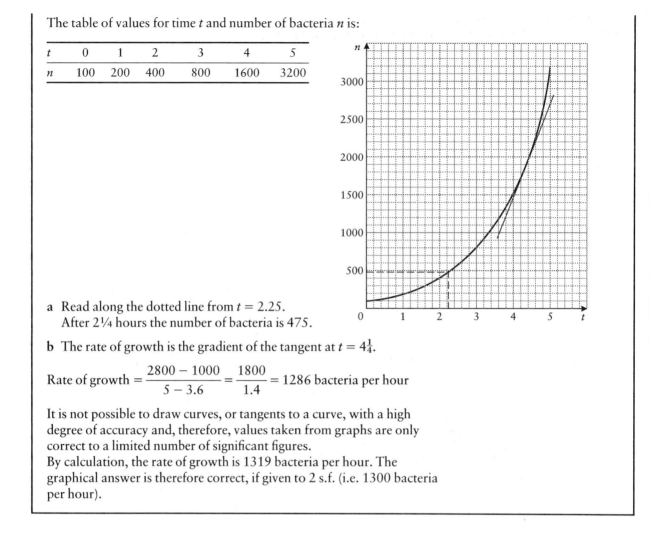

a Read along the dotted line from $t = 2.25$.
After 2¼ hours the number of bacteria is 475.

b The rate of growth is the gradient of the tangent at $t = 4\frac{1}{4}$.

$$\text{Rate of growth} = \frac{2800 - 1000}{5 - 3.6} = \frac{1800}{1.4} = 1286 \text{ bacteria per hour}$$

It is not possible to draw curves, or tangents to a curve, with a high degree of accuracy and, therefore, values taken from graphs are only correct to a limited number of significant figures.
By calculation, the rate of growth is 1319 bacteria per hour. The graphical answer is therefore correct, if given to 2 s.f. (i.e. 1300 bacteria per hour).

EXERCISE 21.5

1 The spread of moss in a lawn is represented on the graph below.

a What area of lawn was covered by moss at the beginning?

b After how long had the area of moss doubled?

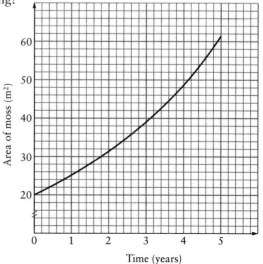

2 A radioactive substance has a *half-life* of one day. This means that at the end of each day the mass of the substance remaining radioactive is half the mass at the beginning of that day.

   a If the mass at the beginning of day 1 was 200 g, draw up a table to show the mass over the following 6 days.

   b Draw the graph of mass against time and find after how long the mass is 70 g.

3 Sasha and Elizabeth buy an antique painting for £1000. They expect its value to increase by 5% per year. They draw a graph to show their estimate of its expected value.

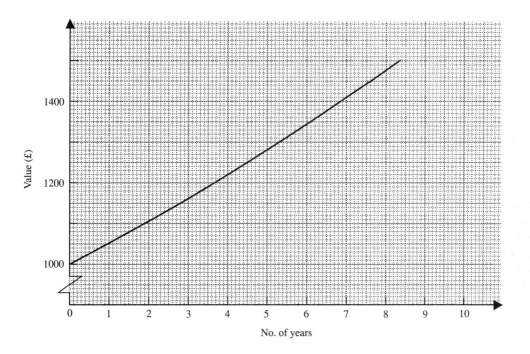

No. of years

Find:

   a the value which Sasha and Elizabeth expect their painting to be worth after 6 years

   b the rate of increase in the painting's value after 5 years.

4 A sum of £1000 was invested in a building society. The amount of money in the account at the end of each of the following 6 years is shown on the graph.

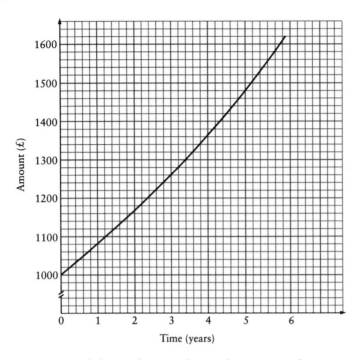

a If no money is withdrawn, how much is in the account after:
   (i) 2½ years   (ii) 5 years?

b Is the rate of growth increasing or decreasing? Give a reason for your answer.

5 A tube containing an isotope of radon is implanted in a patient and emits alpha rays. The radon has a half-life of 4 days and is implanted for 8 days. The graph shows the mass of radon during the 8-day period.

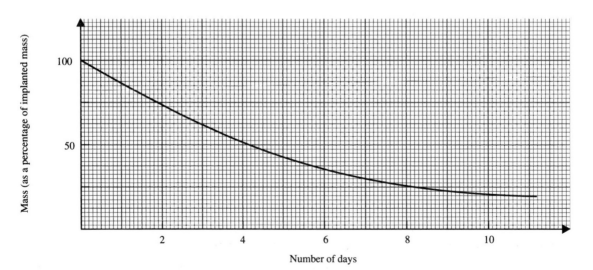

Find:

a (i) the mass of radon remaining after 8 days
  (ii) the mass of radon remaining after 3 days

b the rate of decay after 6 days.

6 A company depreciates the value of a CNC lathe every year. Using the reducing balance method, the company gives the value of the lathe at the end of each year.

Time (years)	0	1	2	3	4	5
Value (£)	5000	4000	3200	2560	2048	1638

a Draw the graph of value V against time t.

b What is the value of the lathe (to the nearest £10) after 2½ years?

c What is the rate of depreciation after: (i) 1 year, (ii) 5 years?

7 Zoë is a scientist checking the ages of artefacts by carbon-dating.
This is based upon the presence of carbon-14, which has a half-life of 5730 years. The presence of carbon-14 is 0.02% in any living item and it starts decaying on death.
The graph below shows the presence of carbon against time.

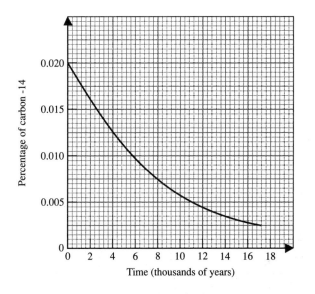

Find:

a the age of a Sumerian sailboat with 0.012% carbon-14

b the rate of decay of carbon after 10 000 years.

c The Chalcolithic period was from 4000 – 3150 BC. What percentage of carbon-14 would you expect to find in any artefact from this period?

22 *Further Algebra*

22.1 Simultaneous equations

Eddie has just bought a new pen and his friend Pete would also like one, but Eddie can't remember how much it cost. He does remember that he bought the pen and a ruler for £2.20.

Writing this information in algebra gives:

$$p + r = 220$$

This does not help Pete to work out the cost of the pen as there are too many values of p and r which would fit the equation.

Fiona then remembers that she bought two of the same type of pen and a ruler for £3.50.

Pete can now work out the cost of the pen:

$$p + r = 220$$
$$\text{and} \qquad 2p + r = 350$$

The extra pen which Fiona bought must have cost $(350 - 220)$ pence, i.e. 130 pence.

Therefore the pen cost £1.30 and the ruler 90 pence.

If an equation has two unknown values (variables), it cannot be solved on its own.

Two variables require **two** equations which are solved at the same time, i.e. **simultaneously**.

Three variables would require three simultaneous equations, etc.

To solve a pair of simultaneous equations the method of **elimination** is used.

Solving simultaneous equations

EXAMPLE 1

Solve the equations: $4x + 3y = 24 \qquad (1)$
$\qquad\qquad\qquad\quad 2x + 3y = 18 \qquad (2)$

The only difference between the left-hand sides of the two equations is that equation (1) has $2x$ more, which must be balanced by the extra 6 on the right-hand side.

Subtracting equation (2) from equation (1) gives:

$$-\begin{array}{r} 4x + 3y = 24 \\ 2x + 3y = 18 \\ \hline 2x \quad\;\; = 6 \\ \therefore x = 3 \end{array}$$

The value of y can be found by substituting the value of x into one of the equations.

Substitute $x = 3$ into (2):
$$\begin{array}{r} 2 \times 3 + 3y = 18 \\ 6 + 3y = 18 \\ 3y = 12 \\ y = 4 \end{array}$$

The solution is $x = 3$, $y = 4$.

(This solution can be checked using the other equation:

Substitute $x = 3$, $y = 4$ into equation (1)
LHS = $4 \times 3 + 3 \times 4 = 12 + 12 = 24 =$ RHS
So the solution is correct.)

EXAMPLE 2

Solve the equations $3x - y = 11$ (1)
$$2x + y = 9 \quad (2)$$

The number of ys in each equation is the same, except for the sign, so, in this case y is eliminated by *adding* the two equations.

Adding equation (1) to equation (2) gives:

$$+\begin{array}{r} 3x - y = 11 \\ 2x + y = 9 \\ \hline 5x \quad\;\; = 20 \\ \therefore \quad x = 4 \end{array}$$

Substituting $x = 4$ into (2):
$$\begin{array}{r} 2 \times 4 + y = 9 \\ 8 + y = 9 \\ y = 1 \end{array}$$

The solution is $x = 4$, $y = 1$.

(To check, substitute $x = 4$, $y = 1$ into (1).)

EXAMPLE 3

Solve the equations $3x + 4y = 18$ (1)

$$4x - 3y = -1 \quad (2)$$

Neither x nor y has the same coefficient in each equation, so this needs to be remedied first.

Method	Working
(i) Decide which variable is to be eliminated.	Eliminate y.
(ii) Multiply one or both equations so that this variable has the same coefficient in each equation (not counting the signs).	Multiply equation (1) by 3 and equation (2) by 4 $9x + 12y = 54$ $16x - 12y = -4$
(iii) Add or subtract the equations, depending on the signs of the variable to be eliminated.	As the coefficients of y have opposite signs, add the equations: $+ \begin{array}{r} 9x + 12y = 54 \\ 16x - 12y = -4 \\ \hline 25x = 50 \end{array}$
(iv) Solve for the remaining variable.	$x = 2$
(v) Substitute into one of the original equations to find the eliminated variable and hence the complete solution.	Substitute $x = 2$ into (1) $3 \times 2 + 4y = 18$ $4y = 12$ $y = 3$ Solution is $x = 2$, $y = 3$
(vi) Substitute into the other original equation to check the solution.	Substitute into (2) LHS $= 4 \times 2 - 3 \times 3$ $= 8 - 9$ $= -1 = $ RHS

EXERCISE 22.1

Solve the following pairs of simultaneous equations and check your solutions:

1. $2x + y = 8$
     $x + y = 6$

2. $x + 3y = 12$
     $x + y = 10$

3. $x + y = 12$
     $x - y = 2$

4. $3x - 2y = 9$
     $x + 2y = 15$

5. $x + 3y = 6$
     $2x + y = 7$

6. $4x + 2y = 10$
     $3x + 5y = 11$

7. $3x + 2y = 18$
     $4x - y = 2$

8. $2x - 3y = 10$
     $3x + 4y = 15$

9. $x - y = -1$
     $2x + 3y = 28$

10. $7x + y = 9$
     $3x + y = -3$

11. $2x + 5y = 15\frac{1}{2}$
     $3x - 4y = -5\frac{1}{2}$

12. $6x + 5y = -17$
     $3x + 2y = -8$

Solving problems

> **EXAMPLE**
>
> An ice cream seller charges a customer £3.20 for three ice cream cornets and two choc-ices.
> The next customer is charged £4.50 for four ice cream cornets and three choc-ices.
> What are the prices of the ice cream cornet and the choc-ice?
>
> Let x pence be the cost of an ice cream cornet
> and y pence be the cost of a choc-ice.
>
> | Then | $3x + 2y = 320$ | (1) |
> | and | $4x + 3y = 450$ | (2) |
>
> Eliminate y:
> | Multiply (1) by 3: | $9x + 6y = 960$ | (3) |
> | Multiply (2) by 2: | $8x + 6y = 900$ | (4) |
>
> Subtract (4) from (3): $\qquad\qquad x = \;60$
>
> Substituting $x = 60$ in (1): $3 \times 60 + 2y = 320$
> $$2y = 140$$
> $$y = \;70$$
>
> An ice cream cornet costs 60p and a choc-ice costs 70p.
>
> (Check by substituting $x = 60$ and $y = 70$ in (2).)

EXERCISE 22.2

1   The cost of 3 tubes of paint and 2 palettes is £6. The cost of 5 tubes of paint and 2 palettes is £9.12.

   Find the cost of one tube of paint and the cost of a palette.

2   A potter makes two types of ware. Type A takes $\frac{1}{2}$ hour to make and sells for £3 each. Type B takes 1 hour to make and sells for £5 each.

   One day he worked for 8 hours and sold the pottery he made for £45.

   How many of each type did he make?

3   Sally is employed by a secretarial agency to be a temp. She is hired by a firm to do 6 hours work at basic rate and 1 hour of overtime. She is paid £58 gross (i.e. before deductions).

   For another firm, she works 5 hours at basic pay and 2 hours overtime. Her gross pay is £60.

   What is her basic hourly rate of pay and what is her overtime rate of pay?

4   For Mother's Day, a cosmetics business advertises a presentation box of 3 soaps and 2 bubble baths for £4.60.

   A de luxe presentation box of 5 soaps and 4 bubble baths costs £8.

   Find the costs of one soap and one bubble bath.

5   A 100 ml bottle of cough medicine is sufficient for 4 adults and 8 children or 6 adults and 2 children.

   What are the dosages for adults and for children?

6   One family claims child benefit for 3 children. The total amount claimed is £26.20.

   Another family claims child benefit for 4 children. The total amount claimed is £34.30.

   Let x be the amount of child benefit for the first child and y be the amount of benefit for subsequent children.
   Find x and y.

7 A holiday for 2 adults and 3 children costs £748. The same holiday for 3 adults and 4 children costs £1056.

What would be the cost of the holiday for 2 adults and 2 children?

8 The difference in price between an airline's economy and club class fares, on one particular flight, is £350.

A couple exchange one club class ticket for two economy class tickets and receive a refund of £100.

Find the costs of economy class and club class fares.

9 The perimeter of a section of chipboard is 690 cm.

The difference between the length and the width is 55 cm.

a Find the length and width of the chipboard.

b Find the area of the chipboard.

10 When the temperature of a steel bar is increased by 20°C, its expanded length is 507.2 mm.

Let l mm be the original length of the bar and e mm be the expansion rate of steel per degree rise in temperature. Then

$$l + 20e = 507.2$$

When the temperature of a steel bar which is twice as long as the first one is increased by 30°C, its expanded length is 1010.8 mm.

a Write down an equation in l and e.

b Solve the two equations to find the original lengths of the bars and their expansion rate.

Graphical solution

Simultaneous equations can also be solved by a graphical method.

The graphs of the two equations are drawn and the solution to the equations is the coordinates of the point of intersection of the graphs since these values of x and y will satisfy both equations.

(For the method of plotting straight-line graphs see p. 202.)

─ **EXAMPLE** ─

Solve, graphically, the equations
$x + 2y = 8$
$3x + 4y = 18$

To draw the lines, use the points where $x = 0$ and $y = 0$.

For $x + 2y = 8$ the points are $(0, 4)$ and $(8, 0)$
For $3x + 4y = 18$ the points are $(0, 4\frac{1}{2})$ and $(6, 0)$

The axes are now drawn and scaled and the points plotted and joined.

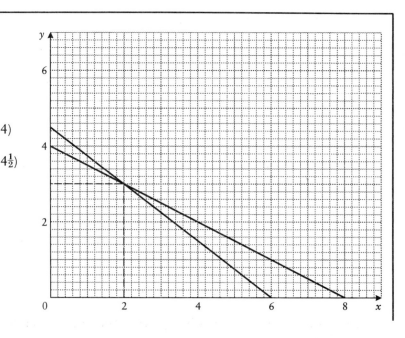

The graphs intersect at the point $(2, 3)$.

Substitute $x = 2$, $y = 3$ into equation (1): LHS $= 2 + 2 \times 3 = 8 =$ RHS
Substitute $x = 2$, $y = 3$ into equation (2): LHS $= 3 \times 2 + 4 \times 3 = 6 + 12$
$$= 18 = \text{RHS}$$

The solution to the equations is therefore $x = 2$, $y = 3$.

EXERCISE 22.3

Solve the following equations by the graphical method:

1 $\quad x + y = 5$	**3** $\quad 4x + 5y = 40$	**5** $\quad 2x + 5y = 15$	**7** $\quad y = 3x + 5$	**9** $\quad y = 6 - 2x$
$\quad 3x + 2y = 12$	$\quad x - y = 1$	$\quad 2x - y = 3$	$\quad 2y = 5x + 9$	$\quad 3y + 4x = 10$
2 $\quad x - 2y = 1$	**4** $\quad 3x - 2y = 0$	**6** $\quad x + 3y = 11$	**8** $\quad y = 7x$	
$\quad x + y = 4$	$\quad 3x + 4y = 18$	$\quad 2x + y = 7$	$\quad 2y = 5x - 9$	

10   Solve graphically the questions in Exercise 22.2.

*22.2 *Inequalities*

An **equation** is a mathematical relationship which is balanced, i.e. what is on the left-hand side of the equation is always equal to what is on the right-hand side.

In many situations, the relationship is not one of equality. In an **inequality** one side is larger than the other.

Examples of inequalities are:

1   The average woman's height is 'less than' the average man's height:

$$\text{Height of average woman} < \text{Height of average man}$$

2   On a cumulative frequency graph, the median is 'greater than' the lower quartile:

$$\text{Median} > \text{Lower quartile}$$

3   In order to win a game a player must throw at least a score of four, i.e. the score on the die must be 'equal to or greater than' four:

$$\text{Score} \geqslant 4$$

4   The number of people standing on the bus should be no more than six, i.e. the number standing should be 'less than or equal to' six:

$$\text{Number standing} \leqslant 6$$

Statements such as those above may be represented on a number line by a **range** of values.

EXAMPLE 1

Represent the inequality $x \leqslant 3$ on a number line.

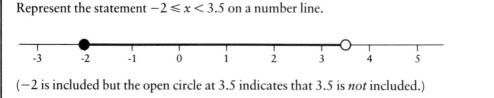

(The 'blob' on 3 indicates that 3 is included.)

EXAMPLE 2

Represent the statement $-2 \leqslant x < 3.5$ on a number line.

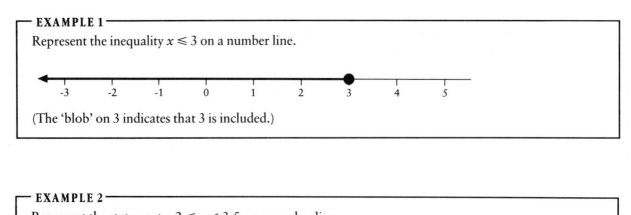

(-2 is included but the open circle at 3.5 indicates that 3.5 is *not* included.)

EXAMPLE 3

A salesman expects to earn between £200 and £300 in commission during a six day week.

a Taking x as the daily amount of commission, write down an inequality which represents the above statement.

b Solve the inequality to find the expected daily commission.

a The inequality is $200 < 6x < 300$

b The expected daily commission is $\dfrac{200}{6} < x < \dfrac{300}{6}$

i.e. $33.34 < x < 50$

Note $33.\overset{.}{3}$ must be rounded up to 33.4 as x must be *more* than this amount.

EXERCISE 22.4

1 Illustrate the following statements on a number line:

   a $x < 5$ **c** $-3 < x < 3$ **e** $-1 < x \leqslant 4$ **g** $x < 5, x > 6$

   b $x \geqslant 0$ **d** $-3 \leqslant x \leqslant 3$ **f** $-7 \leqslant x < -2$ **h** $x < -3, x \geqslant 3$

2 Write down the inequalities which are illustrated on the following number lines.

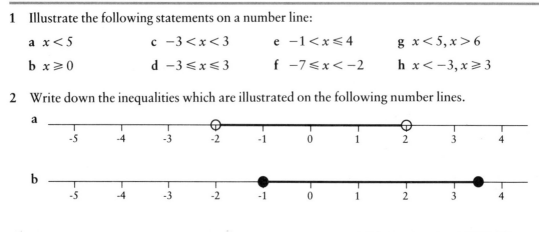

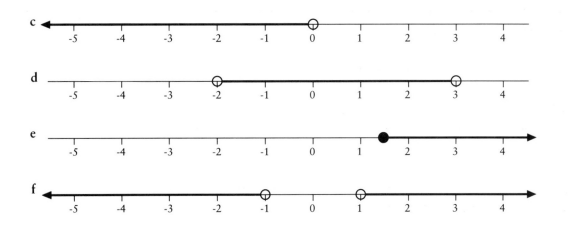

3 The number of beads required to make a necklace is at least 35.

   a Write down an inequality which describes this statement.

   b Write down an inequality for the number of beads needed for 5 necklaces.

4 To buy five new paint brushes will cost an artist between £1 and £6.60, depending on quality.

   a Write down an inequality describing this statement.

   b What is the price range for one brush?

5 An office requires three new mobile telephones and cannot afford to spend more than £540.

   a Write this statement as an inequality.

   b Solve the inequality to find the maximum cost of one machine.

6 A shop estimates that they need one basket for every 20 customers.

   The number of customers per day is between 500 and 780. If x is the number of baskets needed,

   a write this statement as an inequality

   b solve the inequality to find values of x.

7 In a school for children with special needs each assistant helps with 4 children. The time available for the children is up to 5 hours per day. If c is the time for one child,

   a write this statement as in inequality

   b find the maximum time the assistant can spend with one child.

8 A physiotherapist estimates that the number of patients treated in one six-day week is more than 180, but less than 280. Let n be the number treated per day and

   a write this statement as an inequality

   b find the number which could be treated in one day.

9 A family with four children spend a day at a theme park. The parents decide that the children must spend not more than £30 on rides.

   a Write this statement as an inequality.

   b What is the allowance per child?

10 A courier estimates that the number of complaints received during a two-week holiday will be at least 10 but not more than 30.

   a Write down an inequality to describe this statement.

   b How many complaints can the courier expect: (i) per week, (ii) per day?

11 A team of four employees checks products on a conveyor belt for faults. The team is expected to check at least 750 items per hour.

   Write down inequalities for the number of items expected to be checked by:

   a the team of four employees

   b one employee.

12 One type of plywood (five-ply) is made by bonding together five thin layers of wood.

The total thickness of the plywood should be between 10 mm and 14 mm, inclusive. Write down an inequality for the thickness of:

a the five layers,

b one layer of single ply.

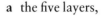

*Solving inequalities

Some of the rules for solving equations can also be used for solving inequalities:

EXAMPLE 1

Solve **a** $x - 5 = 9$ **b** $x - 5 \geqslant 9$

a Adding 5 to each side gives $x = 14$.

b Similarly, adding 5 to each side gives $x \geqslant 14$.

EXAMPLE 2

Solve **a** $x + 5 = 3$ **b** $x + 5 < 3$

a Subtracting 5 from each side gives $x = 2$.

b Similarly, subtracting 5 from each side gives $x < -2$.

EXAMPLE 3

Solve **a** $4x = 15$ **b** $4x > 15$

a Dividing each side by 4 gives $x = 3\frac{3}{4}$.

b Similarly, dividing each side by 4 gives $x > 3\frac{3}{4}$.

EXAMPLE 4

Solve **a** $\dfrac{x}{4} = 20$ **b** $\dfrac{x}{4} \leqslant 20$

a Multiplying each side by 4 gives $x = 80$.

b Similarly, multiplying each side by 4 gives $x \leqslant 80$.

But there are some rules for solving equations which, when applied to inequalities, change the sign:

1 Interchanging the two sides of the equation:

  e.g.   if $x = y$ then $y = x$

  but   if $x < y$ then $y > x$ (e.g. $2 < 3$ but $3 > 2$)

2 Multiplying (or dividing) by a negative number:

  e.g.   if $-x = -4$ then $x = 4$

  but   if $-x > -4$ then $x < 4$ (e.g. $-5 < -4$ but $5 > 4$)

Remember, when solving inequalities you may:

- add any number to both sides
- subtract any number from both sides
- multiply or divide both sides by any positive number
- multiply or divide both sides by any negative number and change the inequality sign.

EXERCISE 22.5

1 Solve the following inequalities:

  a $4x < 12$ c $3x + 2 \leqslant 11$ e $2x - 7 \geqslant 10$

  b $x + 2 > 9$ d $x - 7 \geqslant 10$ f $7 - 2x < 3$

2 A student buys a sketch pad and some pencils. The sketch pad costs £2.52 and pencils cost 62p each. Let x be the number of pencils bought.

  a Write down an expression for the total cost of pad and pencils.

  The student has saved £5.00.

  b Write down an inequality in x.

  c Solve the inequality to find the values of x.

3 Omar specialises in tooled leather work. He decorates, among other items, cases for spectacles and sunglasses. To make a case, he requires twice the length of the spectacles plus 3″ for the flap. Let x be the length of the spectacles.

  a Write down an expression in terms of x for the length of leather needed for one case.

  The pieces of leather which Omar has cut to make the cases vary in length from 21″ to 35″.

  b Write down two inequalities in x.

  c Solve the inequalities to find the lengths of the smallest and largest pairs of spectacles which will fit the cases.

4 Tonia is stocktaking. There are only five packs of computer disks left in stock so more need to be ordered. Tonia knows that there should be at least 20 packs in stock. Let x be the number of packs ordered.

  a Form an inequality in x for the total number of packs in stock.

  b Solve the inequality to find the values of x.

5 A small office is to be re-equipped. An area of $55\,m^2$ is needed for the new office equipment, photocopier, filing cabinets etc. Working space is also needed for three clerical staff who each have desks.

  Let $x\,m^2$ be the space allowed for each employee.

  a Write down an expression for the total area of office spaced needed.

  The total area of office space available is $90\,m^2$.

  b Write down an inequality and solve it to find the maximum space allowable for each member of staff.

6   Frances has been prescribed some pain killers by the doctor. The dose is 3 tablets x times per day.

   a Write down an expression for the total number of tablets taken per day.

The total number of tablets taken in one day should not exceed 8.

   b Form an inequality and solve it to find x.

7   A day centre allocates £500 to buy Zimmer frames and a manual wheelchair.

The number of Zimmer frames bought is x and they cost £35 each.

   a How much money remains?

At least £300 will be needed for the wheelchair.

   b Write down an inequality in x, and solve it to find the number of Zimmer frames which could have been bought.

8   Four friends are planning a holiday. They have £240 saved towards it.

Let £x be the amount they each have to save to pay for the holiday.

   a Write down an expression for the total cost of the holiday, in terms of x.

The holiday will cost at least £600.

   b Write down, and solve, an inequality in x to find the least amount they each must save.

9   Don travels on holiday to France. He wishes to buy several bottles of perfume for presents.

The perfumes each weigh 200 grams and his suitcase, when packed, weighs 23 kg.

Let x be the number of bottles of perfume bought.

   a Write down an expression, in terms of x, for the total weight of case and perfume.

Don does not wish to exceed the weight allowance for luggage, which is 25 kg.

   b Write down an inequality and solve it to find the maximum number of bottles of perfume Don can pack in his case.

10   When products, such as chemicals or food stuffs, are 'packed off' at the end of the production process, there is a difference in the weight of the ingredients at the beginning of the process and the total weight of the product packed off at the end of the process.

The *yield* is the weight which is packed off as a percentage of the initial weight.

A firm manufactures drinking chocolate which is sold in tins containing 250 g.

The firm decides that the yield must be at least $99\frac{1}{4}$%.

   a If the ingredients for a batch of drinking chocolate are weighed in at 100 kg, what is the minimum weight which must be packed into the tins?

Let x be the number of tins filled by this batch of drinking chocolate.

   b Write down an inequality, in terms of x, for the total weight in the tins.

   c Solve the inequality to find the minimum number of tins of drinking chocolate which must be produced from 100 kg of the product.

*22.3 *Removing brackets*

To multiply out a bracket in an expression of the form $2x(x + 3)$

each term in the bracket must be multiplied by $2x$, i.e. $2x(x + 3) = 2x^2 + 6x$

To multiply out a bracket in an expression of the form $(2x + 4)(x + 3)$

each term in the second bracket is multiplied by $2x$ and by 4, i.e.

$$(2x + 4)(x + 3) = 2x(x + 3) + 4(x + 3)$$
$$= 2x^2 + 6x + 4x + 12$$

Collecting like terms gives $(2x + 4)(x + 3) = 2x^2 + 10x + 12$

EXAMPLE 1

Multiply $(3x - 2)$ by $(2x + 1)$

$$(3x - 2)(2x + 1) = 3x(2x + 1) - 2(2x + 1)$$
$$= 6x^2 + 3x - 4x - 2$$
$$= 6x^2 - x - 2$$

Brackets of this type can be removed without the intermediate stages being shown if the following stages of working are carried out mentally and only the answer is written down.

To expand $(2x + 4)(x + 3)$:

The final answer will have three terms, i.e. an x^2, an x and a constant term.

The x^2 term is calculated by multiplying the x term in the first bracket by the x term in the second bracket:

$$(2x + 4)\,(x + 3) \longrightarrow 2x^2$$

The x term is calculated by multiplying the x term in one bracket by the constant term in the other bracket and adding the two resultant terms.

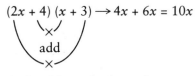

$$(2x + 4)\,(x + 3) \longrightarrow 4x + 6x = 10x$$

The constant term is calculated by multiplying the constant term in the first bracket by the constant term in the second bracket.

$$(2x + 4)\,(x + 3) \longrightarrow 12$$
$$\therefore (2x + 4)\,(x + 3) = 2x^2 + 10x + 12$$

EXAMPLE 2

Expand $(3x - 4)(2x - 3)$

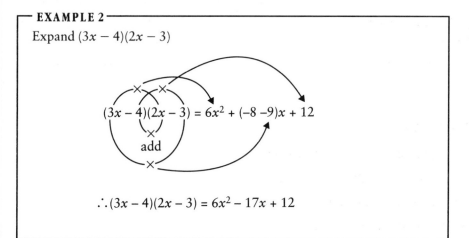

$$(3x - 4)(2x - 3) = 6x^2 + (-8\ -9)x + 12$$

$$\therefore (3x - 4)(2x - 3) = 6x^2 - 17x + 12$$

EXERCISE 22.6

Remove the brackets from the following:

1 $(x + 3)(x + 4)$ 6 $(x - 3)(x - 7)$ 11 $(2x + 5)(2x - 5)$

2 $(x + 2)(x - 1)$ 7 $(x + 1)(x - 2)$ 12 $(3x - 4)(3x + 4)$

3 $(x - 5)(x - 3)$ 8 $(x - 6)(x - 2)$ 13 $(x + 2)(x + 2)$

4 $(x + 1)(x + 4)$ 9 $(x + 3)(x - 3)$ 14 $(x - 1)(x - 1)$

5 $(x + 4)(x - 2)$ 10 $(x + 1)(x - 1)$ 15 $(3x + 1)(3x + 1)$

EXERCISE 22.7

1 The diagram shows a picture x cm square, mounted on a rectangular piece of card. The borders at the top and bottom are 1 cm wide and the borders at the sides are 2 cm wide.
   Write down an express in terms of x for:

   a the width of the mount

   b the height of the mount

   c the area of the mount.

   d Expand the brackets to give the area as a quadratic.

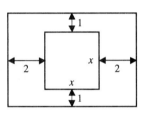

2 A box is made by cutting squares of side x cm out of the corners of a rectangle 10 cm by 12 cm, as shown in the diagram. The sides are then folded up along the dotted lines.

   a What is the length of the box, in terms of x?

   b What is the width of the box, in terms of x?

   c What is the area of the base of the box?

   d Expand the brackets to give the base area as a quadratic.

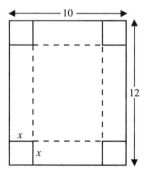

3 A hospital consulting room has a screen along the length which divides off an area 2 m wide. The remaining area is twice as long as it is wide.

   The screen is moved so that it is now across the width of the room dividing off an area 3 m wide.

   For the remaining part of the room, write down, in terms of x:

   a its length   b its width   c its area.
   d Expand the brackets.

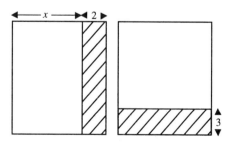

4 A motel increases the number of beds in some of its rooms to sleep one extra person. At the same time, a £3 reduction is made on the cost per person.

If a room used to sleep x persons and the cost was $10x$:

a write down in terms of x, the number of persons a room now accommodates

b write down, in terms of x, the cost per person

c write down an expression for the total cost of a room and expand the brackets.

5   During the recession a small manufacturing company had to reduce its workforce by $2x$. At the same time, the remaining work force was expected to increase productivity by x.

If previously the workforce was 10 and production was 6 items per person:

a what is the size of the new workforce,

b what is the new number of items made per person?

c What is the production rate for the workforce?

d Expand the brackets.

22.4 Rearranging formulae

The formula which converts degrees Fahrenheit to degrees Celsius is

$$C = \frac{5}{9}(F - 32)$$

It may, however, be necessary to convert degrees Celsius to degrees Fahrenheit. In this case, the formula needs to be **rearranged**, or **transposed**, to give F in terms of C, i.e. F is made the subject of the formula.

EXAMPLE 1

a Rearrange the formula $C = \frac{5}{9}(F - 32)$ to give F in terms of C.

b Use the transposed formula to convert 15°C to °F.

a The method is the same as for solving equations.

$$C = \frac{5}{9}(F - 32)$$

(i)	Multiply through by 9:	$9C = 5(F - 32)$
(ii)	Remove the bracket:	$9C = 5F - 160$
(iii)	Transpose 160:	$9C + 160 = 5F$
(iv)	Dividing through by 5 gives the formula for F:	$F = \dfrac{9C + 160}{5}$

b When $C = 15$

$$F = \frac{9 \times 15 + 160}{5}$$

$$= \frac{135 + 160}{5}$$

$$= \frac{295}{5}$$

$$= 59$$

$$\left(Check. \quad C = \frac{5}{9}(F - 32) \quad = \frac{5}{9}(59 - 32) = \frac{5}{9} \times 27 = 15 \right)$$

EXAMPLE 2

The profit ($£P$) made when an article is sold for a price $£S$ with a percentage profit of $x\%$, can be calculated from the formula:

$$P = \frac{Sx}{100 + x}$$

a Find P when $x = 12$ and $S = 392$.

b Rearrange the formula to make x the subject.

c Find the percentage profit if a profit of £33 is made when an article is sold for £253.

a

$$P = \frac{392 \times 12}{100 + 12} = \frac{4704}{112} = £42$$

b

$$P = \frac{Sx}{100 + x}$$

(i) Deal with the fraction by multiplying each side by $(100 + x)$:

$$P(100 + x) = Sx$$

(ii) Multiply out the bracket:

$$100P + Px = Sx$$

(iii) Collect x terms on one side, other terms on the opposite side (in this case, it is easier to collect x terms on RHS to avoid a negative sign for $100P$):

$$100P = Sx - Px$$

(iv) Take out a common factor of x:

$$100P = x(S - P)$$

(v) Divide each side by $(S - P)$ to find the value of x:

$$\frac{100P}{S - P} = x$$

---

c $P = £33,\quad S = £253$

$$\text{Profit \%} = x = \frac{100P}{S - P} = \frac{100 \times 33}{253 - 33} = 15\%$$

EXERCISE 22.8

1 A silversmith makes jewellery by setting stones into silver. The stone are surrounded by a bezel of silver as shown:

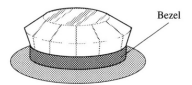

Bezel

The length of the bezel (L) is the circumference of the stone (C) plus one and a half times the thickness of the silver (T),

i.e. $L = C + 1\frac{1}{2}T$

or $L = \pi D + 1\frac{1}{2}T$

where D is the diameter of the stone.

a Find the length of the bezel needed for a stone of diameter 8 mm using silver of thickness 0.6 mm.

b Rearrange the equation to give T in terms of L and C.

c An oval stone has a circumference of 30.35 mm and a bezel length of 30.47 mm.
What was the thickness of the silver used?

2 The number of mosaic tiles, 1 cm square, needed to surround rectangular mirrors with dimensions x cm by y cm, is

$$N = 2(x + y) + 4$$

a How many tiles are needed for a mirror which is 14 cm by 20 cm?

Glass for a mirror is 30 cm wide and there are 170 tiles left.

b Rearrange the formula to give y in terms of N and x.

c Use your formula to find the length of glass which should be cut to use up all the tiles.

The craftsman decides to make some of the mirrors square.

d Adapt the original formula and find the number of tiles needed for a mirror which is 30 cm square.

e Rearrange the formula to give x in terms of N.

f What should the dimensions of a mirror be if there are 150 tiles available for the surround?

3 The total cost $£T$ of legal action is given

by $T = 1200b + 350s + 50c$

where b is the number of days a barrister is used, s is the number of days a solicitor is used and c is the number of days a clerk is used.

a Find the total cost if the barrister works for 4 days, the solicitor works for 10 days and the clerk works for 28 days.

b (i) Rearrange the formula to find the number of days the barrister works in terms of s, c and T.
(ii) If $T = 3950$, $s = 3$ and $c = 10$, find b.

c (i) Rearrange the formula to find the number of days the clerk works in terms of b, s and T.
(ii) If the total cost was £10 900, the barrister worked for 5 days, and the solicitor worked for 11 days, for how many days was the clerk employed?

4 The return on capital employed (ROCE) is calculated using the formula:

$$\text{ROCE} = \frac{\text{Net profit}}{\text{Capital}} \times 100$$

$$\text{or } R = \frac{P}{C} \times 100$$

a What is the return if $P = £2520$ and $C = £8000$?

b Rearrange the formula to P in terms of R and C.

c What was the net profit if $C = £6500$ and $R = 26\%$?

5 The cardiac output C, of a person is given by

$$C = HS$$

where C is the heartbeat rate and S the volume of each stroke.

Sally is an athlete. When at rest, she has a heartbeat of 35 beats per minute and a stroke volume of $130\,cm^3$.

a Find Sally's cardiac output.

b (i) Rearrange the formula to find Sally's heartbeat rate in terms of C and S.

Sally's friend, Gillian, is not an athlete, but she has the same cardiac output as Sally.

(ii) Find Gillian's heartbeat rate if her stroke volume is $60\,cm^3$.

6 Every chocolate bar I eat will be a gain of 230 calories. If I then walk briskly, I will lose 6 calories per minute.

The excess calories which I have eaten are given by:

$$c = 230b - 6t$$

where c is the number of calories, b is the number of chocolate bars, and t is the time in minutes.

a Calculate the excess number of calories if I eat two chocolate bars and then walk briskly for 20 minutes.

b Rearrange the formula to give t in terms of c and b.

c If I eat three chocolate bars, for how long will I need to walk to use up all the extra calories?

7 Naismith's rule for hill walking is to allow 1 hour for every 4 km walked plus 1 minute for every 10 m climbed.

The formula is:

$$t = \frac{d}{4} + \frac{h}{600}$$

where t is the time in hours, d is the distance walked in kilometres and h is the height climbed in metres.

a Calculate the time which should be allowed for a walk which covers a distance of 8 km and a climb of 900 m.

b Rearrange the formula to give d in terms of T and h.

c Find an estimate for the distance walked if the time taken was 6 hours and the height climbed was 1050 m.

8 The deposit required when hiring a self-catering apartment is 10% of the cost per person hiring the apartment plus a charge of £50, which is returnable if no damage is caused, i.e.

$$D = \frac{CN}{10} + 50$$

where D is the deposit, C is the cost per person and N is the number of people hiring the apartment.

a Calculate the deposit for 4 people on a holiday which costs £220 per person.

b Rearrange the formula to give N in terms of C and D.

c How many people occupy an apartment on a holiday costing £180 per person if the deposit is £158?

9 The power, P watts, of a battery source, is given by:

$$P = V^2/R$$

where V volts is the voltage and R ohms is the resistance.

a Find P when $V = 240$ and $R = 70$.

b (i) Rearrange the formula to find R in terms of V and P.
(ii) Find the resistance when the voltage is 240 volts and the power is 3000 watts.

c (i) Rearrange the formula to find V in terms of P and R.
(ii) Find the voltage when the power is 2000 watts and the resistance is 90 ohms.

Art & Design
ASSIGNMENTS

Numeracy Core Skills Matrix

Element	Range	Assignments											
		1	2	3	4	5	6	7	8	9	10	11	12
3.1	1	✓				✓							
3.1	2			✓		✓							
3.1	3	✓	✓	✓		✓		✓					
3.1	4			✓		✓							
3.1	5			✓		✓							
†3.1	6			✓		✓							
3.2	1	✓	✓	✓	✓	✓	✓	✓	✓	✓		✓	✓
3.2	2	✓	✓	✓	✓	✓	✓	✓	✓	✓		✓	✓
3.2	3	✓	✓	✓	✓	✓	✓	✓		✓			
3.2	4	✓			✓	✓			✓	✓	✓		
3.2	5	✓	✓				✓	✓	✓			✓	
3.2	6				✓						✓		
3.2	7	✓	✓				✓	✓	✓			✓	
3.2	8	✓	✓		✓	✓	✓	✓	✓	✓			✓
3.2	9		✓		✓	✓		✓	✓				✓
3.2	10	✓	✓				✓						
†3.2	11		✓										
†3.2	12	✓					✓						✓
†3.2	13	✓	✓				✓						✓
3.3	1	✓	✓			✓	✓	✓	✓				✓
3.3	2			✓		✓							
3.3	3					✓							
3.3	4	✓	✓	✓	✓	✓	✓	✓	✓				✓
3.3	5	✓	✓				✓		✓				
3.3	6				✓				✓				
†3.3	7				✓				✓			✓	

† denotes element required only at GNVQ Level 3. All other elements are required at GNVQ Level 2.

Assignment **AD1**

The size of its contents and the fragility of the article will often dictate the actual dimensions of a 'container', which will usually be derived from some basic shape such as a cuboid, cylinder, pyramid, etc. The following questions relate to various packaging problems and available design space.

1.1 Estimate the size of a drinks can. Measure it accurately and see how accurate you were with your estimation.

A drinks can has a diameter of 60 mm and its height : diameter ratio is 5 : 2.

a What will be the dimensions of the curved surface area available to the designer as advertising space?

b If visually only half the can is visible when stacked, what is the actual area which needs to catch the eye?

1.2 A goblet is to be presented in a cuboid pack.
If the maximum diameter of the goblet is 8 cm with a height of 20 cm what will be:

a the dimensions of the cuboid pack

b the area of card required (you can ignore any flaps needed)?

EXTENSION

1.3 Tankards are dispatched from the manufacturer in boxes of 20, where each individual item is packed in a box measuring 12 × 12 × 20 cm. Investigate the most economical and packaging for a box of 20 tankards.

a What are the possible dimension options for the box?

b State what dimensions will utilise the minimum area of card and find this area.

c If the weight of card used is 300 grams per square metre, what will be the weight (in kilograms) of 50 such boxes?

1.4 The area of card ('net') for a closed cuboid-shaped container is as shown with the flaps top and bottom of the box being indicated.

The ratio of the dimensions of a box, length : width : height, are 5 : 3 : 2.

What will be the dimensions of the box which has a flap 15 cm wide?

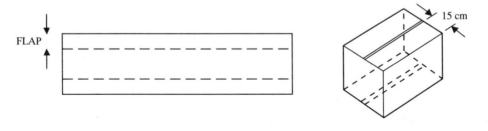

Assignment AD2

2.1 A maquette for a large piece of sculpture work approximates to the combination of cylinders and sphere shown. If the final statue is to be 2 metres high, find:

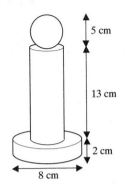

5 cm

13 cm

2 cm

8 cm

a the overall scale factor enlargement which needs to be applied

b (i) the dimensions of the cuboid of material from which the statue will be produced

    (ii) the initial volume of material.

c If the figure is to be carved in wood from a tree trunk, what will be the minimum diameter of tree trunk which will be suitable?

2.2 Artists sometimes ensure the correct relative sizes of figures within their artwork by sighting the object at arms length, noting the height on a pencil, and then relating this height to that of the other detail on the canvas. The diagram illustrates the technique.

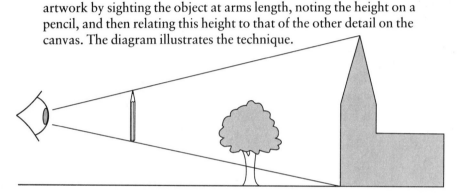

a A tree registers 12 cm and a church spire 15 cm on the pencil. If the tree is actually 25 m high, what is the actual height of the church spire?

b If 1″ = 2.54 cm and 12″ = 1 foot, what is the height of the church spire in feet?

c Irrespective of the size of canvas what must the ratio **pencil measurement : actual dimension** always be?

2.3 The diagram represents a perspective drawing of equally spaced apartment doors along a hotel corridor.

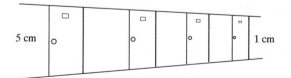

5 cm

1 cm

a Given that the height of the first door = 5 cm and the height of the fourth door = 1 cm, find the heights of the two remaining doors.

b These heights are in a sequence. What is this sequence (number pattern) called? If the drawing were extended to show other apartment doors along the corridor, what would be the height of the 8th apartment door?

c If the width of the first appears as 2 cm on the drawing, calculate the widths of the next three doors (assuming the drawing is accurately constructed).

Assignment AD3

A design business has prepared an advertisement measuring 14 cm wide by 7 cm deep, which it wishes to place in either a newspaper or periodical.

3.1 Compare the costs of placing this advertisement (black and white) in:

a A design magazine with the following standard rates:

Full page . . .	£750
Half page . . .	£450
Quarter . . .	£250
Eighth . . .	£139
Sixteenth . . .	£79
Thirty-second . . .	£49

The typed page size for this magazine is 257 mm × 181 mm.

b A national daily which charges £82 per standard column cm (scc). The format used is a column length of 360 mm, with each column occupying approximately 35 mm.

c A local newspaper which charges £1.85 per column cm. (The format used in this case is a 9 column display with a typed page width of 44 cm.)

3.2 Produce a set of questions, where responses can be easily recorded, to survey public opinion on the most effective form of advertising. Your survey should consider all popular forms of advertising such as television commercials, media, poster, direct mail, telephone etc. and examine any differences in opinion between the sexes. Illustrate the data obtained and draw conclusions.

Assignment AD4

The recipe for a quality ceramic mix (porcelain) is given in terms of units in the table below.

4.1 The potter estimates that 25 kg of mix is required to produce his designs.

a Extend the table and enter in a third column the **actual** weights of each component required.

	Units	Weight (kg)
China clay	53	
Potash Feldspar	25	
Fine-ground Quartz	17	
White Bentonite	5	

The costs of purchasing these components is given below along with associated transport costs for the area in which the potter lives. All figures given are exclusive of VAT.

b Calculate the minimum total cost of purchasing the above components for the initial small run requiring 25 kg. Include transport costs and VAT at 17.5%

c The potter is commissioned to produce a series of large pieces requiring an estimated 120 kg of mix.
Recalculate parts **a** and **b** to find the minimum total cost of purchase and delivery in this case.

d The final ceramic work is required to undergo reduction firing at 2236°F.
Use the formula $C = \frac{5}{9}(F - 32)$ to convert this temperature to degrees Centigrade.

Weight (kg)	0.5	1	5	10	25	50	100
China clay			£4.97	£8.95	£14.33	£26.01	£47.19
Feldspar potash		£1.77	£6.32	£11.38	£20.15	£36.27	£65.79
Quartz			£4.34	£7.87	£10.26	£18.46	£33.23
White Bentonite		£1.56	£4.75	£8.50	£12.50	£21.00	£37.50

Transport rates to local area							
Up to	50 kg	75 kg	100 kg	150 kg	200 kg		
	11.50	15.50	19.50	27.50	37.50		

4.2 A potter makes three different styles of drink container (mugs, cups, beakers), each in four different glaze patterns for a local craft shop.

e If the shop stocks all designs how many different drink containers will the shop have on its shelves?

The four glaze patterns are denoted A, B, C, D.
If a drink container is selected at randon, what will be the probability of choosing:

f a mug in pattern A or B

g a cup or beaker in pattern C or D?

4.3 The potter travels to a number of large retailers in different countries to seek new markets for his mugs. He wishes to travel from London to each of the following cities: Paris, Madrid, Lisbon, Rome and Bonn.
Assuming that he wishes to travel the shortest distance and that direct travel is possible between all of the cities listed, in which order should the potter visit the cities?

Assignment AD5

5.1 Estimate the height of any sculpture you have produced. Measure its height accurately to check your estimation.

In a model box layout for a proposed exhibition of sculpture and artwork a lifesize figure 2 metres in height appears as a 2.5 cm high object.

The relationship

$$\text{Scale factor} = \frac{\text{Image height}}{\text{Object height}}$$

gives the connection between the true and scaled dimensions.

a What is the scale factor reduction being employed?

b A large canvas measuring $3\,\text{m} \times 4\,\text{m}$ is to be displayed behind the sculpture. If a rectangle of card is to be cut and used in the 'model box' to assess the relative proportions, what will be the dimensions of this piece of card (in cm)?

c To assist with these and further such calculations a graph is prepared linking the two quantities, A = actual dimension (m) and M = model dimension (cm)

Use the above information to produce this graph.

What equation connects the variables A and M?

5.2 The data given in the table shows how the Arts Council has allocated its government grant over the period 1971–1991.

Arts Council Expenditure (£ thousands)				
	1971–72	1981–82	1986–87	1990–91
National companies	3508	22418	31480	40005
Regional arts	605	9133	24637	34550
Art	605	4982	6844	7274
Drama	2419	14945	20531	23640
Music	2419	15775	23268	29095
Dance	484	3321	6844	9092
Literature	242	1661	1369	1818
Other	1814	9963	20531	34550
Total				

a Calculate the totals and produce a suitable statistical illustration to show the change in Arts Council expenditure over the 20-year period.

b Determine the percentage increase in grant over the 20-year period.

c Examine the data and determine which heading has seen the largest increase in its allocation of grant between 1971–72 and 1991–92.

5.3 The editor of a theatre publication asks an employee to examine the level of interest of the general population in the theatre, and to see if there are any connections or conclusions that can be drawn. Produce suitable questions which could be put to a random group of people and provide the following data:

- the number of visits made to the theatre each year
- the amount spent on this leisure activity in a year
- the age and sex of the person being interviewed
- type of theatre visited (national, regional, local)
- occupational category, etc.

5.4 Use the data given in the table below to produce a pie chart indicating the division of advertising expenditure by medium for 1991.

Display advertising expenditure by medium

	£m 1986	1987	1988	1989	1990	1991	% of total 1991
Press*	2,136	2,370	2,680	2,983	2,964	2,893	51
TV	1,674	1,872	2,127	2,286	2,325	2,303	41
Poster and transport	193	216	244	271	282	267	5
Cinema	19	22	27	35	39	42	1
Radio	91	111	139	159	163	149	3
Total	4,112	4,591	5,217	5,734	5,773	5,654	100

(*Source:* The Advertising Association' Advertising Statistics Yearbook 1992, tables 4.3.1, 4.3.2)

Find the mean and range of the advertising expenditure by medium in the six years 1986–91.
Use the data in the next table to produce a bar chart showing the trend in television advertising expenditure from 1986 to 1991.

Television advertising expenditure

	£m 1986	1987	1988	1989	1990	1991	% of total 1991
Transmission charges	1,440	1,623	1,849	1,990	2,004	1,974	86
Production costs	234	249	278	296	321	329	14
Total	1,674	1,872	2,127	2,286	2,325	2,303	100

(*Source:* The Advertising Association's *Advertising Statistics Yearbook 1992,* tables 6.1.1, 6.1.2)

(A sectional bar chart could be used to indicate transmission charges and production costs as a proportion of the total costs.)
Make any necessary calculations to determine whether there have been any major changes in the ratio of production costs to transmission costs during the period 1986–1991.

Assignment **AD6**

As part of an exercise in package design, consideration is being given to producing an aerosol can which will contain a given volume of product. To maintain the correct aesthetic proportions it is initially assumed that the cap height is a fifth of the total height. The can and cap radii are 2.5 cm.

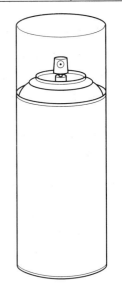

    a If the volume of the cap is 100 cm³, what is the height of the can?

    b If a third of the can volume is taken up by propellant gas, what volume of product does it contain?

    c If a similar can is to contain 500 cm³ of the product, what will be the resulting can and cap heights?

    d What area of the original can's surface will be available for a 'label' design?

Assignment **AD7**

7.1 The diagram depicts a 50 mm lens focussed on a 2 m high person at a distance of 25 metres from the camera.

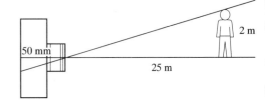

    a What will be the corresponding image size?

    b What scale factor enlargement is involved?

    c If this 50 mm lens is replaced by a 120 mm lens, what will be the size of an object 25 metres from the camera which produces the same image size found in **a**?

The diagram indicates the relative sizes of the image for the same object at the same distance from the camera when using lenses of different focal length.
Examine the link between focal length and image size.
Construct a table and enter the missing values x and y.

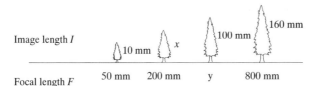

7.2 The diagram shows the strip of film within a typical 36 exposure 35 mm cassette. The dimensions of each negative are 35 mm × 24 mm and there is a 2 mm gap between all 36 exposures. The leader consists of a length equal to a further two exposures plus a tab of equal length. The film strip is fixed to the cassette spindle of 0.8 cm diameter and following the 36 exposures a further length equal to one exposure plus the spindle circumference is added.

a What is the total length of the 36-exposure film strip?

b What will be the total length required for a 24-exposure film?

c In the case of a manual film advance mechanism what is the distance moved by the film between each exposure?

d The film advance lever moves through some 120 degrees between exposures each time producing a complete turn of the take-up spool. Calculate the approximate diameter of the take-up spool.

7.3 Camera motor drives can be operated in either continuous or single shot mode. They usually operate in $\frac{1}{4}$–$\frac{1}{6}$ second cycles. The diagram depicts the sequence where after the shutter fires, camera components such as wind on, mirror return, exposure recalculation etc. take place before the shutter fires again.

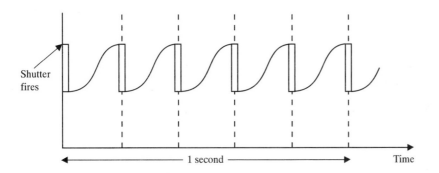

a At how many cycles per second is the motor drive operating?

b How quickly would you be able to use up a 36 exposure film with the motor drive in this continuous mode?

c Operating in this mode the motor drive batteries will only deliver sufficient power for 5 minutes.

Use this figure to calculate the number of **complete** 36 exposure films that could be loaded and run in this continuous mode before the batteries expire.

7.4 A survey is to be conducted into the preferences of the photographic public for various brands, speeds and type of film.
Produce a set of suitably constructed questions to provide data on the number of films purchased per year in terms of the following:

- type of film purchased (b/w, colour negative or transparency)
- film format (35 mm, 110, etc.)
- ISO rating
- preferred brand.

Conduct a survey using your questions. Illustrate your findings and state what conclusions you can make.

Assignment AD8

8.1 In the process of framing a picture (25 cm by 35 cm) I need to cut out a card surround.

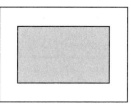

   a The card is to have a width of 5 cm all round.
   What will be the dimensions of the original rectangle of card?

   b What proportion of the card will have been removed in this operation?

8.2 The diagram shows a large picture frame which is to accommodate a canvas measuring 25 inches by 32 inches. Corners are mitred and the picture framing material being used is 2 inches wide.

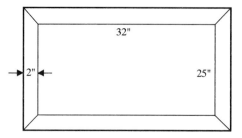

   a What will be the minimum continuous length of framing material required?

   b What would be the amount required for a picture measuring 35 inches by 47 inches?

   c The dimensions of a picture are in the ratio 2 : 3.
   What will be the actual size of picture that can be accommodated with 250 cm of framing material with width 5 cm?

8.3 In selecting work to be part of an exhibition of photographic work a selection is made at random from eight equally good prints.
The eight prints are made up of wildlife, landscape, seascape and portraiture, with one black & white and one colour print covering each subject.

   a What is the probability that the choice is a colour portrait?

   b If two prints are chosen, at random, what is the probability that they are wildlife or a landscape in colour?

Assignment AD9

A designer is contracted to produce marketing material for a company. Apart from producing the design of the materials, the designer is in charge of the complete operation from initial ideas through to final completed and delivered product.
The designer's costs involve charging for time spent producing draft designs (8 hours), meetings for discussion with the client and presentation of designs to

the client (3 hours including travelling time), incorporating requested alterations and production of final copy (2 hours).

    a If the designer charges £60 per hour to simply cover his overheads, what contribution will this initial design process make to the final bill?

Following agreement from the company about the actual design to be used, the designer has been asked to advise on printing costs and arrange for the printing of 50 000 copies.

The cost of setting up and printing from the designer's copy are £300 for the plates plus an amount charged per 1000 copies depending on the quality of paper used.

These figures are:

	Grade A	Grade B	Grade C
	£84	£76	£68 per 1000 copies

    b What will be the cost of using Grade A paper?

    c What will be the saving if Grade C paper is used?

In the original costings the designer adds in a contingency amount to ensure an adequate profit margin.

    d If this is 10% of the figure in **a** how much is actually added?

The company eventually settles for the best paper option (Grade A).

    e What will be the final amount which the company must pay (including VAT)?

Assignment AD10

The following draft schedule has been put together by a design team as the basis for a product and package design presentation to a client. A range of approximate timings have been assigned to each stage of the presentation so that some idea of the overall duration of the presentation can be obtained and adjustments made if necessary. Determine:

    a the maximum presentation time

    b the minimum presentation time.

A	Introduction and reminder of design brief	(3–10 min)
B	Initial ideas – slides and description of design process (6 slides)	(2–5 min each slide)
C	Short-listed designs – reasons for rejecting some (3 slides)	(4–10 min each slide)
D	Final design and reason for selection	(5–10 min)
E	Introduction of original artwork, product prototype and packaging	(15–20 min)
F	Question-and-answer session leading to acceptance or modification of the design 'package'	(15–45 min)

Assignment **AD11**

A cardboard transparency mount has the shape shown in the diagram so that it can be folded to enclose a single film frame. The 'opening' is a rectangle 34 mm × 23 mm and the final mounted transparency measures 5 cm by 5 cm.

    a What is the area of card used in each transparency mount?

    b What area of card will be required to mount 36 exposures?

    c If each transparency is 2 mm thick, what is the minimum volume that will accommodate all 36 transparencies?

It is common for photographers to take up to 38 exposures by careful film loading.

The probability that when a film is processed it has 36, 37 or 38 exposures is given by the following table:

No of exposures	36	37	38
Probability	0.8	0.15	0.05

    d If a film processing operator selects one film at random, what is the probability that it has either 37 or 38 exposures?

Assignment **AD12**

12.1   Many people asked to select one of the following shapes for writing paper or a picture frame would choose C. In C, the dimensions are such that the ratio of the smaller side to the larger side is the same as the ratio of the larger side to the sum of both sides.
This ratio is known as the Golden Ratio.

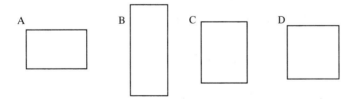

    a If the height of C is h and its width w, write the above statement algebraically.

The Greeks were aware of this proportion, and its use is apparent in much of their architecture.
Classical art and photography have also made use of this ratio to place the central feature of the picture in the most pleasing position.

In the diagram below the main feature will need to be placed so that the Golden Ratio $a/b = b/(a + b)$ applies.

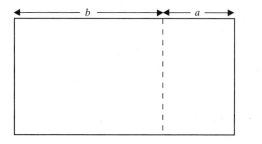

b Assuming the rectangle is 10 cm long find the values of a and b. (This should be approached by forming a table with four columns as indicated. Let b take values from 5.0 increasing by 0.1 each time and calculate a and the two ratios accordingly.)

b	$a = 10 - b$	a/b	$b/(a+b)$

c Hence state the values of a and b for a rectangle with length 10 cm.

12.2 The dimensions of paper sizes A1, A2, A3, A4, A5 etc. are connected in such a way that each is rectangular and a piece of A3 represents two pieces of A4. A4 divides to give two pieces of A5 etc., as shown below:

a If A3 measures 297 mm by 420 mm what will be:
  (i) the dimensions of A4 paper
  (ii) the perimeter of a piece of A5 paper?

b What will be the ratio of the areas for paper sizes A5 : A3?

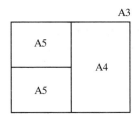

Design students can easily produce their own A5 sketch books by cutting up sheets of A1 paper and adding a spiral binding.

c How many A5 sheets can be obtained from a single sheet of A1 paper?

d If each sketch book has 30 pages, how many complete books can be produced from 20 sheets of A1 paper?

Business

ASSIGNMENTS

Numeracy Core Skills Matrix

Element	Range	1	2	3	4	5	6	7	8	9	10	11	12
3.1	1					✓							
3.1	2	✓						✓					
3.1	3				✓	✓			✓			✓	
3.1	4	✓						✓					
3.1	5	✓						✓					
†3.1	6	✓						✓					
3.2	1		✓	✓	✓	✓	✓		✓	✓	✓	✓	
3.2	2		✓	✓	✓	✓	✓		✓	✓	✓	✓	
3.2	3		✓	✓	✓	✓			✓	✓	✓	✓	
3.2	4		✓	✓	✓	✓			✓	✓	✓	✓	
3.2	5					✓	✓		✓				
3.2	6					✓							✓
3.2	7					✓	✓		✓				
3.2	8		✓	✓	✓	✓	✓		✓	✓	✓	✓	
3.2	9				✓	✓			✓	✓		✓	
3.2	10						✓		✓				
†3.2	11												
†3.2	12				✓				✓				
†3.2	13								✓				
3.3	1					✓	✓		✓				
3.3	2	✓		✓				✓		✓	✓		✓
3.3	3										✓		✓
3.3	4	✓	✓	✓	✓	✓	✓	✓	✓		✓		✓
3.3	5						✓		✓				
3.3	6					✓							✓
†3.3	7								✓				✓

† denotes element required only at GNVQ Level 3. All other elements are required at GNVQ Level 2.

Assignment B1

Construct a series of questions which can be used to survey people on the facilities (e.g. shops, banks, post office, doctors, dentists, community facilities such as recreation centres etc.) that they would like to see provided locally. The questions should differentiate between male/female responses and between different age groups.

Conduct a survey of 50 people and display your findings pictorially.

Assignment B2

Creation and distribution of wealth for a business, such as the manufacture of traffic cones, can be described under the heading of 'value added', given by the relationship:

Value added = Turnover (total sales) − Raw material and services costs

The business has a turnover of £100m with raw material and services costs amounting to £60m.

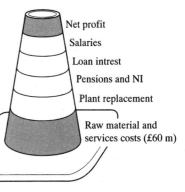

   a What will be the value added amount for this business?

'Value added' is made up of salaries (£10m), pension contributions (£5m), National Insurance contributions (£2m), loan interest (£10m), replacement of plant (£5m) and net profit.

   b What is the net profit made by the business?
      Express this as a percentage profit figure.

   c If this net profit figure is distributed among the headings of tax, dividends to shareholders and reinvested money in the ratio 2 : 3 : 3, what will be the amount distributed as dividends to shareholders?

Assignment B3

The pie chart given below shows the projected capital expenditure for a County Council.

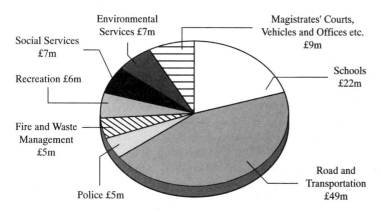

   a What is the total capital budget involved?

   b Produce a table which gives the various headings and the associated capital expenditure.
      Calculate the angles for each sector of the pie chart.

c If Government reduces local authority funding so that a total of £22m is lost from this capital budget, what will be the percentage reduction in the budget?

d If the budget for each of the services is reduced by this percentage, what will the new figures be?

e Will the pie chart constructed to reflect these changes differ from the original?

Assignment B4

A manufacturing company has basically two major considerations in calculating total cost of production: fixed costs and variable costs.
Fixed costs (FC) are defined as costs which do not change as a result of a change in output, in the short term. Variable costs (VC) on the other hand rise as output rises.
The graph shows the link between FC and VC.

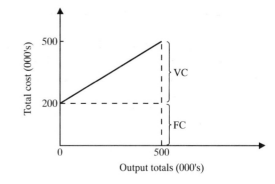

a Use this graph to complete the table below.

FC	No. of units (000's)	Total cost	Cost per unit
	100		
	500		

b If the FC is increased by 50% because of the installation of new plant, produce the new graph if the new plant results in a variable cost per unit of 50p.

The graph below shows how the income increases as the number of goods sold increases.

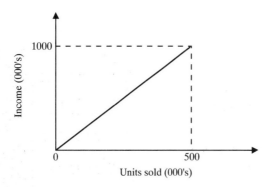

c From this graph determine the price at which each unit is sold.

d Superimpose the two graphs in **b** and **c** by drawing them accurately on graph paper, with the same axes and scales. From the point where the two graphs intersect (the **break-even point**) find the number of units which the company must sell before it makes a profit.

Assignment B5

Estimate the size of a sheet of A4 paper. Measure it carefully to check your estimate.

5.1 A small business has its filing system organised in box files which it keeps on shelves for ready access.
If each box file measures 380 × 280 × 80 mm:

    a how many files can be accommodated on a shelf of length 1.75 m?

    b what length of shelf will be needed to accommodate 30 files?

In the interests of security the business decides that lockable filing cabinets would be a preferable form of storage. The dimensions of a typical four-drawer filing cabinet are 470 mm wide, 620 mm deep and 1320 mm high, each drawer front measuring 410 mm wide by 290 mm deep.
Assume that each drawer has these dimensions and accepts box files with the above dimensions.

    c How many three-drawer filing cabinets would be required to accommodate 75 box files?

    d If four-drawer, and two-drawer cabinets are also available, what combination of these three types would be necessary to accommodate 100 box files?

5.2 The business is undergoing expansion and as part of this process decides to refurbish the area used by its office staff. Apart from the redecoration which takes place, new furniture and computing equipment is to be purchased and installed.
The different aspects of this process are given below together with the likely range of time for each stage to be completed:

- Relocate existing equipment and personnel (2 days)
- Order furniture (delivery 3–4 weeks)
- Order computing equipment (delivery 2–3 weeks)
- Rewire and add additional computer network cable (2 days)
- Redecorate (5 days)
- Order carpet (delivery up to 4 weeks)
- Lay carpet (1 day)
- Install furniture and computing equipment (2 days)

    e Produce a network which schedules this project and takes into account the order in which the above must be done.

    f Determine how long the office will not be operational and give both the maximum and minimum times for completion of the project.

5.3 The four drawers of a filing cabinet are labelled **Finance, Marketing, Personnel, Sales.**
The file for Mr Alun Edwards has been placed in one of the filing cabinet drawers.
The secretary is sure that it has been correctly filed in alphabetical order but cannot remember whether it is filed under A for Alun or E for Edwards, but knows that it is in one of the four drawers.

    g List all the places where the file could be located.

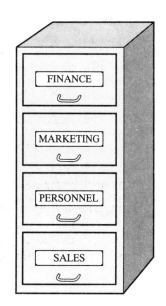

Assignment **B6**

A company is looking to smarten up its image when clients are invited to presentations in its boardroom and orders conference room furniture to produce the arrangement shown.

If the diameter of the semicircular end tables is 1.75 metres, find:

a the total area of the two semicircular tables

b the total rectangular area of veneer needed to laminate these two tables on the top and bottom surfaces

c the perimeter of each of the semicircular tables

d the total length of edging strip required during the manufacture of the two tables.

e The rectangular tables in the layout below each have dimensions in the ratio 2 : 3.
What will be the overall length and width of the final conference room table arrangement?

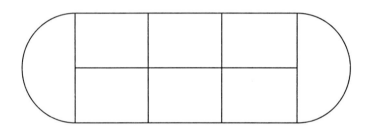

Assignment **B7**

Produce a questionnaire which will assess public attitudes to the practice of direct mailing (often referred to as 'junk mail') and telephone selling.
Ensure that your questions will provide data on:

- differences in attitude depending on age/sex/occupation
- the measure of responses made to these two forms of sales and marketing – how many people have replied positively to the different approaches?

Conduct a survey and show the data obtained in a variety of forms.
What conclusions can be drawn about the benefits of direct mailing?

Assignment B8

A large multinational oil company is developing a site on an upgraded stretch of road as a new petrol station. The station is of the self-service type with six pumps, one of which is for diesel only and the remaining five deliver 4-star or unleaded petrol.

During the construction process the builders need to sink three fuel storage tanks, one for each type of fuel, each of which is cylindrical with a radius of 3 m and a length of 8 m.

   a What is the volume of each tank?

   b The hole excavated to take each of the tanks is a cuboid. What will be:
     (i) the minimum dimensions of the cuboid
     (ii) the total volume of soil removed?

   c If the average fill of any fuel is 20 litres, how many cars can be filled from a full storage tank with unleaded petrol?

   d The bar chart indicates the number of litres of each type of fuel sold in a day with the price per litre attached. Find a figure for the total daily income.

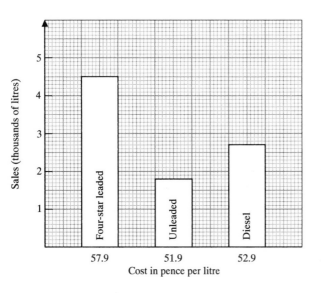

Statistics show that the number of cars on the road using unleaded, diesel and leaded fuel is in the ratio 5 : 2 : 3.

   e If a car pulls in to the petrol station what is the probability that it uses diesel fuel?

   f If this driver pulls up at a pump without paying too much attention, what is the probability that the pump dispenses non-diesel fuel?

Assignment B9

The table shows the distribution of salaries of employees in a medium-sized company.

Salary range S (£000's)	No. of employees
$10 \leqslant S < 12$	15
$12 \leqslant S < 15$	13
$15 \leqslant S < 20$	10
$20 \leqslant S < 25$	7
$25 \leqslant S < 30$	3
$S \geqslant 30$	2

    a Illustrate the data in an appropriate way.

The management structure within the company is the traditional one with senior managers (SM), middle managers (MM), and other employees (OE). Use the distribution to find:

    b the total number of employees

    c the number of managers, given that SM salaries >30 K and MM salaries >20 K.

    d What is the ration of SM to MMs?

    e What proportion of the workforce is non-management?

If I approach someone in the staff canteen what is the probability that they are:

    f a middle manager

    g a senior manager

    h not a manager?

If I sit down at a table with two occupants, what is the probability that both are:

    i senior or middle management

    j a middle manager or a non-management employee?

Assignment B10

WEEKLY HOUSEHOLD EXPENDITURE, 1990-91

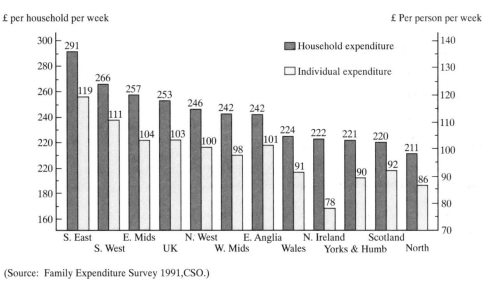

(Source: Family Expenditure Survey 1991,CSO.)

10.1 This dual bar chart compares weekly household expenditure with individual expenditure. Use this chart to find:

  a the region of the UK where the difference between these two types of weekly expenditure is: (i) greatest, (ii) least.

  b the region of the UK where the difference between these two types of weekly expenditure expressed as a percentage is: (i) greatest, (ii) least.

Complete the following statements:

  c Weekly household expenditure in the UK can be expected to be within the range _____ to _____ .

  d The range of weekly individual expenditure in the UK is _____ .

10.2 The table below gives data on types of pension held (P.P.P = Personal Pension Plan).

PENSIONS HELD BY TYPE

	Company contrib	Company non-contrib	P.P.P. emps	P.P.P. self-emp	SERPS	Only state pension
All adults	24.0	6.2	7.8	4.9	11.4	30.1
Sex						
Men	34.3	7.6	9.7	7.5	14.1	23.5
Women	14.3	4.9	6.1	2.4	9.0	36.2

  a Illustrate the figures for all adults by means of a pie chart.

  b Use the data for men and women to construct a dual bar chart, similar to the one above, which compares the difference in percentages of both sexes holding each different type of pension.

Assignment **B11**

The money markets influence the spot and forward rates for currency exchange on a daily basis.

In the case of someone owning property abroad and transferring money into their foreign bank account the rate applicable at the time of transfer is important.

The table below shows an extract from the financial section of a newspaper and gives these exchange rates on a particular day.

Helen has visited her bank on the day before to transfer £3500 sterling into her French bank account:

> **a** What is the maximum number of francs she can expect to be credited to her account in France?
>
> **b** What is the least number of francs which will have been credited?
>
> **c** Express the difference between these two figures in **a** and **b** as a percentage difference between the two rates.
>
> **d** If the bank charges £30 to make the transfer, what is the true range of exchange rates that will apply?

STERLING RATES		
	Closing Market Rates	Previous Closing Rates
Australia	2.0788-2.0832	2.1118-2.1147
Austria	17.74-17.77	17.68-17.72
Belgium	51.95-52.06	51.93-52.04
Canada	2.0302-2.0332	2.0435-2.0465
Denmark	9.84-9.86	9.83-9.85
France	8.57-8.58	8.56-8.58
Germany	2.5225-2.5258	2.5177-2.5209
Hong Kong	11.53-11.54	11.59-11.60
Ireland	1.0389-1.0419	1.0389-1.0419
Italy	2.494-2.498	2.495-2.499
Japan	158.16-158.42	157.62-157.89
Netherlands	2.8361-2.8396	2.8303-2.8338
Norway	10.94-10.95	10.93-10.94
Portugal	259.01-259.64	259.83-260.46
Spain	207.14-207.44	207.25-207.55
Sweden	11.72-11.74	11.75-11.77
Switzerland	2.1400-2.1500	2.1200-2.1400
USA	1.4935-1.4945	1.5015-1.5025
ECU	1.3066-1.3081	1.3048-1.3067

Assignment B12

12.1 A medium-sized business has a number of photocopying machines which can be used by any member of the workforce. The use of these machines is monitored by the resources manager who records the readings for the numbers of copies made on each machine at the end of each week. The table below gives the readings for one machine over a six-week period.

Week	1	2	3	4	5	6
No. of copies	5238	6789	6523	7181	6955	5714

    a Illustrate this data in a suitable manner to indicate any fluctuations over the six-week period.

    b Find the total number of copies made during the six-week period.

    c Calculate the mean number of sheets used per week.

    d How many reams of paper have been used by this one machine (1 ream = 500 sheets)?

    e If the paper costs £1.32 per ream, what is the total cost of the paper used on this machine during the six-week period?

12.2 If an employee goes to photocopy a document, s/he will find the copier usable or inoperable. If the probabilities of a particular photocopier being inoperable through either a paper jam, no toner or no paper are in the ratio 1 : 2 : 3, find the probability of a photocopier being inoperable through:

    f a paper jam

    g no toner or no paper.

    h If two copiers are found to be inoperable with each having one of the above faults, write down all the possible combinations of faults.

12.3 While in the process of preparing a report during the weekend, a manager realises that a document is required urgently. In order to obtain this vital component of the report the manager goes into the office to make a copy of the necessary document.
Assuming that

    • the manager takes 3 minutes to locate the document in the filing system
    • the copier takes 2 minutes to warm up and become operational
    • the actual copying process takes 30 seconds
    • it takes 1 minute to replace the document in the filing system

what is the order of the above events so that the complete process takes the minimum time?

Health and Social Care
ASSIGNMENTS

Numeracy Core Skills Matrix													
		Assignments											
Element	Range	1	2	3	4	5	6	7	8	9	10	11	12	13
3.1	1	✓		✓										
3.1	2		✓				✓		✓					
3.1	3	✓		✓			✓	✓			✓	✓	✓	
3.1	4		✓				✓		✓					
3.1	5		✓				✓							
3.1	6		✓				✓		✓					
3.2	1	✓	✓	✓	✓	✓		✓	✓	✓	✓	✓	✓	✓
3.2	2	✓	✓	✓	✓			✓	✓	✓	✓	✓	✓	✓
3.2	3	✓			✓				✓	✓	✓		✓	
3.2	4	✓		✓				✓			✓		✓	
3.2	5			✓		✓		✓					✓	
3.2	6					✓								
3.2	7				✓			✓					✓	
3.2	8	✓	✓						✓	✓	✓	✓	✓	✓
3.2	9	✓				✓		✓		✓			✓	
3.2	10							✓					✓	
3.2	11				✓									
3.2	12				✓			✓					✓	
3.2	13							✓					✓	
3.3	1				✓			✓					✓	
3.3	2				✓				✓					
3.3	3								✓					
3.3	4	✓		✓				✓	✓		✓		✓	
3.3	5			✓				✓					✓	
3.3	6		✓				✓							
3.3	7						✓							✓

Assignment HSC1

The charts given are the standardised charts connecting weight and height for
both males and females. The scales shown are metric but where conversions
are required use 1 metre = 39 inches, 1 kilogram = 2.2 pounds.

a Find the weight range for a male of normal weight whose height is 5′ 9″.

b Using the mid-range values:
  (i) what is the difference in weights between a 5′ 7″ male and female
      as a percentage of the female weight?
  (ii) how tall (to the nearest inch) will a woman be if she is the same
      weight as a 5′ 5″ man?

If the weight is below 80% of the normal weight for height, the individual's
nutrition is probably inadequate as a result of poor diet or disease.
If the weight is 20% or more above normal, the cause of that obesity is
probably poor diet or disease.

c In the case of a 5′ 6″ female, use the mid-point of the normal weight
     range to calculate the minimum weight for obesity and the maximum
     weight for being underweight.

d An alternative method of considering this weight issue is in terms of a
     body mass index.
     This is obtained by dividing the person's weight (in kilograms) by the
     square of the person's height (in metres).
  (i) What will this index be for a 6′ 0″ male whose weight is at the
      upper limit of the normal weight range?
  (ii) If an index value of more than 27 constitutes obesity, what weight
      gain would be needed for this 6′ 0″ male to be regarded as obese?

e Are you above or below the weight for your height?
     Measure your height and weight accurately to check your answer.

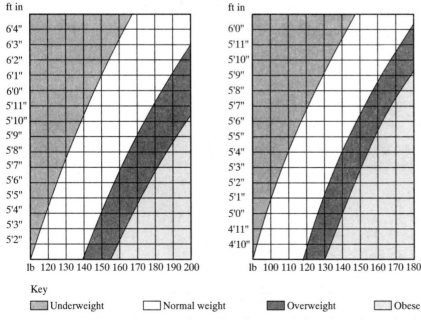

WEIGHT TABLE: MEN

WEIGHT TABLE: WOMEN

Key

▨ Underweight   ☐ Normal weight   ▨ Overweight   ☐ Obese

Assignment HSC2

A person's daily calorie requirements usually relate to the type of activity undertaken.

We can divide daily activity into four main groups: sleep, lightly active, moderately active and very active.

Each of these is defined below and the table gives the likely calorie requirements (in kcal per hour) for both males and females.

Lightly active: sitting, reading or writing
Moderately active: easy walking, washing, cooking, shopping
Very active: hard walking, strenuous physical exercise, labouring
etc.

	Male	Female
Sleep	65	50
Lightly Active	85	70
Moderately Active	200	160
Very Active	340	270

a (i) A person's typical 24-hour period consists of 8 hours sleep, 9 hours light activity, and 7 hours moderate activity. What will be the calorie requirement for both males and females in this case?

  (ii) If this typical person is awake, what is the probability that he or she is involved in moderate activity?

b Examine your own day and divide it into activity levels. Hence calculate the corresponding calorie intake figure.

c A period of time consists of sleep and light activity in the ratio 3 : 5 and equates to a recommended calorie intake of 1550 kcal.
Assuming that the person is male, what will be the number of hours spent sleeping?

d Devise a series of questions which can be used to survey people's eating habits and produce figures for total daily calorie intake.
Compare the results of your survey with figures produced from the above table and comment on the extent to which eating habits provide more or less than the recommended daily calorie intake.

Assignment HSC3

Estimate the size of a single bed. Check your estimation by accurate measurement.

The actual layout of beds in a hospital ward is subject to health and safety requirements as well as operational considerations.
Assume a bed size of 2 m × 1 m and a regulation gap of 2 m between the beds, to allow nursing staff to operate behind the curtain screening, together with a minimum 3 m wide 'corridor' for access at the foot of the beds.

a Examine possible ward layouts and find the minimum dimensions of a rectangular 15-bed ward with 2 rows of beds. (Squared paper may be found useful.)

Hospital beds are usually made up by two nurses using a well-practised routine. In the case of the bottom sheet this would involve placing the sheet on the mattress with approximately equal overlap all round, folding under each side and then folding under the top and bottom.

The standard size of a single sheet is 70×100 inches and a mattress measures 3 feet $\times$ 6 feet $\times$ 6 inches deep.

    b What will be the true width of sheet tucked under the mattress?

The top sheet (and blankets) are placed with no overlap at the head of the bed. The two sides and bottom are tucked under as described above, and the top turned down.

    c What will be the area of this top sheet under the mattress?

    d What proportion of the total sheet area does this represent?

    e What is the area of a single sheet in square feet?

    f What is the volume of a mattress in cubic feet?

Assignment HSC4

The data given below compares the birth and death rates (per 100 of the population) for both the UK and the world.

    a Examine the data and comment on any trends that you observe.

    b If the total UK population is 57 237 000, find the actual number of births and deaths in 1990.

    c What is the ratio of births to deaths for the UK in 1990?

    d Assuming that any trends continue what will be the likely figures for the year 2000?

    e If the sequence shown by the world birth rate figures continues, express in symbolic notation, the world's birth rate after 1950. When would the world birth rate be less than 22?

	Birth Rate		Death Rate	
	UK	World	UK	World
1950	16	38	12	20
1960	18	35	12	15
1970	15	32	12	12
1980	13	29	12	10
1990	14	26	12	9
2000				

EXTENSION

Using the given data and any other information necessary, find out if there has been an overall population increase in: **a** the UK   **b** the world.

Assignment **HSC5**

A social care worker has arranged to make a series of visits in the district on a particular day. The places to be visited are indicated on the accompanying scale map and the only issue is in which order the visits should be made to minimise distance travelled and hence the time spent travelling. Each visit can be assumed to last 30 minutes. By considering the distances between each location to be visited, the time taken to travel each connecting distance by car can be calcualted.

Assume an average speed of 35 mph, and that the care worker starts from home (H).

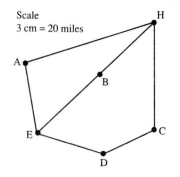

Scale
3 cm = 20 miles

a Find the route which minimises the distance travelled and state the total distance travelled during the day's visiting.

b Use the distances found in **a** to calculate the time intervals between visits.
   If the first appointment is scheduled for 0900 hours in the social care workers diary, give the remaining diary entries in the form of location and time of arrival.

EXTENSION

c The social care worker travels by private car and is allowed to claim a mileage allowance amounting to 47 pence per mile. This amount is taxed at source (at the 20% rate) and the resulting amount added to the worker's monthly salary.
   What will be the true amount received by the worker for this day's travelling?

Assignment **HSC6**

6.1 Many people take vitamin supplements on a daily basis and these are usually in the form of pills of varying shapes and sizes.
   The pills I take with my breakfast consist of 2 large (L), 3 medium (M) and 1 small (S). I swallow one at a time in any random order.

a Find the probability that the first pill I take is a medium pill.

b List all the possible combinations of the first two pills taken.
   Find the probability:
   (i) that the second pill taken is a large pill
   (ii) that the two pills are different.

c Find the probability that the first 3 pills taken are all different sizes.

6.2 A dietician is conducting research into the extent to which people use vitamin supplements as part of their daily diet.
   Construct a suitable questionnaire which will allow data collection and provide answers to questions such as:
   • What types of supplement are taken and what are the most popular?
   • How does the use of health supplements vary with age?
   • What quantities of supplements are normally taken?
   • For how long have people who take supplements been doing so?
   • What are people's reasons for taking vitamin supplements?

Assignment ■HSC7■

In a creche facility the safety of the children is assured by using a soft environment.

This is usually created from poly foam shapes covered in an easily washable covering.

In setting up such a facility regular shapes such as cuboids, cylinders, triangular cross-section lengths etc. are to be included.

The dimensions, in inches, of each of these shapes are as shown.

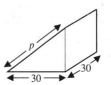

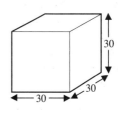

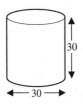

a Calculate the volume of each solid and hence the total volume of foam material used.

b Calculate the surface area of each solid and find the total area of covering material required. (The sloping edge p is 42.4 inches.)

c How many of each shape will be required to form the steamroller shown?

d The cube shapes eventually need recoving.
If you have 30 m² of material available, how many of the cubes can you cover?

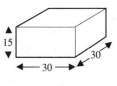

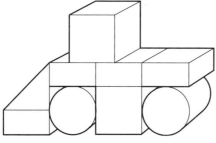

Assignment ■HSC8■

The figures given below relate to elderly persons in residential care in Great Britain. The total figure is approximately 265 000 distributed amongst various types of residential accommodation as follows:

Local Authority	39.4%
Registered Voluntary	11.9%
Registered Private	48.7%

Use these figures to:

a calculate the actual number of elderly persons in each type of accommodation

b produce a pie chart to illustrate the data

c find the percentage of the population in residential care (assume population of GB is approximately 53 million).

d Investigate the weekly costs of accommodation in private nursing homes and produce a bar chart of your findings. What is the range of these weekly costs?

Assignment HSC9

A residential care home looks after 20 senior citizens who each pay an average basic fee of £295 per person per week. The home operates on a shift system with three full-time qualified nursing staff and 14 additional part-time care assistants.

Staff costs account for approximately 35% of the care home's income, food costs for approximately 20%, and general running costs 20%. The remainder of the home's income is profit.

    a What is the total weekly income from its residents?

    b What is the actual profit per week?

    c What is the weekly wage bill?

The salary paid to the full-time nursing staff is £14 000 per annum and the hourly rate for care assistants is £4.25. Assume that the salaried staff are paid for 52 weeks and that 6% National Insurance is paid in the case of all staff.

    d Calculate the total weekly wage bill if each of the part-time care assistants work an average of 20 hours per week.

    e If a pay rise of 3% is awarded to the staff, what will be the new percentage figure for staff costs?

    f By how much would the weekly fees have to rise to ensure that the original profit margin remains unchanged?

Assignment HSC10

It is well known that cereals provide a source of essential vitamins and minerals. Figures relating to nutritional content, dietry fibre and amounts of vitamins and minerals can be found on the side panels of most cereal and other packets.

The table below is a typical example from a cereal packet:

Vitamins and Minerals	per 100g	% RDA
Thiamin (Viamin B1)	1.2 mg	30
Riboflavin (Vitamin B2)	1.5 mg	28
Niacin	16.0 mg	26
Folic Acid	300 µg	30
Vitamin B12	2.3 µg	34
Iron	7.7 µg	19

1 mg (milligram) = 1 thousandth of a gram.
1 µg (microgram) = 1 millionth of a gram.

The Recommended Daily Amount (RDA) is now an EU-agreed figure for certain vitamins and minerals which for an average adult would avoid deficiencies and ensure good health.

a Find the ratio of vitamins B1 : B2 in 100 g of cereal.

b Find the RDAs for the vitamins and minerals listed.

c Given that a bowl of cereal actually weighs 45 g, add a further two columns of values to the table with headings **per 45 g** and **% RDA**.

Assignment HSC11

Sugar is recognised as a contributory factor in tooth decay, and for those who cannot give it up, finding an alternative to cane sugar with a better 'sweetness quotient' would be beneficial.
The 'sweetness quotient' of fruit sugar (fructose) compared with cane sugar is in the ratio 1.7 : 1.
Each form of sweetner is a carbohydrate and 1 gm of carbohydrate provides 16 kJ of energy.

One level spoo....... of cane sugar or fructose weighs 5 grams. Mrs Wills presently takes two level teaspoons of cane sugar in tea and one level spoonful of cane sugar in coffee. On a certain day Mrs Wills drinks four cups of coffee and three cups of tea.

a What weight of cane sugar will be consumed?

b How much energy (in kJ) does this amount represent?

c How much energy (in kJ) can be saved by switching from cane sugar to fructose?

d If 1 kcal = 4.18 kJ, what does this energy figure equate to in calories?

Assignment HSC12

An average packet of throat lozenges contains four bubble packs of six lozenges with the overall dimensions as indicated. Each of the six 'bubbles' is circular with a diameter of 20 mm and a depth of 8 mm.

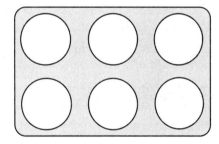

a Find the surface area of one bubble.

b **Volume of bubble = Cross-sectional surface area × Depth.**
Find the volume of one bubble.

c If a single lozenge takes up a volume 10% less than the 'bubble', what will be the total volume of the lozenges in the packet?

d The directions for use contain the instruction 'dissolve one lozenge in the mouth every 2–3 hours'.

If the first lozenge in the packet is taken is at 0800 hours on Wednesday and periods of sleep occurs between 2300 hours and 0700 hours the next day, between which times will the last lozenge in the packet be taken?

Assignment HSC13

Figures 1 and 2 relate to trends associated with asthma.

    a Comment on the trend observed in Figure 1.

    b Determine the total number of admissions represented by Figure 2.

    c If this number of patients accounted for a total of 2539 bed days, what was the average stay in hospital for an asthma patient in 1991?

    d What is the probability of the next person admitted to hospital with asthma being between 15 and 35 years?

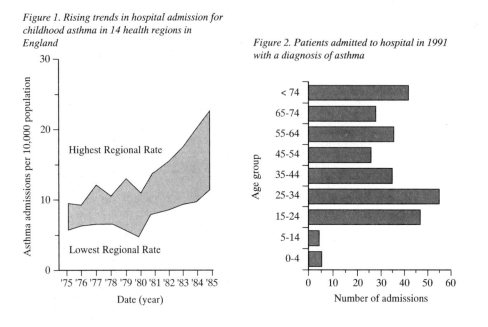

Figure 1. Rising trends in hospital admission for childhood asthma in 14 health regions in England

Figure 2. Patients admitted to hospital in 1991 with a diagnosis of asthma

EXTENSION

Figures 3 and 4 are taken from a medical report and relate to mortality from heart attacks and heart disease.

    e What conclusions do you think should be drawn from these charts and contained within the report?

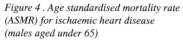

Figure 4 . Age standardised mortality rate (ASMR) for ischaemic heart disease (males aged under 65)

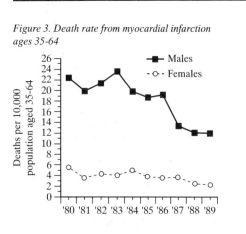

Figure 3. Death rate from myocardial infarction ages 35-64

Leisure and Tourism

ASSIGNMENTS

Numeracy Core Skills Matrix

Element	Range	1	2	3	4	5	6	7	8	9	10	11	12	13
3.1	1			✓				✓						
3.1	2					✓					✓			
3.1	3			✓					✓	✓		✓		✓
3.1	4	✓				✓					✓			
3.1	5	✓				✓					✓			
†3.1	6					✓								
3.2	1	✓			✓		✓	✓	✓	✓		✓	✓	✓
3.2	2	✓		✓	✓		✓	✓	✓	✓		✓	✓	✓
3.2	3	✓			✓		✓		✓	✓		✓		
3.2	4			✓	✓			✓	✓				✓	
3.2	5				✓			✓					✓	✓
3.2	6								✓					
3.2	7				✓			✓					✓	✓
3.2	8	✓			✓		✓		✓	✓		✓	✓	✓
3.2	9			✓	✓		✓	✓	✓	✓			✓	✓
3.2	10				✓								✓	✓
†3.2	11			✓									✓	
†3.2	12			✓	✓		✓	✓			✓			
†3.2	13				✓			✓						✓
3.3	1				✓			✓					✓	✓
3.3	2		✓			✓				✓	✓			
3.3	3		✓			✓	✓							
3.3	4	✓		✓	✓			✓				✓	✓	✓
3.3	5	✓			✓			✓		✓			✓	✓
3.3	6	✓											✓	
†3.3	7	✓											✓	

† denotes element required only at GNVQ Level 3. All other elements are required at GNVQ Level 2.

Assignment **LT1**

The diagram shows the typical seat layout in a jumbo jet (Boeing 747) and clearly indicates first class, business class, economy (tourist) class and designated smoking and non-smoking seats.

    a Find the percentage of business class seats.

    b Find the ratio of business to economy class seats.

    c How many seats on the aircraft are smoking seats?

    d What percentage of the seats on the aircraft are non-smoking?

If I am assigned a seat in row 23, at random, what is the probability that it will be:

    e an aisle seat

    f a window seat

    g not an aisle or window seat?

    h I am travelling economy class. Given a random allocation of seats within the economy class section, what is the probability that I sit in a non-smoking window seat?

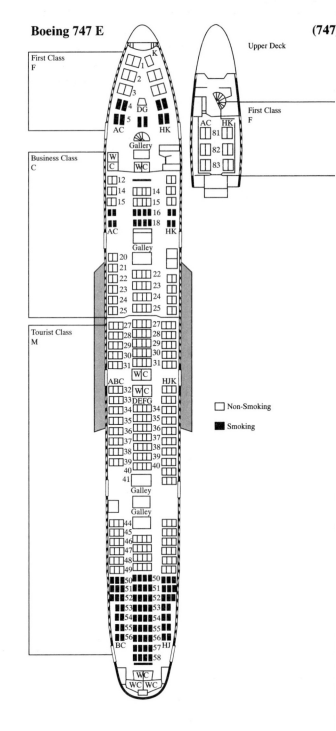

Boeing 747 E

(747

Upper Deck

First Class F

Business Class C

Tourist Class M

Non-Smoking

Smoking

EXTENSION

During the second part of my journey I transfer to a smaller plane (Fokker 50) which is a single class (economy) plane with seats on one side of the plane designated as smoking. What is the probability that:

    i I sit in a non-smoking seat window seat on this flight

    j I sit in a non-smoking economy class window seat on **both** flights?

Fokker 50

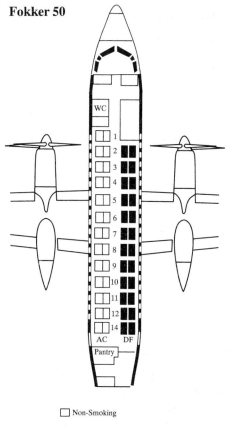

☐ Non-Smoking

■ Smoking

Assignment ▐LT2▌

Presentation of data to provide the desired visual impact is an important part of statistics.
The two sets of data given relate to the following:

- popular holiday destinations
- airport usage

In each case select and use a suitable method to present the data pictorially.

Top 10 destinations of British tourists in Europe

Country of destination	Number of British visitors
Austria	786 300
France	7 177 000
Germany	1 303 110
Greece	1 674 875
Ireland	2 355 000(1)
Italy	1 711 634
Netherlands	832 300
Portugal	1 100 000
Spain	6 144 813
Switzerland	536 230

(*Source:* World Tourism Organisation)

Airports used

Airport	Passengers (millions)
London Heathrow	40.3
London Gatwick	21.4
Manchester	10.8
Glasgow	3.9
Birmingham	3.5
Luton	2.8
Edinburgh	2.5
Belfast	2.2
Newcastle	1.5
East Midlands	1.4
London Stansted	1.3

Assignment **LT3**

Before embarking on your air travels you may need to estimate the weight of your luggage. You can check your estimation by weighing the luggage accurately. Zoe estimates that her luggage weighs 18 kg. She then proceeds to use her bathroom scales to check that her baggage weight is less than the maximum 20 kg allowance.

a Her scales are actually marked in stones (where 14 pounds = 1 stone). The reading she obtains is as indicated.
If there are 2.2 pounds to the kilogram, how much does her luggage weigh (in kilos)?

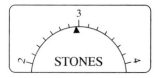

b When Zoe reaches the airport she discovers that her luggage is in fact 3.4 kg overweight. How should the reading on her scales have looked?

c At the airport she is charged for her baggage being overweight. The particular airline she is travelling with charges an administrative fee of £3 plus £2 for each kilogram overweight.
  (i) How much will Zoe have to pay if her luggage is 1 kg overweight?
  (ii) How much would she have to pay if her luggage was 2 kg overweight?
  (iii) What if her luggage was 3 kg overweight, or 4 kg, or . . . ?

d Work out the connection between excess weight (E kg) and excess baggage charge (£C).

e Sketch the graph of the relationship derived in **d** above.

During her journey Zoe transfers to a different carrier who charges different rates for excess baggage.
In this case the connection between weight and excess baggage charge is given by the graph shown below.
Use this graph to find the cost if Zoe's luggage is:

f 2 kg overweight

g 10 kg overweight

Find also:

h the administrative charge

i the charge per kilogram overweight.

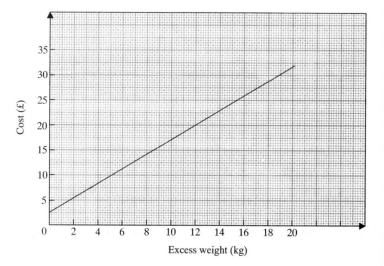

Assignment LT4

A Leisure Centre pool complex includes a Jacuzzi suite consisting of three circular pools.

The diagram indicates the layout of these pools and the distance between the centres of any two pools is 6.75 m. The depth of each pool is 1 m.

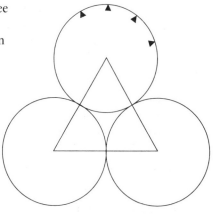

a Find the surface area of each pool.

b The volume of water in each pool, which is cylindrical, can be found by using the relationship
Volume = Surface area × Depth.
Find the volume of water in each pool.

c If each person using the pool requires 1.5 m of the perimeter to be accommodated comfortably, what is the maximum capacity of the three Jacuzzi pools?

d If the 16 water jets in each pool are equally spaced around the walls, what is the distance between these jets?

e It is found that if N people use the Jacuzzi on a Monday, the number of people using it on the following Friday is $3N + 10$. A check one Friday revealed that 100 people used the Jacuzzi. How many people used it the previous Monday?

EXTENSION

The cafeteria/bar of the leisure centre has a number of circular tables, diameter 1 m, occupying a 10 m × 8 m room. Each table requires a further 1 m wide surround for the chairs and free movement when people are seated.

a How many tables can be arranged in the room?

b If 10 sets of tables and chairs were required, what would be the dimensions of the smallest room that could accommodate them?

Assignment LT5

As a research worker for a consumer magazine, you are asked to investigate possible links between annual income, popular holiday destinations, annual expenditure on holidays etc. in order to provide data for a forthcoming article in the magazine.

a Design a suitable questionnaire which will produce the required data and carry out a survey.

b Use the data collected to illustrate possible correlations.

c State any apparent conclusions.

EXTENSION

The graph shows a possible connection between two variables, the number of people taking holidays and the holiday cost per person.

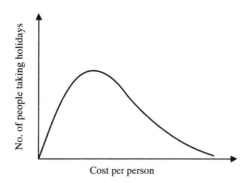

a State the connection between the two variables as shown by the graph.

b (i) What question(s) would you need to put to a sample of the public in order to test the validity of your statement?

(ii) Decide how sampling should take place and collect an adequate amount of data.

Assignment LT6

The pool in a Recreation Centre is used throughout the week by members of the public who may be either members or non-members of the recreation centre.

The rates fall into two categories for members (non-members) and are as follows.
Category 1: Adults £1.35 (£1.80)
Category 2: Juniors/Senior Citizens/Concessionary £0.65 (£1.10)

The table below details the average number of persons using the pool in a week.

	Member	Non Member
Adults	867	1024
Juniors	387	563
Seniors	203	98
Concessionary	31	57

a Produce a figure for the total week's income from the pool.

b Calculate the average payment per user.

c As a marketing strategy to increase the usage of the pool by non-members, a reduction in rates is to be announced which will apply for a trial week. If a 20% increase in attendance by non-members can be expected, what is the maximum percentage reduction that can be applied to the non-member rates so that the total week's income remains as calculated above?
(Assume that the number of members using the pool remains the same.)

Assignment LT7

The Leisure Centre pool is in the form of a cuboid, as indicated. The pool is 50 m long and 10 m wide with a depth of 2 m.

a Calculate the volume of water in the pool.

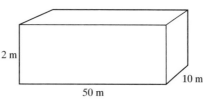

In the interests of health, the pool is emptied annually and thoroughly cleaned.
Some regrouting may be required if the pool is of a tiled construction.
The main costs involved are for the cleaning of the internal pool surfaces
(£1.65 per m²) and water replacement (£1.32 per m³).

b Calculate the total internal area of a pool.

c Calculate the total cost of cleaning and refilling the pool.

d The water drains out at 3 m³ per minute and flows in at 1 m³ per minute.
Cleaning is performed at a rate of 1m² per min.
Approximately how long (to the nearest hour) will the pool be out of action?

Estimate the length and width of the pool in your local Leisure or Recreation Centre.
Check your estimate to see how accurate you were.

EXTENSION

The pool is 50 m long by 10 m wide and has a cross-section as indicated with a shallow end depth of 1 m and a deep end depth of 3.5 m. The pool is 50 m long by 10 m wide.

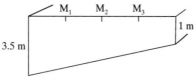

a Find the volume of water in the pool.

b In the interests of safety, depth markings are required at regular intervals along the pool edge. Estimate the depth at the mid-point M_2. What will be the readings at points M_1 and M_3 which are at the quarter and three-quarter distances?

Assignment LT8

The map shows part of the French Autoroute network with the distances (in kilometres) between main cities included.

a Identify three routes from Calais to Narbonne.

b What is the shortest route from Calais to Narbonne?

c Estimate the total expected toll charge during the journey from Calais to Narbonne. Assume that the toll is 1 Franc per 4 kilometres and that ring roads around all main cities are free and account for $\frac{1}{10}$th of the total distance travelled.

d Reims is three quarters of the distance from Calais to Troyes. What is the distance from Calais to Reims?

e Assuming 1 kilometre = $\frac{5}{8}$ mile, convert this distance into miles.

f The average speed for the journey is 60 mph. Find the time to get from Calais to Reims.

Assignment LT9

A specialist travel company is reviewing its marketing strategy and considering various forms of advertising to increase its sales.
One option which it includes as part of this strategy is a TV commercial.
The local television franchise operates on the scale of charges below. Charges depend on the particular time slot and whether the commercial lasts 10, 20 or 30 seconds. The cost of running a commercial is always calculated to the nearest second.

Rates	10 seconds	20 seconds	30 seconds
0930 - 1200	£120	£205	£240
1200 - 1700	£180	£310	£360
1700 - 2300	£600	£1020	£1200
2300 - 2500	£240	£410	£480

a Use the chart given to find the best time to screen the commercial if the message is to appeal to the maximum number of housewives. What is this time (to the nearest hour)?

b What will be the cost of screening a 26 second commercial at this time?

c How much cheaper will it be to screen the same commercial between 1200 and 1700 hours?

d The television company applies a 20% surcharge if a commercial is required to be screened on a specified day.
If the travel company requests that its commercial should be screened on a Friday, what will be the cost for 8 weeks in the case of **a** and **b** above?

e The TV company offers a 'volume discount' of 2% for expenditure between £20 000 and £30 000. If the travel company wishes to take advantage of this discount, what will be the minimum number of Friday screenings, between 1700 and 2300 hours, that it will need to finance?

TV viewing patterns

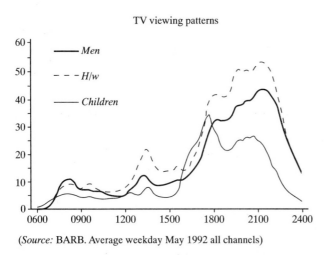

(*Source:* BARB. Average weekday May 1992 all channels)

Assignment LT10

This assignment specifically concerns the analysis and interpretation of charts, diagrams and tabulated data.

10.1 The chart shows the number of holidays of four nights or more taken by residents of Great Britain.

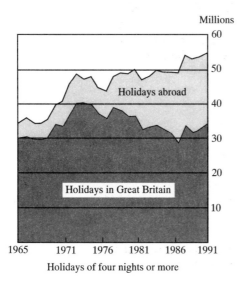

Holidays of four nights or more

(*Source:* British National Travel Survey. British Tourist Authority)

a Examine the chart and comment on:
  (i) the general trend observed
  (ii) any correlation between the peaks and troughs.

b How many holidays were taken in Great Britain in 1987?

c How many holidays were taken abroad in the same year?

d In which year were holidays in Great Britain at their peak?

e How many holidays were taken abroad in this year?

10.2   The bar chart has been produced from the tabulated data for the year 1991.

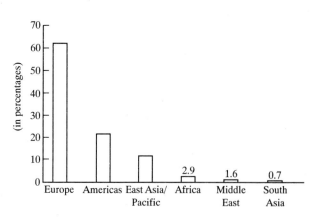

Share of each region in international tourist arrivals (1950-1991)

	Shares (in percentages)				
	1950	1960	1970	1980	1991
Africa	2.07	1.08	1.51	2.54	
Americas	29.61	24.11	22.95	21.32	
East Asia/Pacific	0.75	0.98	3.04	6.82	
Europe	66.60	72.66	70.76	65.55	
Middle East	0.78	0.91	1.17	2.98	
South Asia	0.19	0.26	0.57	0.79	
World	100.00	100.00	100.00	100.00	

(*Source:* World Tourism Organisation)

a   Use this bar chart to find the entries needed and complete the 1991 column.
    (Make sure that your figures give the correct total.)

b   Use the completed table to identify which part of the world has undergone the greatest change in terms of tourism popularity.

c   Perform a simple survey with an appropriate sample of people to see whether these figures are reflected locally.

10.3   The next two tables used in this assignment relate to UK travellers to EEC countries and contain information on:

   • the number (thousands) travelling to each EEC country
   • the average length of stay (days)
   • the average expenditure per visit (£).

a   By considering figures for the percentage growth in numbers of tourists for each country, find which country has the greatest percentage growth in number of tourists between 1980 and 1988.

b Use the two averages given to produce the average expenditure per day for 1980.
Hence find the countries which attracted (i) the greatest and (ii) the least average daily expenditure.

c Perform a similar investigation for 1988. Are the countries identified in (c) parts (i) and (ii) the same in both years?

Table	UK travellers abroad: numbers (by destination countries/areas) 1978 to 1988										
Principle country visited	1978 ('000)	1979 ('000)	1980 ('000)	1981 ('000)	1982 ('000)	1983 ('000)	1984 ('000)	1985 ('000)	1986 ('000)	1987 ('000)	1988 ('000)
United States	554	808	1,093	1,201	970	780	719	722	946	1,245	1,486
Canada	228	278	289	313	239	243	200	193	221	314	337
North America	782	1,087	1,382	1,514	1,299	1,023	919	914	1,167	1,559	1,823
Belgium/Luxembourg	520	538	671	614	894	831	776	755	761	642	758
France	2,686	3,208	3,844	4,513	5,002	5,058	4,482	4,523	5,188	5,321	5,032
West Germany	794	1,016	944	1,115	1,101	1,091	1,294	1,321	1,258	1,397	1,329
Italy	831	989	1,102	1,051	1,068	1,154	1,184	1,066	1,103	1,188	1,036
Netherlands	571	642	729	711	838	784	868	949	868	940	1,060
Denmark	106	127	136	170	175	128	136	151	154	152	131
Irish Republic	1,437	1,466	1,430	1,409	1,440	1,472	1,552	1,462	1,425	1,545	1,823
Greece	471	613	855	935	1,000	869	1,048	1,319	1,520	1,842	1,715
Spain	2,627	2,651	2,617	3,040	3,688	4,278	5,022	4,175	5,887	6,559	6,828
Portugal	211	273	364	401	472	547	573	709	956	903	1,108
Western Europe EEC	10,255	11,522	12,743	13,959	15,678	16,211	16,936	16,430	19,120	20,488	20,820

Table	UK travellers abroad: average length of stay, average expenditure per visit and per day (by destination countries/areas) 1976 to 1988							
	Average length of stay (days)				Average expenditure per visit (£)			
Principle country visited	1976	1980	1984	1988	1976	1980	1984	1988
United States	26.7	22.6	24.2	20.1	189.7	317.4	524.2	561.1
Canada	30.6	27.1	26.8	24.5	157.6	210.3	351.6	459.4
North America	28.2	23.5	24.8	20.9	177.9	295.0	486.5	542.3
Belgium/Luxembourg	5.0	3.9	3.4	4.3	45.2	65.1	89.8	123.9
France	7.9	7.3	6.7	7.8	58.9	97.5	118.4	189.7
West Germany	10.6	10.0	8.6	8.0	65.0	109.6	157.9	182.4
Italy	14.4	12.2	12.7	11.7	100.6	172.4	243.6	340.6
Netherlands	7.2	7.0	5.4	4.9	58.5	91.2	111.0	151.1
Denmark	10.7	8.8	8.0	7.4	91.0	124.1	148.9	272.0
Irish Republic	10.4	9.3	8.7	7.0	63.3	94.4	116.4	166.5
Greece	16.4	15.7	15.2	14.8	120.5	192.5	252.1	296.7
Spain	13.1	12.8	13.0	13.1	98.6	163.4	213.4	276.0
Portugal	17.8	12.7	14.0	12.9	140.4	182.6	228.5	288.3
Western Europe EEC	10.7	10.2	9.9	10.2	76.9	129.3	168.7	233.2

Assignment **LT11**

During a flight from Spain I am invited to buy drinks and duty free goods in either £ sterling or pesetas. The airline rate is quoted as 210 pts. = £1. The actual bank rate on the day I travel is 195 pts = £1.

If I buy a bottle of duty free spirits on the plane priced at £8.90 and I pay in pesetas, calculate:

  a how much I pay in pesetas

  b the amount in £ sterling that the airline will receive for my pesetas

  c the extra percentage profit being made by the airline if I pay in pesetas.

I am travelling on a charter flight and wish to purchase an alcoholic drink from the bar.
I buy a gin and tonic, plus a bottle of wine to have with my lunch, at a total cost of £3.70.

  d Find the cost in pesetas.

  e Find the amount in pounds which I would receive for these pesetas.

  f How much do I save (in £ sterling) by **not** paying in pesetas?

Assignment **LT12**

12.1 Many airports have a frame into which you can place your hand baggage to ensure that it complies with the accepted dimensions. This frame measures 23″ × 13″ × 9″.

  a What is the maximum volume for a bag which is cuboid in shape?

  b In the case of a barrel bag (or cylindrical shape package), what will be the maximum area of one end?

  c **Volume of cylinder = Area of end × Length.** What is the maximum volume that can be accommodated as cabin baggage?

  d Find the surface area of baggage in the form of:
   (i) the largest possible cuboid
   (ii) the largest possible cylinder.

12.2 The success of a local airport is often evident from the increase in the number of take-offs and landings each day. The number of flights per day has increased over the last three years for one particular airport and it has been observed that the number of flights per day has followed the sequence 3, 5, 7.
If the success of the airport continues how many flights per day can be expected in:

  a 3 years time?

  b 10 years time?

  c Produce a general formula from which these and subsequent flight figures can be obtained.

12.3 When large aircraft land at international airports the considerable quantity of baggage very often arrives in the baggage hall on one or more carousels.

I land at an airport where there are six carousels operating in the baggage hall and luggage is allocated to two carousels at random. Draw up a possibility space diagram to show all possibilities where two carousels are used and find:

a the probability that the luggage from my plane appears on two adjacent carousels

b the probability that my own single piece of luggage arrives on an even-numbered carousel

c the probability that my luggage arrives on the even-numbered of two adjacent carousels.

Assignment LT13

The cross-section of the channel tunnel approximates to a circle. The trackway is positioned such that it divides the circumference of this circle in the ratio 1 : 3.

If the tunnel has a diameter of 50 metres and is 45 km long, calculate:

a the length of a steel support girder, maintaining the shape of the tunnel above the trackway

b the area of steel casing used in the construction of the tunnel walls

c the total length of girder material used, given that steel support girders are placed every six metres along the length of the tunnel

d the volume of seabed removed during the course of construction.

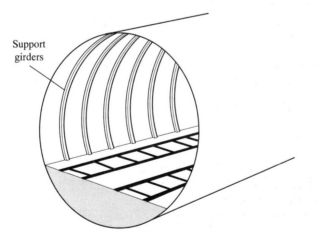

Manufacturing
ASSIGNMENTS

Numeracy Core Skills Matrix														
		Assignments												
Element	**Range**	1	2	3	4	5	6	7	8	9	10	11	12	13
3.1	1		✓						✓					
3.1	2		✓									✓		
3.1	3	✓	✓	✓	✓	✓	✓		✓	✓			✓	
3.1	4		✓									✓		
3.1	5		✓									✓		
3.1	6		✓									✓		
3.2	1	✓	✓	✓	✓	✓	✓	✓	✓	✓		✓	✓	✓
3.2	2	✓	✓	✓	✓	✓	✓	✓	✓	✓		✓	✓	✓
3.2	3			✓		✓				✓				✓
3.2	4	✓			✓	✓	✓	✓						✓
3.2	5	✓		✓	✓	✓	✓		✓	✓		✓	✓	✓
3.2	6		✓									✓		
3.2	7	✓		✓	✓	✓	✓			✓			✓	✓
3.2	8			✓					✓	✓				✓
3.2	9	✓		✓	✓		✓	✓						✓
3.2	10	✓		✓			✓			✓				
3.2	11	✓												
3.2	12	✓		✓		✓	✓	✓					✓	
3.2	13	✓		✓		✓	✓	✓					✓	
3.3	1	✓	✓	✓	✓	✓		✓	✓	✓		✓		✓
3.3	2		✓									✓		
3.3	3		✓									✓		
3.3	4	✓	✓	✓	✓	✓	✓	✓	✓	✓		✓	✓	✓
3.3	5	✓		✓	✓	✓	✓	✓				✓	✓	✓
3.3	6	✓									✓			
3.3	7	✓			✓						✓			

Assignment M1

1.1 A production line is filling bottles with non-alcoholic wine.
When the bottles reach the fill point it takes 2 seconds to fill four bottles simultaneously and then a further 3 seconds to bring the next four bottles into position ready to be filled.
Each bottle has a capacity of 75 ml.

Find:

a how many bottles are filled per hour

b how many litres of wine is being bottled per hour

c total production during an 8-hour day.

Further down the line each bottle has a cork inserted. Each cork is a cylinder with diameter 22 mm and length 45 mm.

d Find the volume of cork required for a day's production.

e 50 corks are stamped out of a single rectangular sheet of cork. Assuming the most economical method, what will be the dimensions of each sheet?

f How many of these rectangular cork sheets will be needed for a single day's production?

The bottles are eventually packed into cases of 12.

g How many cases will be needed to accommodate one day's production?

1.2 The winery regularly produces bottles in 75 ml and 150 ml for 3 large supermarket chains, each of which has its own brand label.
List all the possible labels which the winery must have available to meet demand.

1.3 If a shop stocks four drinks in three different types of container (can, bottle and carton), how many different items will be found on display in the shop?
At any one time, the shop has 30 cans, 10 bottles and 15 cartons on its shelves.
If a customer is equally likely to buy any type of container, find the probability that the customer buys:

a a can

b a can or a bottle.

EXTENSION

A foil top of depth 45 mm is added to hide the cork and is in the form of a crimped circular foil shape.
The external bottle diameter is 35 mm.
Examine actual wine bottles. Consider ways of producing foil caps in the most economical fashion from rectangular sheets of foil.
What area of foil is required for a single foil cap?

Assignment **M2**

2.1   The importance of recycling to the environmentally conscious will be apparent, but for some people this form of selective waste disposal will not be of major importance and in buying goods some people will not be persuaded by the 'green' argument.

Imagine that you are employed by a paper company presently manufacturing a variety of paper-based products from raw materials. Before committing itself to using recycled paper, the company commissions a survey to see which of its product range the public would still purchase if manufactured from recycled pulp.

Devise a suitable questionnaire to gauge public opinion if the company's product range includes toilet tissue, kitchen roll, paper handkerchiefs, writing paper, envelopes etc.

Organise your data into groups based on sex, age and income.

2.2   Estimate the weight of glass in a wine bottle. Weigh it to check your estimate.

The chart below indicates the weight of glass bottles collected from 13 districts in Hampshire.

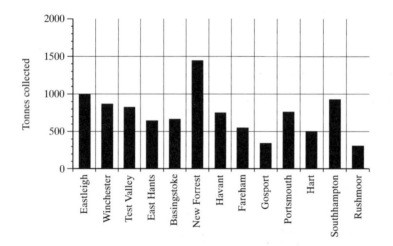

a   Find the total weight of glass collected (in tonnes).

b   Find the average weight per district.

c   How many district totals fall below this average figure?

2.3   The map opposite shows the proximity of bottle banks to a main recycling depot.
The scale of the map is 1 cm = 4 km.
The depot has one lorry to make collections and it makes no more than 3 collections in any one day.

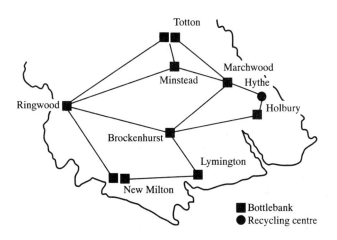

a What is the minimum number of days required to complete collections from all the centres indicated, some of which have more than one bottle bank?

b What is the furthest distance the lorry driver will have to travel in one day?

c If three collections are made on one day, what will be the minimum distance travelled?

d Use the table below giving population by district, in conjunction with the chart opposite to determine the most environmentally friendly district (i.e., the district which recycles the greatest amount of glass per head of the population).

Area	Population present		
	1991		
	Total persons	Males	Females
HAMPSHIRE	1,523,742	746,383	777,359
Districts			
Basingstoke and Deane	141,823	70,179	71,644
East Hampshire	101,606	49,701	51,905
Eastleigh	103,742	50,904	52,838
Fareham	97,496	47,795	49,701
Gosport	73,185	35,502	37,683
Hart	79,083	39,839	39,244
Havant	118,078	56,869	61,209
New Forest	158,898	76,193	82,705
Portsmouth	177,142	86,747	90,395
Rushmoor	80,850	40,808	40,042
Southhampton	195,906	95,868	100,038
Test Valley	99,348	49,428	49,920
Winchester	96,585	46,550	50,035

Assignment **M3**

A computer-controlled lathe is being used to produce metal bushes from a continuous rod of material.
The work involves cutting the shape from the rod and then parting off the finished turning from the rod.
The dimensions of the bush are shown in mm. There is a centrally drilled hole of diameter 5 mm. Parting off is accomplished with a 1.6 mm wide parting tool.
Find:

    a the volume of metal in each bush

    b the volume of waste in producing a single bush.

If the usable length of alloy rod fed through the chuck is 1.35 m find:

    c how many bushes can be produced from a single usable length of rod

    d the amount of waste material from each rod

    e the percentage waste from each usable rod length.

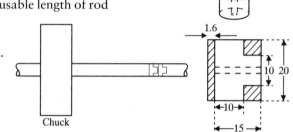

Chuck

Assignment **M4**

A spot-welding robot is being used in the manufacture of metal cuboid lockers.
The rate of spot welding is one weld every 4 seconds with the gap between each weld being 5 cm. A typical locker has the dimensions indicated with a single shelf welded to the casing on three sides.
The welding occurs along all the sides and between each side and both the top and bottom.

    a Find the total length to be welded.

    b How many welds will be required?

    c Assuming a continuous process, find the time taken to complete the welding process.

    d If the door is 157 cm × 25 cm with a flange (projecting edge) of 9 mm, what is the original size sheet of metal used?

Examine a locker construction and produce diagrams of the sheet metal shapes involved.
Use these to calculate the total area of metal sheet required for each locker.

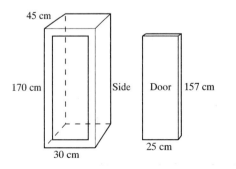

In another locker design 40 welds are applied to the back, 15 to the front and 25 to each of the two sides.
What is the probability that, at any one time, the weld is being applied to:

    e the front

    f the front or the side of the locker?

Assignment **M5**

In the production of specialised metal alloys from the molten state, various combinations of raw materials are mixed together in fixed proportions. The melt is usually poured into moulds to produce ingots which can either be cuboid in shape or of a trapezium cross-section.
Tungsten steel (which is used to manufacture cutting tools) and stainless steel have the following approximate percentage compositions:

Tungsten steel: 94% Iron + 5% Tungsten + 1% Carbon
Stainless steel: 73% Iron + 18% Chromium + 8% Nickel + 1% Carbon

Find:

    a the weights of iron and tungsten required to produce 20 tonnes of tungsten steel

    b the weights of chromium and nickel to be found in 45 tonnes of stainless steel.

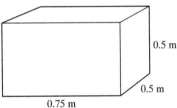

    c If each ingot is cuboid-shaped measuring 0.75 m × 0.5 m × 0.5 m and the density of tungsten steel is 7700 kg per cubic metre, find how many ingots will be produced by the 20 tonnes of tungsten steel.

EXTENSION

If the ingot mould has a length of 0.75 m with a cross-section which is a trapezium with parallel sides 0.5 m and 0.4 m with height 0.5 m and length 0.75 m, find:

    d the difference in volume of an ingot compared with the original cuboid shape

    e the additional number of ingots produced from the 20 tonnes of tungsten steel.

    Area of trapezium = $\frac{1}{2}(a + b)h$

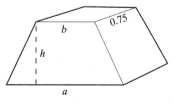

Assignment M6

In Assignment M1 the corks were 22 mm in diameter and cut from sheets of 45 mm thick cork.
The diagrams illustrate two possible ways in which this could be done.

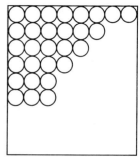

Method 1

    a Investigate which method would be the most economical.
Examine each method and determine the amount of waste produced.
Do your calculations confirm your original estimate?

    b Use Method 1 and assume an 8 mm gap between each cork and 4 mm between each cork and the edge of the sheet.
Find the area required for:
     (i) two corks
    (ii) three corks
   (iii) four corks
   (iv) n corks.

    c The actual process produces 50 corks at a time from cork sheet using Method 1.
What are the minimum dimensions of each cork sheet?
(Use of squared paper may help.)

    d Calculate the volume of waste cork from each sheet with these dimensions.

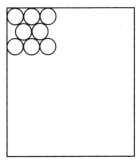

Method 2

The 'waste' from this process is collected and passed to a manufacturer of cork floor tiles.
A typical floor tile measures 300 mm × 300 mm and is 4 mm thick.

    e How many corks will need to be produced before there is sufficient cork waste to manufacture a packet of 10 cork tiles?

Assignment M7

Heavy-duty 250 mm diameter plastic pipe used for gas mains is stacked after production as shown in the diagram.

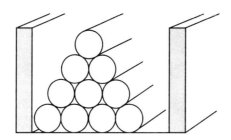

    a How many pipes will there be in the bottom layer if the stack is:
     (i) 2 rows high
    (ii) 3 rows high
   (iii) 15 rows high?

b What will be the total number of pipes in a stack which is:
  (i) 2 rows high
  (ii) 3 rows high
  (iii) 4 rows high?

c Give a sequence for the total number of pipes in n rows in terms of the total number in $n-1$ rows.

If there are r rows in the stack, the formula $S_r = \frac{1}{2}r(r+1)$ can be used to find the total number of pipes stacked this way.

d Verify that this formula gives the same answers for **b** above.

e If the stack is placed between two retaining walls 20 m apart, what is the maximum number of pipes that this stack can contain?

EXTENSION

Use Pythagoras' theorem to find the height h indicated in the diagram and hence calculate the vertical height of the stack referred to in part **e**.

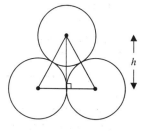

Assignment M8

The surveyor for a double-glazing company produces the window diagram shown below with the overall dimensions 1750 mm × 1150 mm. The three window areas are equal with two side-opening windows and the centre area having a top opening section.
The corners are mitred as indicated and the internal frame uprights and cross-member fixed as shown.

a If the constructor is working with 5 cm wide UPVC extrusion, what is the minimum length of extrusion needed?

b If the cost per metre is £2.38, what does the basic frame cost?

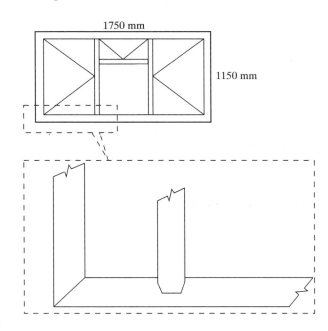

1750 mm

1150 mm

Assignment M9

Paint-spraying is being performed by a robot which is coating 2 m lengths of 50 mm square cross-section metal tube. After each pass of the spray nozzle the metal length is rotated through 90 degrees until all four sides are coated.

a The paint coating is 0.01 mm thick.
What volume of paint will be used per length?

b Some paint misses its target, leading to a wastage of paint equal in volume to 20% of the paint on the tube.
Calculate the volume of paint required to coat a run of 300 lengths of tube.

c A similar robot is used to put the initial coat of paint on both sides of a circular road sign.
Assuming similar wastage, what volume of paint will be required if the sign has a diameter of 0.6 metres?

Assignment M10

An engineering company manufactures three components: X, Y and Z. As part of quality control, batches of these components are regularly checked. On one inspection the number of defectives found in each batch of 100 components was found to be as follows:

Component	X	Y	Z
No. of defectives	5	4	7

a Find the probability of selecting from a batch of component Y, a non-defective component

b If a selection is made from each batch, what is the probability of picking at least one defective component?

EXTENSION

c If selections are made from two batches, chosen at random, find the probability of selecting:
   (i) a defective component X and a non-defective component Z
   (ii) a non-defective component X and a non-defective component Y.

A device made by the company includes all three components. The operation, and hence the reliability of this device, depends on these three components. It is found that the device will operate satisfactorily if two out of the three components function properly.

d Using the above figures find the probability that the device will operate satisfactorily.
(A tree diagram approach may help.)

Assignment M11

11.1 The network A shows a road system round four factory blocks.
Each block is a square of side 100 metres. The total length of roadway is 1300 m.
Factory security personnel start from their base at a corner of one block
and patrol by walking along each side at least once per tour.
Explain why it is necessary for the security personnel to walk 1600 m to
patrol the site once.
Networks B, C and D are other possible layouts of similar factories.
Copy and complete the table given below.

Lay-out	Length of roadway	Shortest distance travelled to patrol the roadway
A	1300 m	1600 m
B		
C		
D		

If security is the only consideration, which factory layout would you
choose and why?
Does it matter where the security base is situated?

11.2 A food production company has asked its sales department to
investigate the market penetration of one of its cereal products.
Imagine that you have been given this task and need to produce a
questionnaire which will allow collection of the following data:

- brand of favourite cereal
- reason for purchase (e.g. price/taste)
- weekly expenditure on cereals
- who in the household eats cereals
- etc.

Use your questionnaire to obtain the above data. From the data:

a Calculate the mean weekly expenditure on cereal products.

b Calculate the range of expenditure per week on cereal products.

c Illustrate your data on weekly expenditure as a bar chart.

11.3 A researcher is looking into people's attitudes to car ownership before
writing an article for a motoring magazine. Construct a series of
questions which will produce data on people's preference for diesel or
non-diesel cars.
Data obtained from the person interviewed should also include:

- preferred fuel (petrol, unleaded, diesel)
- age grouping
- size of car preferred
- details of present vehicle

Assignment ▮M12▮

A manufacturer of wooden pallets for forklift loading of heavy electrical goods produces them to an overall length of 1100 mm and width of 1000 mm. They look like this:

Three lengths with cross-sections of 100 mm × 70 mm maintain the gap for the forklift with 9 lengths of 100 mm × 15 mm forming the top and 3 lengths of 100 mm × 15 mm forming a base.

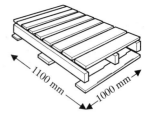

a What is the total length of each type of wood required for a single pallet?

b If both forms of timber come in rough-sawn 5 m lengths, how many lengths of each will be required for 50 pallets?

c When complete, the pallets are stacked in the manufacturer's yard ready for delivery.
In the interests of safety the maximum height of any stack is 20 pallets. If 240 pallets are stacked, what will be the dimensions of the minimum rectangular ground area taken up by the stack?

Assignment ▮M13▮

Manufactured articles which require careful handling (such as electrical goods) are usually packaged with surrounding polystyrene packing so that minor damage to the exterior packaging is unlikely to damage the article itself.
A microwave oven with dimensions 390 mm (H) × 558 mm (W) × 450 mm (D) is packed in a box with dimensions 405 mm (H) × 575 mm (W) × 467 mm (D).

a Calculate the volume taken up by the microwave oven.

b Calculate the volume of 'protection' surrounding the oven.

c What percentage of the box is occupied by the microwave oven?

d If these boxed ovens are stacked a maximum of 3 high on a 2 metre square pallet, how many boxes will be placed on each pallet?

e If these pallets were then placed in a container for transhipment to Japan, how many pallets would occupy one container if the container floor dimensions were 7 m by 3 m?

f How many microwave ovens would be shipped in a single container with these dimensions?

g If the boxes were loaded without using pallets and stacked 4 high, what would be the maximum number of boxes that the container would hold?

Solutions to Exercises

Note. Solutions are given for exercises with a 'closed' numerical answer. They are not provided for 'open-ended' questions and for some questions leading purely to an illustration (e.g. a pie-chart or graph).
Numerical answers are generally given correct to 3 significant figures.

Exercise 1.1

1 a 5 tens b 7 hundreds c 3 thousands d 4 units
  e 6 tenths f 2 hundredths
2 a 10, 17, 21, 45, 54, 86
  b 14, 23, 32, 104, 203, 230
  c 6, 60, 61, 600, 601, 610
  d 11, 99, 101, 110, 999, 1001
  e 297, 300, 399, 400, 420
3 7510 4 2369
5 a 430   d 132   g 516
  b 16700   e 590   h 7030
  c 20000   f 935.8   i 130
6 a 32   d 40.3   g 0.0027
  b 3   e 0.65   h 0.051
  c 40   f 0.065   i 0.0002
7 a 100 b 400 c 4100 d 6200

Exercise 1.2

1 41.9   2 180.3   3 133.97   4 16.7
5 16.71 6 51.75   7 169.4   8 702.36
9 1770   10 7.8   11 72.31   12 47.86

Exercise 1.3

1 26   2 36   3 5   4 1   5 1   6 7
7 0   8 66   9 133   10 2   11 £4.96
12 4   13 £78.01   14 a 988 b £4755
15 a 2 h 7 min (127 min) b £19.05
16 7 packs, £1.35   17 a 47.5 miles b £12.92
18 £1183.80   19 £160.50
20 a 7.39 kg b 135   21 a 9 b 14.6 cm

Exercise 1.4

1 a 2 b −4 c −10 d 4 e 6 f 40 g 0 h −49
2 a −1 b 17 c −13 d 20 e −3 f 0 g 50 h 36

Exercise 1.5

1 a −18 b −3 c 28 d $1\frac{3}{4}$ e −15
  f −27 g 8 h 36 i −1 j −10

Exercise 1.6

1 1, 4, 9, 16, 25, 36, 49, 64, 81, 100
2 1, 8, 27, 64, 125, 216
3 a 5 b 11 c 25 d 15 e 14
4 a (i) 3 (ii) −4 (iii) 9
  b 2 c (i) 3 (ii) 5
5 1 + 3 + 5 + 7 + 9
6 8   7 27   8 a 2 b 3 c 6 d $\frac{1}{2}$ e −4
9 3   10 100

Exercise 1.7

1 a 1 × 15 b 1 × 27 c 1 × 36 d 1 × 64
     3 × 5   3 × 9   2 × 18   2 × 32
                           3 × 12   4 × 16
                           4 × 9   8 × 8
                           6 × 6
  e 1 × 100
     2 × 50
     4 × 25
     5 × 20
     10 × 10
2 a (i) 1, 2, 3, 4, 6, 8, 12, 16, 24, 48
     (ii) 1, 2, 3, 4, 6, 8, 9, 12, 18, 24, 36, 72
  b 1, 2, 3, 4, 6, 8, 12, 24
3 64, 144, 116, 2620
4 a 5, 10, 20, 25 b 5, 10, 25 c 5, 10
  d 5, 25 e 5, 10, 20
5 a 240, 87, 96, 255 b 240, 96 c 240, 255

Exercise 2.1

1 9.74   2 0.36   3 147.5   4 29
5 0.53   6 4.20   7 1250   8 0.004
9 270   10 460.0

Exercise 2.2

1 a 3500 b 240 c 1200 d 300 e 250
  f 10 g 40 h 5
2 a 9 b 0.06 c 24
3 Incorrect calculations are c, d, e, f, h, i.

Exercise 2.3

1 52p   2 6 tins   3 5   4 a 27p b 3p
5 2m   6 25p   7 £10.91   8 £3.86
9 £1458.90   10 26

Exercise 2.4

1 11.8   2 73700   3 2.70   4 0.173   5 88.9
6 29.0   7 21.4   8 26.0   9 0.786   10 882.65
11 0.829   12 11   13 3.3

Exercise 2.5

1 a 7.9×10^5 b 4.6×10^{-3} c 3.13×10^4
  d 9.41×10^{-5} e 1×10^5 f 2.82×10^{-4}
  g 1.57×10^4 h 4.7×10^7 i 3.4×10^{-2}
  j 2.7×10^{-6} k 5×10^{-1} l 1.4×10^{-7}
2 a 7530 b 240 c 0.0019 d 0.837 e 0.0451
  f 40420 g 192000 h 0.000974
  i 0.0000068
3 a 6×10^4 b 5.18×10^0 c 4×10^1
  d 1.35×10^4 e 2.174×10^3 f 4×10^{-2}
  g 4.32×10^{-5} h 2.84×10^4 i -5×10^{-4}
  j 6×10^1
4 390   5 8 minutes 20 seconds

Exercise 2.6

1 a 2.3×10^{-5} kg b 8.70 m
2 3.5×10^4, 266.6 m   3 W\$756.25
4 4.096×10^7 5 2.303×10^{13} 6 1.34×10^7
7 a 1.32×10^5 b 362   8 106 days   9 \$4595
10 228 years

Exercise 3.1

1 a 8 b 8 c 18 d 9 e 7 f 9
2 a $\frac{2}{3}$ b $\frac{3}{4}$ c $\frac{2}{9}$ d $\frac{1}{3}$ e $\frac{3}{4}$
  f $\frac{2}{3}$ g $\frac{6}{13}$ h $\frac{2}{3}$
3 $\frac{2}{3}$ 4 a $\frac{9}{16}$ b $\frac{3}{16}$ 5 $\frac{3}{16}$ 6 $\frac{1}{4}$ 7 $\frac{4}{7}$
8 a $\frac{20}{9}$ b $\frac{31}{6}$ c $\frac{59}{12}$ d $\frac{111}{10}$ e $\frac{35}{4}$
  f $\frac{38}{3}$ g $\frac{143}{20}$ h $\frac{143}{7}$
9 a $1\frac{2}{7}$ b $7\frac{1}{5}$ c $3\frac{1}{3}$ d $7\frac{5}{8}$ e $13\frac{10}{11}$
  f $10\frac{7}{12}$ g $8\frac{4}{5}$ h $23\frac{1}{2}$

Exercise 3.2

1 $1\frac{3}{20}$ 2 $\frac{1}{24}$ 3 $\frac{2}{3}$ 4 $\frac{3}{4}$ 5 $\frac{1}{2}$ 6 $5\frac{1}{20}$
7 2   8 $\frac{7}{8}$ 9 $\frac{3}{20}$
10 a 6 b (i) $\frac{1}{4}$ in (ii) $\frac{11}{16}$ in   11 $\frac{1}{12}$
12 $\frac{2}{15}$ 13 a $\frac{1}{12}$ b 3
14 a $\frac{3}{25}$ b 400 mg aspirin, 40 mg ascorbic acid,
60 mg caffeine
15 $3\frac{5}{12}$ 16 7 in   17 $\frac{3}{16}$ in   18 $1\frac{7}{8}$ in

Exercise 3.3

1 $\frac{7}{10}$ 2 $1\frac{1}{3}$ 3 12   4 $1\frac{1}{9}$ 5 $7\frac{3}{20}$
6 $1\frac{5}{7}$ 7 a $\frac{3}{5}$ b 1 in
8 a $1\frac{1}{4}$ cm b 3 cm   9 £7.60
10 a $\frac{1}{4}$ b 6   11 $\frac{3}{4}$ stone
12 a 13 g b $\frac{3}{4}$ g   13 13   14 a £288 b 15
15 $1\frac{1}{8}$ in   16 a $7\frac{1}{2}$ in b $2\frac{1}{2}$ in

Exercise 3.4

1 a $\frac{8}{12} = \frac{2}{3}$, $0.\dot{6}$, b $\frac{1}{4}$, 0.25 c $\frac{5}{8}$, 0.625
2 a 0.1 b 0.5 c 0.75 d 1.45 e 4.84
  f $2.8\dot{3}$ g 7.4 h $3.14285\dot{7}$
3 a $\frac{1}{2}$ b $\frac{1}{4}$ c $\frac{2}{3}$ d $1\frac{1}{3}$ e $1\frac{3}{10}$
  f $2\frac{4}{5}$ g $3\frac{3}{5}$ h $2\frac{3}{20}$ i $\frac{1}{8}$ j $\frac{3}{8}$
5 a Insert d.p. into numerator 1 place from right.
  b Multiply numerator by 2 and change to tenths.
  c Insert d.p. into numerator 2 places from right.
  d Change to tenths then divide by 2.
  e Multiply numerator by 4 and change to hundredths.
6 34   7 a (i) $1\frac{2}{3}$ (ii) 1.67 b 80p
8 a 20 sheets b (i) $20\frac{5}{6}$ (ii) 20.83
9 (i) $4\frac{2}{3}$ hours (ii) 4.67 hours
10 (i) $3\frac{1}{5}$ hours (ii) 3.20 hours
11 (i) $1\frac{1}{4}$ (ii) 1.75

Exercise 4.1

1 5 : 6   2 4 : 5 : 10   3 20 : 9
4 a 3 : 2 b 10 : 1 c 12 : 1 d 1 : 4 e 4 : 3
  f 3 : 2 g 3 : 8 h 3 : 2 i 2 : 3
5 a 8 b 2 c 1.2 d 0.6 e 3.2 f 2.6
6 410 and 1025   7 $13\frac{1}{2}$ kg   8 3 : 20
9 a 125 b 200   10 3 : 16   11 28 floz
12 1 : 8   13 a 720 b 480   14 40 : 1   15 66

Exercise 4.2

1 £260, £390   2 £1500, £4500, £6000
3 £48, £32, £24   4 £1750, £1250, £1000
5 1360 g, 240 g   6 20
7 a £6318, £4212 b £15 760 c £9924
8 £26 154, £34 872, £17 436, £26 154
9 27, 45   10 40
11 a (i) 5 : 3 (ii) £7.50, £4.50 b 7.33, £4.67
12 £24   13 1813   14 a 192 b 720

Exercise 4.3

1 £3.18   2 £2.66   3 £1.26   4 £1.84   5 £4.40
6 £242   7 £430.50   8 44   9 200   10 4 hours
11 £1845   12 84   13 $\frac{11}{16}$ in

Exercise 4.4

1 a 1 cm b 4.8 cm c 1.1 m (110 cm)
  d 2.88 cm
2 a 20 cm b 1.24 m (124 cm)
  c 1.68 m (168 cm) d 75 ft e 90 in (7.5 ft)
3 a 45 in b 60 in × 24 in
4 a 1 : 40 b 48 in
5 a 1.05 m × 0.40 m b 0.65 m
6 100 m × 450 m   7 12.8 m^2
8 a 1 : 72 b 11 ft × 8 ft   9 3.65 m, 1.25 m
10 a 1 : 200 b 3.24 m^2

Exercise 4.5

1 a (i) 7 cm (ii) 14 cm × 12 cm (iii) 8 mm
  b (i) 93 cm (ii) $13\frac{1}{2}$ cm
    (iii) 69 cm × 60 cm
2 a 9 ft 2 in b 39.7 cm
3 a 20.4 m b 68 ft
4 a 6 cm × 3 cm b 1.24 m
5 a 8.8 cm b 5 m
6 a 1 : 150 b $2\frac{2}{3}$ cm
7 a 1 ft : 30 m b 6.3 ft
8 a 1 : 130 b 3.0 cm c 39 m

Exercise 5.1

2 a metres b millimetres c kilograms
  d kilometres e millimetres
3 5000 mm 4860 cm $\frac{1}{2}$ km 750 m
4 $\frac{3}{8}$ kg
5 a 1.232 km b 32 mm c 0.626 kg
  d 73.1 cl e 16.2 ml f 12 700 m
  g 0.0591 litres
6 230 g   7 20 days   8 1.55 kg
9 2.65 cm   10 665 litres
                    (665.8 litres including disinfectant)

Exercise 5.2

2 a 3.25 ft b 2 lb 8 oz c 5.5 yards
  d 27 in e 55 oz f 2.5 gal
  g 28 pt h 14 floz

3 $\frac{3}{4}$ pint   4 a 46.5 ft b 15.5 yards
5 $6\frac{1}{8}$ (6.125) oz   6 5 yd × $2\frac{1}{2}$ yd   7 40
8 5   9 20 yd 2 ft 4 in   10 $1\frac{1}{2}$ ft × $1\frac{1}{6}$ ft

Exercise 5.3

1 9 km
2 **a** 15 oz **b** 15.5 oz **e** 14.6 oz
3 **a** 454 g **b** 5.3 oz **c** 2.3 kg
   d 336 g **e** 0.5 oz
4 **a** 0.219 gal **b** 4.4 gal
5 3.52 miles per litre
6 **a** 152 (150) mm **b** 14.6 (14.8) in
   c 17.5 (16) ft **7** 80 kph
8 **a** 42 lb **b** 2 lb **9** 6 in **10** 25.4 kg
11 1.60 m − 1.83 m **b** 22.9 m
12 **a** 77.8 g **b** 0.579 troy ounces
13 57 mm, 89 mm, 22 mm, 32 mm
14 28

Exercise 5.4

1 6.4 cm, 2.5 in **2** Approx, 2.3 m to 5 m
3 335 g **4** 98.5 °F **5** 15 min 10.6 s
6 **a** 30 mph **b** 50 kph **7** 5 psi

Exercise 6.1

1 **a** 20% **b** $12\frac{1}{2}$% **c** 70% **d** 65% **e** $66\frac{2}{3}$%
   f 36% **g** 175% **h** 250%
2 **a** $\frac{3}{5}$ **b** $\frac{1}{4}$ **c** $\frac{1}{10}$ **d** $\frac{17}{20}$ **e** $\frac{3}{20}$ **f** $1\frac{3}{20}$
   g $\frac{3}{8}$ **h** $\frac{1}{3}$
3

a		0.75	75%
b	$\frac{1}{2}$		50%
c		0.125	$12\frac{1}{2}$%
d	$\frac{1}{3}$	0.3	
e	$\frac{3}{8}$		$37\frac{1}{2}$%
f		0.7	70%
g	$\frac{7}{20}$	0.35	
h	$\frac{2}{3}$		$66\frac{2}{3}$%
i		0.6	60%
j	$\frac{5}{8}$	0.625	

Exercise 6.2

1 **a** £1.38 **b** £318.62 **c** £22.12 **d** £13.91 **e** £5.17
   f £8.73 **g** £97.20 **h** £44.20

Exercise 6.3

1 **a** £10.12 **b** £4.07 **c** £5.50 **d** £10.79 **e** £10.04
2 **a** £108.18 **b** £1.05 **c** £792.00 **d** £233.75
   e £156.00 **f** £21.69

Exercise 6.4

1 **a** £24.00 **b** £8.40 **c** £14.08 **d** 36p **e** £10.39
2 **a** £49.77 **b** 59p **c** £51.20 **d** £23.76 **e** £59.43
   f £1.09

Exercise 6.5

1 **a** 80.0% **b** 3.45% **c** 175% **d** 50%
   e 54.5% **f** 130%
2 **a** +23.1% **b** +20.0% **c** +375% **d** −20.0%
   e −45.5% **f** +464%

Exercise 6.6

1 **a** 18% **2 a** 260 **b** 78 **3** 12%
   4 a 20000 **b** 7500 **c** 36.2%

5 **a** 406 **b** 146 **6** £2.64 **7** £3.43
8 £1335.70 **9** 616 **10** £2240

Exercise 7.1

1 £172.20 **2** £479.67 **3** £6.43 **4** £11582.40
5 £98.28 **6** £23700 **7** £7320 **8** £186.82
9 £5244 **10** 151.36 **11** £5.526 **12** £36.95
13 **a** £259.70 **b** £155.75 **c** £441
14 £4.2667

Exercise 7.2

1 £344.10 **2** £259.89 **3 a** £3.50 **b** 4
4 £163.68 **5** £8.43 **6** £199.80 **7** £280
8 £162.40 **9** £245.33 **10** £121.50
11 £266.53
12 Andrews £163.18; Collins £214.92;
    Hammond £210.94; Jali £254.72
    Longman £246.76
13 £4.45

Exercise 7.3

1 £1560 **2** £24.72 **3** £1883.20
4 £493.20 **5** £1138 **6** £1456
7 **a** Firm B by £500 **b** Firm A by £250
8 £233.55 **9** £94 **10** £48 **11** £99.40
12 £304 **13** £380.70

Exercise 7.4

1 £59.04 **2** £56.40 **3** £3.99 **4** £228.70
5 £182 **6** £362 **7** £243.50 **8** £26 **9** £440
10 1570 Fr **11** £52.38 **12** £89.20

Exercise 7.5

1 **a** (i) £3445 (ii) £1055 (iii) 211
   b (i) £5165 (ii) £1785 (iii) £357
   c (i) £5165 (ii) nil (iii) nil
2 £396 **3** £34.28 **4 a** £535.60 **b** £373
5 £37.18 **6** £557 **7** £39.92
8 **a** (i) £5165 (ii) £1035 (iii) £207
   b (i) £3445 (ii) £2327 (iii) £465.40
9 £39.40 **10** £49.10 **11** £6.13 **12** £595
13 £30.50

Exercise 7.6

1 **a** £2001.25 **b** £1354.75 **c** £2915
2 **a** £3920 **b** £3490
3 **a** £112.10 **b** £60.38 **c** £137.20
4 £5951.25 **5** £444.90 **6** £5163 **7** £444.48
8 £207.92 **9** £292.40 **10** £5466.25
11 £447.81 **12** £276.83 **13** £5524.25

Exercise 8.1

1 **a** 235.8 Sch **b** 24920 Pts **c** $161.16
2 **a** £19.90 **b** £5.03 **c** £2.44
3 £16 **4 a** £57.09 **b** 28.5p
5 **a** 1678.80 DM **b** 6023.78 Sch
6 **a** 1370250 Lira **b** 320250 Lira **c** £70.93
   d £7.68
7 **a** 945 Fr **b** £94.03 **c** £5.97

Exercise 8.2

1 a £1 b £1 c £7.97 2 a £3 b £6
3 a £304.98 DM; 243.34 SFr; 2338.35 Sch
  b (i) £570 (ii) £5.70 c £226.43

Exercise 8.3

1 6.15 am; 0615
2 Ten past eleven in the evening; 2310
3 Half past nine in the morning; 9.30 am
4 Twenty to two in the morning; 0140
5 Ten to two in the afternoon; 1.50 pm
6 Twenty past ten in the evening; 10.20 pm
7 9.50 pm; 2150
8 Quarter to eleven in the morning; 1045
9 12.25 am; 0025
10 Four minutes to five in the afternoon; 4.56 pm

Exercise 8.4

1 14 minutes 2 0655 3 Nine thirty 4 0942
5 a 1623 b 28 minutes 6 1 hour 45 minutes
7 a 1945 b 2030

Exercise 8.5

1 a 20 minutes b 4 c 39 minutes
  d 1451, 1543 (or 1551)
2 a 5 b 0030 Belgium time c 25 minutes
  d 0930 e 1 hour f 1335

Exercise 8.6

1 £118.62 2 a 1155 b 1650
3 a Ease of access to airport; Departure time or arrival
    time in Naples; Experience of the airline.
  b American: 2335; Virgin: 0040
4 £94.09 5 1313 6 £256.27
7 £321 8 5.09 pm 9 65.8%
10 a 1045 b 2100 British time

Exercise 9.1

1 Discrete   2 Continuous   3 Continuous
4 Continuous   5 Qualitative   6 Continuous
7 Continuous   8 Qualitative   9 Discrete
10 Qualitative 11 Discrete   12 Qualitative

Exercise 10.1

1 a total population of the town
  b people asked at a particular time in a particular
    shopping street
  c Specify the intended catchment area of the new
    shopping centre. Use the electoral role for this area to
    select a random sample.
2 a all the students in the college
  b She only asks people in the common room, and she
    only asks girls.
  c Find students' enrolment numbers, and select 50
    random numbers in the range of numbers given.
3 a all cars in the UK
  b The police only check cars between 5pm and 6pm.
  c Sample at different times of the day on different days
    of the week on different roads.

4 a the soil in his garden
  b only one sample. Soil beyond the range of his throw
    cannot be sampled.
  c Draw a plan of the garden and divide into numbered
    squares. Use random sampling to choose several
    squares and take samples from these areas.
5 a all teenagers
  b Carol only asked people entering a tobacconist's. The
    sample is biased towards smokers. Carol should only
    ask teenagers.
  c Obtain a list of pupils in the school; select a random
    sample from the list.
6 a any homes in the telephone area
  b The salesgirl only asks those with a telephone. The
    sample includes only those who are at home when the
    salesgirl rings.
  c The salesgirl needs to know the number of homes in
    the area. She needs to use the rating register (used in
    water rates) to identify homes. Their reference
    numbers can be used to obtain a random sample.
7 a all cars owned by people in an area
  b Peter only asked people at home during one
    afternoon. The responses came from a small part of
    the town.
  c Use the DVLC in Swansea to produce a list of cars
    registered as being owned by people in the required
    area. Use random numbers to obtain a sample of the
    required size.
8 a all people who travel to work in John's area
  b People at the station would be biased towards those
    using a train to go to work.
  c Use the electoral role and ask a random sample from
    this how they travel to work. If they do not work,
    delete them from the sample. Continue with a random
    selection until you have a suitable number who do
    work.

Exercise 10.3

1 a Analyse rainfall for the given period over several
    years.
  b Devise a questionnaire, survey or experiment.

Exercise 11.1

(Frequencies only are given)
1 8, 7, 5, 5, 4, 3, 1, 2, 1, 1, 1, 0, 1, 0, 1
2 1, 3, 5, 10, 19, 6, 6
3 18, 17, 13, 7, 4, 2, 1, 0, 1
4 4, 8, 9, 8, 9, 6, 2, 2, 2
5 a 1, 4, 4, 4, 8, 5, 4, 3, 5, 1, 1
  b 1, 8, 15, 8, 6, 2
6 1, 14, 23, 19, 6
7 5, 6, 2, 8, 10, 12, 3, 4
8 9, 11, 8, 11, 5, 8, 12, 11, 5
9 1, 7, 15, 16, 9, 2
10 31, 13, 15, 1
11 1, 0, 5, 16, 13, 4, 1

Exercise 12.1

1 a East Lynne b 50 c 410
4 a 175 b 8.3% c 4 : 1
7 a Soft white baps b 6
  c 61.9(62)%

9 a 20 b Evensong c 110
11 a Plymouth – Roscoff b $3\frac{3}{4}$ hours
   c $2\frac{1}{2}$ hours
13 a 5 b Train c 150

Exercise 12.2

1 a Oak b Oak 80; Elm 10; Chestnut 20;
   Beech 40; Conifer 70; Cedar 25 c 245
6 a A; Adverts on hoarding B are aimed at more
   prosperous suburban inhabitants.
   b 2 c Football club and health education
10 a £30 000 b £27 500 c £2500 d Central
   support; reputation; length of franchise
17 a Estate 1 has more occupants in professional jobs;
   Estate 2 has more occupants in 'blue collar' jobs.
   b (i) 10% (ii) 38% c 30%
18 a (i) 15 (ii) 4 b 70% c The Maples
20 a Chandler b 20 c 18 : 7 d 44%

Exercise 12.3

4 a 160 b 120 c 220 d 140
6 a 40° b 25 c 50 d $\frac{5}{18}$
10 40 476; 20 238; 85 714
12 a 298 b 46 c 306
16 a 325 b 290 c 210 d 87.8%
18 a 72.2% b 458 000 acres

Exercise 12.4

5 a 1 040 000 b 1927, 1951, 1974 c 1940
6 a Tiredness as the week goes by b 226
7 a £75 (6) b £200 c There are more points plotted
   around 1984 which fit the straight line.
   d 1976
8 b 8 am – 9 am heating was turned on
   c after 8.20 pm
9 a 52.5 (±0.5) in b 4 – 6 years
   c It will slow down and eventually stop.
11 a continuous line
   b December (London), October (Nice)
   c June (both) d February
12 b Summer is peak time, but numbers of passengers
   could be declining, whereas winter numbers seem to
   be increasing.
14 a August; new registration letter
   b 21 . c 185 d 31

Exercise 12.5

2 b A low absence rate is more likely on Mondays and a
   high one on Fridays.
3 b Book 1: Science fiction
   Book 2: Child's story
   Book 1 has a greater number of long words and Book
   2 has a greater number of short words.
4 There has been a move to 'Ultimate Style' from 'Danish
   Design'.
6 There are more women than men over the age of 60.
7 b The experimental results are very close to the expected
   results.
8 There were less faults on the new model.

Exercise 13.1

1 £130 2 68.27 mph 3 38.58
4 The ages are given to the last complete year. A person
   aged 17 is between 17 years 0 days and 17 years 364
   days old. Therefore, the true mean is probably above
   $28\frac{3}{4}$; hence John is probably correct.
5 1.848 m 6 104.8 7 a 1.29 m b Yes
8 a 1125 b 75 w.p.m.
9 a £496.14 b £5.04 10 13.5
11 a 164 lb b 32.8 lb
   c $13\frac{2}{3}$ (13.7) lb per week
12 a 21.9°C b (i) 18.75°C (ii) 24°C
13 a 51.78 m b 67.89 m
   c Considerable improvement (over 16 m)
14 Average is 40.9 mpg. Therefore, taking values to 2 s.f.,
   he is justified.
15 6 min 5 seconds

Exercise 13.2

1 a 4 b 4 2 Blue 3 110 – 114
4 a 12.5 b 11 5 6.35 kg 6 1
7 a James and Linda b 5ft $2\frac{1}{2}$ in c Mode
8 a 50p b 44p
9 a £10 000 b £10 000 c £16 800
   d Mode or median
10 a 9.00 – 11.00 b 70 – 75
11 a 18 b 16 12 St Lucia
13 a £112 b £112 14 a 4 b 2.5
15 4:55 (4 min 55 sec)

Exercise 13.3

1 Mode 2 Median 3 Mode
4 Median 5 Mean
6 Mean or median 7 Median
8 Mean 9 Mean
10 Any, but the mean is preferable.

Exercise 13.4

1 6 2 26.60 min (= 26 min 36 s)
3 7.79 words
4 a 1.43 b 1 c 0 d Median
5 a 4.17 b 4 6 a 7.5 b 7.06
7 a 3.5 b 3.28 8 a 1 b 1
9 a 4.08 b 4 c Median
10 a 2.42 b 2.5 11 a 2.94 b 3
12 a 0.52 b 0 c Mean
13 a 19 b 19.3
   c Close match between mean and median

Exercise 13.5

1 17 in 2 a 12.6 min b 10 min
3 a (i) 31.8 (ii) 36.3
   b (i) 50 (ii) 25 4 34 5 8.9
6 a 38.2, 41 b 56, 22 c Beach 2. It has a slightly higher
   average number of shells and is more consistent.
7 a £16.10, £2.55, £16.82, £2.60
   Similar ranges, but Club 2 has a higher mean.
   b £15.80, £16.95
   c Club 1: distribution is positively skewed since
   median < mean; Club 2: distribution is negatively
   skewed since median > mean.

8 a 122.3, 82.5 **b** (i) 30 (ii) 30
   c Blood pressure high on day 8, both pressures below
   normal on day 10.
9 a 55.8 cm, 55.5 cm **b** 51.0 cm, 114 cm
   c The first archer, who is more consistent
10 a 50.3, 48.7 **b** 4.47, 2.94 **c** Machine 3 has a mean
   close to 50 but is variable.
   Machine 5 is producing ball bearings which are
   consistently below size and should be adjusted.

Exercise 14.1

1 **a** 32 **b** 28 **c** 35 **d** 7 **e** 8
2 **a** 58 **b** 44 **c** 71 **d** 27
   e (i) 4 (ii) 83 (iii) 80
3 **e** 8   4 **e** 30(±1)   5 **e** 16(±1)
6 **e** 89%   7 **e** (i) 10 (ii) 10
8 **e** 4(±$\frac{1}{2}$)   9 **e** 88   10 **e** 96(±1) seconds
11 **e** (i) 10 (ii) 52
13 **b** (i) 190 g (ii) 74 **c** (i) 34 kg (ii) 21 kg

Exercise 15.1

1 $\frac{13}{15}$ 2 $\frac{3}{10}$ 3 $\frac{8}{9}$ 4 $\frac{1}{3}$ 5 $\frac{2}{5}$

Exercise 15.2

1 $\frac{3}{10}$ 2 $\frac{1}{6}$ 3 $\frac{1}{2}$ 4 **a** $\frac{1}{2}$ **b** $\frac{1}{13}$ **c** $\frac{1}{52}$
5 $\frac{6}{11}$ 6 **a** $\frac{1}{3}$ **b** $\frac{7}{9}$ 7 $\frac{3}{4}$ 8 $\frac{2}{5}$
9 $\frac{1}{124}$ 10 $\frac{17}{20}$

Exercise 15.3

1 **a** $\frac{1}{4}$ **b** $\frac{2}{13}$ **c** $\frac{21}{52}$ **d** $\frac{2}{13}$
2 $\frac{1}{2}$ 3 $\frac{7}{10}$
4 **a** $\frac{1}{2}$ **b** $\frac{7}{10}$ **c** $\frac{3}{5}$
5 $\frac{7}{20}$ 6 **a** $\frac{1}{2}$ **b** $\frac{1}{4}$ **c** $\frac{3}{4}$
7 **a** $\frac{5}{8}$ **b** $\frac{3}{8}$ 8 **a** $\frac{3}{8}$ **b** $\frac{1}{2}$
9 **a** $\frac{1}{2}$ **b** $\frac{1}{4}$ **c** $\frac{9}{20}$ 10 **a** $\frac{5}{18}$ **b** $\frac{8}{9}$

Exercise 15.4

1 **a** $\frac{1}{9}$ **b** $\frac{1}{18}$ **c** $\frac{1}{18}$ 2 **a** $\frac{1}{4}$ **b** $\frac{1}{2}$
3 **a** $\frac{1}{4}$ **b** $\frac{3}{16}$ 4 **a** $\frac{1}{6}$ **b** $\frac{1}{12}$
5 **a** $\frac{1}{3}$ **b** $\frac{1}{8}$
6 **a** $\frac{1}{8}$ **b** $\frac{1}{2}$ 7 **a** $\frac{1}{4}$ **b** $\frac{1}{2}$ **c** $\frac{1}{6}$
8 **a** $\frac{1}{4}$ **b** $\frac{1}{2}$ **c** $\frac{1}{6}$ 9 **a** $\frac{1}{2}$ **b** $\frac{1}{10}$ **c** 0
10 **a** $\frac{1}{9}$ **b** $\frac{1}{3}$ **c** $\frac{1}{3}$
11 **a**

Hester:

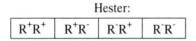

R⁺R⁺	R⁺R⁻	R⁻R⁺	R⁻R⁻

b

Child:

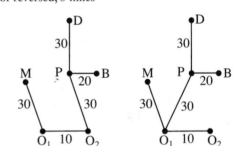

R⁺R⁺	R⁺R⁺	R⁻R⁺	R⁻R⁺	R⁺R⁺	R⁺R⁻	R⁻R⁺	R⁻R⁻	R⁻R⁻	R⁺R⁺	R⁻R⁻	R⁻R⁺	R⁺R⁻	R⁺R⁻	R⁻R⁻	R⁻R⁻

c $\frac{1}{4}$; $\frac{3}{4}$
12 **a** $\frac{1}{3}$ **b** $\frac{2}{3}$ **c** $\frac{1}{2}$
13 **a** $\frac{1}{6}$ **b** $\frac{1}{2}$ **c** $\frac{3}{4}$ 14 **a** $\frac{1}{8}$ **b** $\frac{3}{8}$
15 **a** $\frac{1}{4}$ **b** $\frac{1}{4}$ **c** 0

Exercise 16.1

1 **a** A – B – F – C **b** B – E – G – D
   c C – F – B – E – G – D
2 **a** 52 min **b** Alton → Farnham → Guildford
   → Leatherhead → Wimbledon
3 **a**

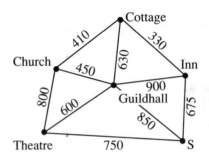

b S → Inn → Cottage → Church → Guildhall →
   Theatre → S or in reverse
c 3215 m (= 3.215 km)
4 **a** A → F → D → M → W → C → A
   or reversed
b 85 miles
c A → F → D → M → W → C → A
   or A → F → D → C → W → M → A
   or reversed, 5 miles
5 **a**

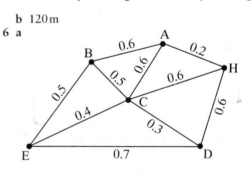

b 120 m
6 **a**

b H → D → C → E → B → A → H or reversed
c 2.6 miles

7 a

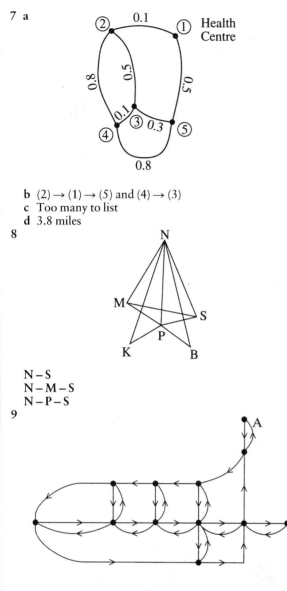

b (2) → (1) → (5) and (4) → (3)
c Too many to list
d 3.8 miles

8

N − S
N − M − S
N − P − S

9

Other solutions are possible.

10 a 12 min
b

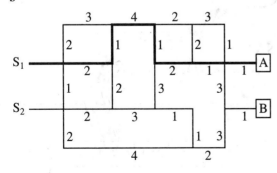

11 a 400 m
b Working anticlockwise:
S → A → E → S → D → S → C → B → S
There are alternative versions of this route which
visit the delivery points in a different order.

Exercise 16.2

1 a equilateral triangle **b** hexagon
c parallelogram
2 a 4, 3, 2, 1 **b** 4, 2, **c** 2
3 a cylinder **b** cube
4 a quadrilateral **b** parallelogram **c** kite
d trapezium **e** trapezium **f** quadrilateral

5

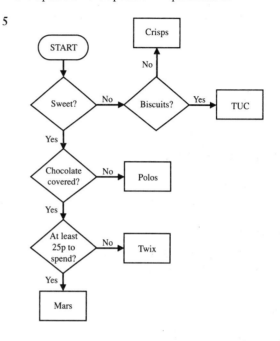

6 a Is it in good condition? **b** Jumble
c Yes **d** Has it been worn in the last two years?
e No **f** OXFAM **g** Keep it.
7 a A: Full price = £5
B : Damaged?
C: Slightly damaged?
D: Half price
E : Reduce by 20%
F : Unsold for 6 months?
G: Destroy
H: Full price
b £4 **c** £3.75
8 A: Enter details of incoming mail in log book
B : Is it a letter?
C: Marked confidential?
D: Do contents match delivery note?
E : Open letters
F : Return to sender
G: Does it contain cash or a cheque?
H: Deliver goods
I : Marked urgent?
J : Hand deliver
K: Put into pigeon holes
9 a A: Assess the patient's injury/condition?
B : Is it an emergency?
C: Is the patient conscious?
D: Is the patient's condition serious?
E : Put into a cubicle for attention asap
F : Send to casualty waiting room
G: Add to waiting list
b (i) Give immediate attention
(ii) Send to the waiting room and add to the list

10 a A: Twin-bed room
      B: Single room
      C: Difficulty climbing stairs?
      D: Ground floor room available?
      E: Over 50 years of age?
      F: First floor room available?
      G: Allocate room
      H: Second floor room available?
      I: Allocate room
      J: No room available
   b (i) First floor, twin-bed room
      (ii) Second floor, single room
11 a A: Goods received
      B: Laundry/washing?
      C: Leisure/entertainment?
      D: Goods larger than 0.5 cu ft?
      E: Beauty products?
   b (i) Area 2 (ii) Area 6 (iii) Area 5 (iv) Area 7

Exercise 17.1

1 $7x + 5y$ 2 $2p - q$ or $q - 2p$ 3 $\dfrac{2a}{b}$

4 $5x - 8$ 5 $\dfrac{y}{4} + 6$ 6 $4a + 3c$

7 $4b + 6r + 2w$ 8 $4r + 3p + 2t$
9 $6l + 8p + 2i$ 10 $22n + 3p$
11 $4t + 5r + 3s$ 12 $3a + 5c$
13 $7f + 5s + 3e$ 14 $2h + 3i + 22s$
15 $28f + 12m + 15w$

Exercise 17.2

1 $5x$ 2 $7n$ 3 $8a$ 4 $2y$
5 $7a + 6b + 4c$ 6 $x + 5y + 9z$
7 $9p + 2q + r$ 8 $5x - 3y + z$
9 $-a - b + 4c$ 10 $3x + 5y$

Exercise 17.3

1 a 11 b −1 c 13 d 6 e $\frac{1}{2}$ f 2 g −30
   h −4 i 0 j 17 k −1 l −2
2 a 1 b −9 c −5 d −6 e 0.3 f −14 g 6
   h 8 i 10 j −5 k 1 l −2
3 a 9 b −24 c 8 d $\frac{4}{3}$ e −5 f $-\frac{3}{4}$ g 38
   h 7 i 28 j 1 k 0 l 14
4 a $\frac{1}{2}$ b 1 c 2 d −4 e $2\frac{1}{2}$ f $-\frac{1}{4}$ g $8\frac{1}{2}$
   h $\frac{3}{5}$ i 3 j −1 k −8 l $4\frac{1}{2}$

Exercise 17.4

1 $5x$ 2 $3mn$ 3 $\dfrac{2y}{z}$ 4 abc 5 $6pqr$

6 $\dfrac{4bc}{d}$ 7 $6xy$ 8 $\dfrac{-2p}{q}$ 9 $\dfrac{9xy}{z}$ 10 a^3

11 a^2b^2 12 $3a^3$ 13 $3a^3b^2$ 14 $-6a^2b^2c$
15 $6a^2b^4c^2$ 16 $9a^2b$ 17 $-18ab^3$ 18 $-2a$

19 x^3y^3 20 $\dfrac{-9a^2b}{c}$

Exercise 17.5

1 x^8 2 x^6 3 x^3 4 x^{-1} 5 $x^0 = 1$

6 $\dfrac{1}{x^2}$ 7 1   8 $\dfrac{3x^2}{2^2}$ 9 $\dfrac{1}{2x^2}$ 10 $4x^2$

11 $-18x^4$ 12 $-\frac{7}{2}$ (or $-3\frac{1}{2}$)

Exercise 17.6

1 $20x + 8y$ 2 $6a - 12b$ 3 $-6p + 12q$
4 $5x - 15y + 10z$ 5 $-a + b + c$
6 $3x^2 - xy + 2xz$ 7 $-a^2 - ab + ac$
8 $2x^3 + 3x^2 + 2x$ 9 $4y^3 - 12y^2 + 4y$
10 $-5x + 10x^2 - 5x^3$ 11 $5x + 2y$
12 $y^2 + y - 12$
13 $9a + 17b$ 14 $8p - 15q$ 15 $x^2 - 11xy$

Exercise 17.7

1 $4(x + 3y)$ 2 $3(p - 2q)$ 3 $5(a + 2)$
4 $5(2b - 1)$ 5 $7(2m - 3n)$ 6 $4(3s + 5t)$
7 $x(y + z)$ 8 $x(y + x)$ 9 $y(y - 2)$ 10 $2y(y - 2)$
11 $3x(2y + 1)$ 12 $5x(1 - 2x)$ 13 $2(a + 4b - 2c)$
14 $3(3x - y - 2z)$ 15 $5(3x - y + 2)$
16 $7(p - 2q + r)$ 17 $2a(a + 2b - 4)$
18 $3p(p + 2q - 3)$ 19 $xy(x + z + y)$
20 $4pq(r - 3p)$

Exercise 17.8

1 $n + 5 = 12$ 2 $n - 7 = 13$ 3 $2n + 4 = 10$
4 $7n = 21$ 5 $5n - 6 = 29$ 6 $\frac{1}{2}n + 10 = 22$
7 $2n - 3 = 3$ 8 $\frac{1}{4}n - 3 = 3$ 9 $2(x + 2x) = 18$
10 $x + (x - 2) + (x + 5) = 27$ 11 $3x + x = 20$
12 $2x + x + 2x + 20 = 135$ 13 $2(x + 2x) = 12.6$
14 $14x + 10(x + 6) + 6(x - 4) = 906$
15 $2(2x) + 3x = 77$ 16 $4 + 2x + (x - 3) = 37$
17 $4x + 2x + x = 1750$
18 $4(3x) + 2(3x) + x + 2(2x) = 10\,350$

Exercise 17.9

1 7   2 20   3 3   4 3   5 7   6 24   7 3
8 24   9 3 cm   10 13 cm   11 5   12 66
13 4.2 ft   14 35   15 22   16 9   17 250
18 1350   19 4   20 3   21 6   22 8   23 3
24 6   25 10   26 8   27 9   28 20

Exercise 17.10

1 4   2 3   3 2   4 $\frac{1}{3}$ 5 9   6 2
7 0   8 10   9 4   10 1   11 3   12 −5.2

Exercise 17.11

1 a (i) $(x + 25)$ pence   (ii) $12x$ pence
      (iii) $10(x + 25)$
   b (i) $12x + 10(x + 25) = 690$ (ii) $x = 20$p
      (iii) 45p
2 a £$(2x + 2.50)$ b £1.25   3 55p
4 a $3x + 4.40 = 50 - 7.50$ b £12.70
5 a $x + 0.3$ b $4x + 7(x + 0.3) = 19.70$ c £1.60
6 a $8x + 5(x + 0.26) = 6.63$ b 41p   7 £1.20
8 68 kg   9 15 min
10 a £$9x$ b £$5(20 - x)$ c £$(4x + 100)$
    d $4x + 100 = 148$ e 12 matches
11 a (i) $2x$ (ii) $2x - 5$
    b $2x - 5 + 2x + x + 15 = 80$; 23
12 a $x + (x - 4) + (x + 6) = 35$ b 7
13 a (i) $2x$ (ii) $2x + 20$
    b $x + 2x + (2x + 20) = 110$; 56

Exercise 17.12

1 3.9   2 5.29   3 2.4   4 2.76   5 1.9   6 3.34